Supplemental Exercises

for Zill's

First Course in Differential Equations
with Modeling Applications

Eighth Edition

Kevin G. TeBeest
Kettering University

THOMSON

BROOKS/COLE

Australia • Canada • Mexico • Singapore • Spain • United Kingdom • United States

To my wonderful wife, Vicki —
for her patience and understanding
while I monopolized the family computer many evenings
and many weekends working on this project.

And to our children — Nathan, Meghan and Caleb.

Special thanks to Katherine Brayton, Assistant Editor of Mathematics in the Brooks/Cole Division of Thomson Higher Education, for her gracious patience and helpful assistance.

Kevin G. TeBeest, Ph.D., is an Associate Professor of Applied Mathematics in the Science and Mathematics Department at Kettering University in Flint, Michigan. He holds degrees in mathematics and mechanical engineering from the University of Nebraska-Lincoln. He has published papers in computational fluid dynamics and heat transfer and one paper in population dynamics. His main interests are differential equations and computational mathematics applied to the deterministic sciences. Besides plinking on the computer, Kevin enjoys touring Michigan's many lighthouses with his family.

CONTENTS

CHAPTER 1: Introduction to Differential Equations

1.1 Definitions and Terminology Subject Correlation Guide

1. classification by order

2. classification by order

3. classification by order

4. classification by order

5. classification by linearity or nonlinearity and homogeneity or nonhomogeneity

6. classification by linearity or nonlinearity and homogeneity or nonhomogeneity

7. classification by linearity or nonlinearity and homogeneity or nonhomogeneity

8. classification by linearity or nonlinearity and homogeneity or nonhomogeneity

9. solution concepts — single differential equation

10. solution concepts — single differential equation

11. solution concepts — single differential equation

12. solution concepts — systems of differential equations

13. solution concepts — systems of differential equations

14. verifying a solution

15. verifying a solution

16. verifying a solution

17. verifying a solution

18. verifying a solution

19. verifying a solution

20. verifying a solution

21. verifying a solution

22. seeking exponential solutions

23. seeking exponential solutions

24. seeking exponential solutions

25. seeking power solutions

26. seeking power solutions

27. seeking power solutions

28. seeking power solutions

29. seeking constant solutions

30. seeking constant solutions

1. State the order of the ordinary differential equation $4y'' + x\,y' = 6y^3$.

   (a) 1st
   (b) 2nd
   (c) 3rd
   (d) 4th

2. State the order of the ordinary differential equation $x^3\,y'' + \cos x\,y^{(4)} = x^2 e^x$.

   (a) 1st
   (b) 2nd
   (c) 3rd
   (d) 4th

3. State the order of the ordinary differential equation $y\,dy = x\,dx$.

   (a) 1st
   (b) 2nd
   (c) 3rd
   (d) 4th

4. State the order of the ordinary differential equation $x^2\,y'' + 2\,x\,y^{(3)} = \sin^2 x$.

   (a) 1st
   (b) 2nd
   (c) 3rd
   (d) 4th

5. State whether the ordinary differential equation is linear or nonlinear. Where appropriate, state whether it is homogeneous or nonhomogeneous. $4y'' + x\,y' = 6y^3$.

   (a) linear and homogeneous
   (b) linear and nonhomogeneous
   (c) linear
   (d) nonlinear

6. State whether the ordinary differential equation is linear or nonlinear. Where appropriate, state whether it is homogeneous or nonhomogeneous. $x^3\,y'' + \cos x\,y^{(4)} = x^2 e^x$.

   (a) linear and homogeneous
   (b) linear and nonhomogeneous
   (c) linear
   (d) nonlinear

7. State whether the ordinary differential equation is linear or nonlinear. Where appropriate, state whether it is homogeneous or nonhomogeneous. $y\,dy = x\,dx$

   (a) linear and homogeneous
   (b) linear and nonhomogeneous
   (c) linear
   (d) nonlinear

8. State whether the ordinary differential equation is linear or nonlinear. Where appropriate, state whether it is homogeneous or nonhomogeneous. $x^2 y'' + 2 x y^{(3)} = \sin^2 x$

    (a) linear and homogeneous

    (b) linear and nonhomogeneous

    (c) linear

    (d) nonlinear

9. How many solutions will a 3rd order ordinary differential equation generally have?

    (a) 1

    (b) 2

    (c) 3

    (d) infinitely many

10. A solution in which the dependent variable is written solely in terms the independent solution is called

    (a) an explicit solution.

    (b) an implicit solution.

    (c) a trivial solution.

    (d) a singular solution.

11. A solution of an ordinary differential equation involving one dependent variable is

    (a) a continuous curve in the plane.

    (b) a discontinuous curve in the plane.

    (c) may be (a) or (b).

    (d) none of the above

12. A solution of a system of two ordinary differential equations involving two dependent variables is

    (a) a pair of curves in the plane.

    (b) a pair of surfaces in 3 dimensions.

    (c) may be (a) or (b).

    (d) none of the above

13. To solve a system of 2 ordinary differential equations   E1: $\dot{x} = f(t, x, y)$ and   E2: $\dot{y} = g(t, x, y)$, one must find

    (a) function x that satisfies E1.

    (b) function y that satisfies E2.

    (c) functions x and y that satisfy both E1 and E2.

    (d) (a) and (b)

14. Verify that $y = e^{2x}$ is a solution of the differential equation $y'' - 2 y' = 0$.

15. Verify that $y = ce^{3x}$ is a solution of the differential equation $y'' - 3 y' = 0$, where c is any arbitrary constant.

16. Verify that $y = e^{-x}$ is a solution of the differential equation $y'' + y' - 2 y = 0$.

17. Verify that $y = \sin 4x$ is a solution of the differential equation $y'' + 16\,y = 0$.

18. Verify that $y = e^{-3x}\sin x$ is a solution of the differential equation $y'' + 6\,y' + 10\,y = 0$.

19. Verify that $y = 2\cos x$ is a solution of the differential equation $y'' + 4\,y = 6\,\cos x$.

20. Verify that $y = 2\,x\,\sin 2x$ is a solution of the differential equation $y'' + 4\,y = 8\,\cos 2x$.

21. Verify that $y = 2\cot 2x$ is a solution of the differential equation $y' + y^2 = -4$.

22. Find all values of m so that the function $y = e^{mx}$ is a solution of the differential equation $y'' + y' - 6\,y = 0$.

23. Find all values of m so that the function $y = e^{mx}$ is a solution of the differential equation $y'' + 3\,y' - 4\,y = 0$.

24. Find all values of m so that the function $y = e^{mx}$ is a solution of the differential equation $y''' - y'' - 6\,y' = 0$.

25. Find all values of m so that the function $y = x^m$ is a solution of the differential equation $x^2\,y'' + x\,y' - 4\,y = 0$.

26. Find all values of m so that the function $y = x^m$ is a solution of the differential equation $x^2\,y'' + x\,y' - 9\,y = 0$.

27. Find all values of m so that the function $y = x^m$ is a solution of the differential equation $x^2\,y'' + 2\,x\,y' - 2\,y = 0$.

28. Find all values of m so that the function $y = x^m$ is a solution of the differential equation $x^2\,y'' + 3\,x\,y' - 8\,y = 0$.

29. Find constant solutions of the differential equation $y' = y - 4y^2$.

30. Constant solutions of the differential equation $y' = 5y - y^2$ are $y(x) = 0$ and $y(x) = 5$.

    (a) Find intervals on the y axis on which a nonconstant solution is increasing.
    (b) Find intervals on the y axis on which a nonconstant solution is increasing.

1. b

2. d

3. a

4. c

5. d

6. b

7. d

8. b

9. d

10. a

11. c

12. b

13. c

14. $4e^{2x} - 2(2e^{2x}) = 0$

15. $9ce^{3x} - 3(3ce^{3x}) = 0$

16. $e^{-x} + e^{-x} - 2(e^{-x}) = 0$

17. $-16\sin 4x + 16(\sin 4x) = 0$

18. $0 = 0$

19. $-2\cos x + 4(2\cos x) = 6\cos x$

20. $4\cos 2x + 4\cos 2x - 8x\sin 2x + 4(2x\sin 2x) = 8\cos 2x$

21. $-4\csc^2 2x + (2\cot x)^2 = -4$

22. $y_1 = e^{2x}$, $y_2 = e^{-3x}$

23. $y_1 = e^x$, $y_2 = e^{-4x}$

24. $y_1 = c$, $y_2 = e^{3x}$, $y_3 = e^{-2x}$

25. $y_1 = x^2$, $y_2 = 1/x^2$

26. $y_1 = x^3$, $y_2 = 1/x^3$

27. $y_1 = c$, $y_2 = 1/x^2$

28. $y_1 = 1/x^2$, $y_2 = 1/x^4$

29. $y_1 = 0$, $y_2 = 1/4$

30. solutions increase on interval $0 < y < 5$ and decrease on interval $y > 5$

1. IVPs: number of solutions

2. IVPs: geometric interpretation of 1st order

3. IVPs: geometric interpretation of 2nd order

4. IVPs: geometric interpretation of 2nd order

5. IVPs: 2nd order

6. IVPs: existence–uniqueness theorem

7. IVPs: existence–uniqueness theorem

8. IVPs: existence–uniqueness theorem

9. IVPs: geometric interpretation of 2nd order

10. IVPs: geometric interpretation of 1st order

11. IVPs: geometric interpretation of 1st order

12. IVPs: geometric interpretation of 1st order

13. IVPs: geometric interpretation of 1st order

14. IVPs: finding arbitrary constant

15. IVPs: geometric interpretation of 1st order

16. IVPs: finding arbitrary constants from 2 ICs

17. IVPs: finding arbitrary constants from 2 ICs

18. IVPs: finding arbitrary constants from 2 ICs

19. IVPs: finding arbitrary constants from 2 ICs

20. IVPs: finding arbitrary constants from 2 ICs

21. IVPs: finding arbitrary constants from 2 ICs

22. IVPs: finding 3 arbitrary constants from 3 ICs

23. IVPs: existence–uniqueness theorem

24. IVPs: existence–uniqueness theorem

25. IVPs: existence–uniqueness theorem

26. IVPs: existence–uniqueness theorem

27. IVPs: existence–uniqueness theorem

28. IVPs: existence–uniqueness theorem

29. IVPs: existence–uniqueness theorem

30. IVPs: existence–uniqueness theorem

31. IVPs: existence–uniqueness theorem

1. How many solutions might an initial value problem have?

   (a) none
   (b) one
   (c) infinitely many
   (d) any of the above

2. When solving an initial value problem $y' = f(x, y)$, $y(x_0) = y_0$, we are seeking a solution to the differential equation that

   (a) contains point (y_0, x_0).
   (b) contains point (x_0, y_0).
   (c) contains point x_0.
   (d) contains point y_0.

3. A solution to an initial value problem $y'' = f(x, y, y')$, $y(x_0) = y_0$, $y'(x_0) = y_1$, is

   (a) a curve that passes point (x_0, y_0) with slope y_1.
   (b) a curve that passes point (x_0, y_1) with slope y_0.
   (c) a curve that contains points (x_0, y_0) and (x_0, y_1).
   (d) a curve that contains points (x_0, y_0) and (y_0, y_1).

4. A solution to an initial value problem $y'' = f(x, y, y')$, $y(1) = 3$, $y'(1) = 5$, is

   (a) a curve that passes point $(3, 1)$ with slope 5.
   (b) a curve that passes point $(1, 5)$ with slope 3.
   (c) a curve that passes point $(1, 3)$ with slope 5.
   (d) a curve that passes point $(3, 5)$ with slope 1.

5. If a 2nd order initial value problem models a real physical problem, we would expect it to involve

   (a) one initial condition.
   (b) two initial conditions.
   (c) one boundary condition.
   (d) two boundary conditions.

6. The theorem for the existence and uniqueness of solutions tells us

   (a) when an initial value problem does not have a solution.
   (b) when an initial value problem has a solution.
   (c) when an initial value problem has one and only one solution.
   (d) all of the above

7. For the ODE $y' = f(x, y)$ to be guaranteed to have a unique solution containing point (x_0, y_0), we must have

   (a) $f_x(x, y)$ and $f_y(x, y)$ be continuous at (x_0, y_0).
   (b) $f_x(x, y)$ and $f_{yy}(x, y)$ be continuous at (x_0, y_0).
   (c) $f(x, y)$ and $f_x(x, y)$ be continuous at (x_0, y_0).
   (d) $f(x, y)$ and $f_y(x, y)$ be continuous at (x_0, y_0).

8. The existence–uniqueness theorem says that the ODE $y' = \sqrt{y}$

   (a) is guaranteed to have a solution containing point $(0,0)$.

   (b) is guaranteed to have a unique solution containing point $(0,0)$.

   (c) is not guaranteed to have a unique solution containing point $(0,0)$.

   (d) does not have a solution containing point $(0,0)$.

9. If we seek the solution to an ODE $y'' = f(x, y, y')$ that passes point $(1,3)$ with slope 5, then the appropriate initial conditions are

   (a) $y(1) = 3$ and $y'(1) = 5$.

   (b) $y(1) = 5$ and $y'(1) = 3$.

   (c) $y(3) = 1$ and $y'(5) = 1$.

   (d) $y(5) = 3$ and $y'(1) = 3$.

10. Without solving the ODE, circle the correct statement about the ODE $y' = y$.

   (a) All solutions to the left of the y axis increase and those to the right of the y axis decrease.

   (b) All solutions to the left of the y axis decrease and those to the right of the y axis increase.

   (c) All solutions above the x axis decrease and those below the x axis increase.

   (d) All solutions above the x axis increase and those below the x axis decrease.

11. What can be said about the solutions to the ODE $y' = \sqrt{x}$?

   (a) The solution has slope 2 when $x = 4$.

   (b) All solutions contain the origin $(0,0)$.

   (c) All solutions contain the point $(4, 2)$.

   (d) All solutions contain the point $(2, 4)$.

12. What can be said about the solutions to the ODE $y' = \sqrt{x}$?

   (a) All solutions are in the left half plane.

   (b) All solutions are in the right half plane.

   (c) All solutions are in the upper half plane.

   (d) All solutions are in the lower half plane.

13. What can be said about the solutions to the ODE $y' = \sqrt{y}$?

   (a) All solutions are in the left half plane.

   (b) All solutions are in the right half plane.

   (c) All solutions are in the upper half plane.

   (d) All solutions are in the lower half plane.

14. What is c if $y = ce^{-2x}$ and $y'(0) = 1$?

   (a) $c = 1$

   (b) $c = -1$

   (c) $c = 1/2$

   (d) $c = -1/2$

15. What can be said about the ODE $y' = y - y^2$?

   (a) The trivial solution is the only solution containing the origin.

   (b) The trivial solution may not be the only solution containing the origin.

   (c) The trivial solution is not a solution.

   (d) The trivial solution is the only solution.

16. If $y = ce^{-2x}$ is a one-parameter family of solutions of an ODE, then find the solution that satisfies the initial condition $y(0) = 3$.

17. If $y = c_1 e^{2x} + c_2 e^{-x}$ is a two-parameter family of solutions of an ODE, then find the solution that satisfies the initial conditions $y(0) = -1$ and $y'(0) = 10$.

18. If $y = c_1 x e^{-x} + c_2 e^{-x}$ is a two-parameter family of solutions of an ODE, then find the solution that satisfies the initial conditions $y(0) = 5$ and $y'(0) = -3$.

19. If $y = c_1 x \ln x + c_2 \ln x$ is a two-parameter family of solutions of an ODE, then find the solution that satisfies the initial conditions $y(0) = 0$ and $y'(0) = -1$.

20. If $y = c_1 \cos 3x + c_2 \sin 3x$ is a two-parameter family of solutions of an ODE, then find the solution that satisfies the initial conditions $y(0) = 2$ and $y'(0) = -3$.

21. If $y = c_1 \cos 2x + c_2 \sin 2x$ is a two-parameter family of solutions of an ODE, then find the solution that satisfies the initial conditions $y(\pi/2) = 3$ and $y'(\pi/2) = -8$.

22. If $y = c_1 x^2 + c_2 x + c_2$ is a three-parameter family of solutions of an ODE, then find the solution that satisfies the initial conditions $y(1) = 5$, $y'(1) = 4$, and $y''(1) = 6$.

23. Without attempting to solve the ODE, determine whether the ODE $y' = x\sqrt{4 - y^2}$ is guaranteed to have a unique solution through the point $(2, 0)$.

24. Without attempting to solve the ODE, determine whether the ODE $y' = x\sqrt{4 - y^2}$ is guaranteed to have a unique solution through the point $(1, 2)$.

25. Without attempting to solve the ODE, determine the largest region in the xy plane in which the ODE $y' = x\sqrt{9 - y^2}$ is guaranteed to have a unique solution.

26. Without attempting to solve the ODE, determine the largest region in the xy plane in which the ODE $y' = x\sqrt{y^2 - 4}$ is guaranteed to have a unique solution.

27. Without attempting to solve the ODE, determine the largest region in the xy plane in which the ODE $xy' = \ln y$ is guaranteed to have a unique solution.

28. Without attempting to solve the ODE, determine the largest region in the xy plane in which the ODE $\sqrt{x}\, y' = y^{2/3}$ is guaranteed to have a unique solution.

29. Without attempting to solve the ODE, determine the largest region in the xy plane in which the ODE $y' = x^2\sqrt{y + 2}$ is guaranteed to have a unique solution.

30. Without attempting to solve the ODE, determine the largest region in the xy plane in which the ODE $y' = \sqrt{xy}$ is guaranteed to have a unique solution.

31. Without attempting to solve the ODE, determine the largest region in the xy plane in which the ODE $y' = (x + y)^{2/3}$ is guaranteed to have a unique solution.

1. d

2. b

3. a

4. c

5. b

6. c

7. d

8. c

9. a

10. d

11. a

12. b

13. c

14. d

15. a

16. $y = 3e^{-2x}$

17. $y = 3e^{2x} - 4e^{-x}$

18. $y = 2xe^{2x} + 5e^{-x}$

19. $y = 2x \ln x - 3 \ln x$

20. $y = 2 \cos 3x - \sin 3x$

21. $y = -3 \cos 2x + 4 \sin 2x$

22. $y = 3x^2 - 2x + 4$

23. The ODE is guaranteed to have a unique solution through the point $(2, 0)$.

24. The ODE is not guaranteed to have a unique solution through the point $(1, 2)$.

25. $\{(x, y) : -\infty < x < \infty, \ -3 < y < 3\}$

26. $\{(x, y) : -\infty < x < \infty, \ y < -2 \ \text{or} \ y > 2\}$

27. $\{(x, y) : x \neq 0, \ y > 0\}$

28. $\{(x, y) : x > 0, \ y \neq 0\}$

29. $\{(x, y) : -\infty < x < \infty, \ y > -2\}$

30. $\{(x, y) : xy > 0\}$ or all points interior to quadrants I and III

31. $\{(x, y) : y \neq -x\}$ or all points off the line $y = -x$

1. population model

2. population model

3. radioactive decay

4. radioactive decay

5. Newton's law of cooling

6. Newton's law of cooling

7. Newton's law with variable mass

8. circuits

9. Newton's law of cooling

10. circuits

11. Newton's law of cooling

12. radioactive decay

13. spread of disease

14. projectile motion

15. Newton's law of cooling

16. population model

17. population model

18. spread of disease

19. chemical reaction

20. population model

21. lake pollution

22. projectile motion

23. circuits

1. According to the Malthusian model for population growth, the population

   (a) increases without bound.
   (b) decreases without bound.
   (c) sometimes increases and sometimes decreases.
   (d) has several constant solutions.

2. According to the Malthusian model for population growth, the rate of change of population is

   (a) constant.
   (b) larger when population is larger.
   (c) larger when population is smaller.
   (d) none of the above.

3. According to the model for radioactive decay, the amount of radioactive substance remaining at time t

   (a) increases.
   (b) decreases.
   (c) sometimes increases and sometimes decreases.
   (d) has several constant solutions.

4. According to the model for radioactive decay, the rate of decay is

   (a) constant.
   (b) larger when less substance is present.
   (c) larger when more substance is present.
   (d) none of the above.

5. Consider an object with initial temperature T_0 placed in a medium with ambient temperature T_m. Newton's law of cooling says that the rate of change of the object's temperature T is proportional to

   (a) $T - T_m$
   (b) $T_m - T$
   (c) $T - T_0$
   (d) $T_0 - T$

6. Consider an object placed in a medium with ambient temperature T_m. Newton's law of cooling says that the rate of change of the object's temperature T is proportional to

   (a) T
   (b) T_m
   (c) $T_m - T$
   (d) $T - T_m$

7. When mass m is variable, Newton's second law is written as

(a) $\dfrac{d}{dt}(mv) = F$

(b) $m\dfrac{d}{dt}(v) = F$

(c) $\dfrac{d}{dt}(mv) = a$

(d) $m\dfrac{d}{dt}(v) = ma$

8. The differential equation that models a single loop circuit is $L\dfrac{d^2q}{dt^2} + R\dfrac{dq}{dt} + \dfrac{1}{C}q = E(t)$. The term $L\dfrac{d^2q}{dt^2}$ represents the

(a) voltage drop across the capacitor.

(b) voltage drop across the resistor.

(c) voltage drop across the voltage source.

(d) voltage drop across the inductor.

9. Consider an object placed in a medium with ambient temperature T_m. Newton's law of cooling says that the object's temperature is modeled by the differential equation $\dfrac{dT}{dt} = k(T - T_m)$ where k is a proportionality constant. What must be true of k?

(a) k is positive

(b) k is negative

(c) (a) or (b), depending on the specific conditions

(d) none of the above can be said without experimentation

10. The differential equation that models a single loop circuit is $L\dfrac{d^2q}{dt^2} + R\dfrac{dq}{dt} + \dfrac{1}{C}q = E(t)$. The term $\dfrac{1}{C}q$ represents the

(a) voltage drop across the capacitor.

(b) voltage drop across the resistor.

(c) voltage drop across the voltage source.

(d) voltage drop across the inductor.

11. When an object at temperature T_0 is immersed in a surrounding medium that is maintained at temperature T_m, then Newton's law of cooling may be applied to determine the object's temperature at time t. Newton's law of cooling applies when

(a) the object us cooler than the surrounding medium.

(b) the object us warmer than the surrounding medium.

(c) either case (a) or (b)

(d) neither case

12. Suppose that $A'(t) = -0.0004332A(t)$ is the model for the decay of radium-226, where $A(t)$ is the amount of radium (in grams) remaining at time T (In years). At what rate is the sample decaying if the sample contains 7 grams of radium?

13. Suppose a student carrying a cold virus returns to an isolated college of 5000 students. Determine a differential equation for the number of people $x(t)$ who have contracted the cold if the rate at which the cold spreads is proportional to the number of interactions between the number of students who have the cold and the number of students who have not yet been exposed.

14. A projectile is propelled upward at 200 ft/sec from a height of 6 ft. What is the differential equation that models the altitude $y(t)$ of the projectile at time t? You may ignore drag. Also include the appropriate initial conditions.

15. An object that has an initial temperature of 500 Kelvin is placed in an oven that is maintained at a temperature of 700 Kelvin. What is the differential equation that models the temperature $T(t)$ of the object at time t? Also include the appropriate initial condition. State whether the porportionality constant is positive or negative.

16. Consider the Malthusian model for population growth.

    (a) Modify the Malthusian model to allow the population to be harvested at a constant rate $h > 0$.

    (b) Determine a constant solution of the modified model, and denote it by P_c.

    (c) What happens if the population exceeds P_c?

    (d) What happens if the population is below P_c?

17. The Malthusian model for population growth does not account for competition for resources within the population.

    (a) Competition for resources adversely affects the population, tending to cause the population to decrease at a rate proportional to the square of the population. Modify the Malthusian model to account for competition within the species.

    (b) Determine a nontrivial constant solution of the modified model, and denote it by P_c.

    (c) What happens if the population exceeds P_c?

    (d) What happens if the population is below P_c?

18. The model for the spread of disease was $\dfrac{dx}{dt} = kx(n + 1 - x)$.

    (a) Determine a nontrivial constant solution of the modified model, and denote it by x_c.

    (b) What happens if the population exceeds x_c?

    (c) What happens if the population is below x_c?

19. The model for the reaction of two chemicals to produce a third chemical C was $\dfrac{dX}{dt} = k(\alpha - X)(\beta - X)$, where k, α, and β are positive constants, and X denotes the amount of chemical C produced. Let us suppose that $\alpha < \beta$.

    (a) Determine two nontrivial constant solutions of the model, and denote them by X_1 and X_2.

    (b) What happens if $0 < X < \alpha$?

    (c) What happens if $\alpha < X < \beta$?

    (d) What happens if $X > \beta$?

20. Suppose that $P'(t) = 0.2\,P(t)$ represents a model for the growth of a population culture (measured in number od cells), where $P(t)$ is the population at time t (measured in hours).

    (a) How fast is the culture growing when the population is 10 million cells?

    (b) How many cells are present if the culture is growing at a rate of 4 million cells per hour?

21. In cleaning Lake Ontario, suppose that pollution input into the lake suddenly ceases and that the pollution present in the lake at time t is always well mixed but decreases as fresh water flows into the lake and contaminated water laves the lake. Suppose that fresh water enters the lake at the same rate that contaminated water leaves the lake — denote this flow rate by r (measured in cubic meters per hour).

   (a) Let $x(t)$ denote the pollution concentration (number of grams of pollutant per cubic meter of lake water) at time t, and let V denote the constant volume of Lake Ontario. What is the total pollution level in the lake at time t?

   (b) At what rate is pollution carried out of the lake?

   (c) If the rate at which the total pollution level decreases equals the difference between the rate at which pollution enters and leaves the lake, what is the differential equation for $x(t)$?

22. Suppose in projectile motion the object experiences a drag that is proportional to the square of the velocity. Let the projectile be propelled vertically upward and let y denote the altitude above ground (up is positive).

   (a) What is the drag force acting on the projectile as it moves?

   (b) What is the differential equation the models tha projectile's altitude y at time t?

23. The differential equation that models a single loop circuit is $L\dfrac{d^2q}{dt^2} + R\dfrac{dq}{dt} + \dfrac{1}{C}q = E(t)$. Suppose a circuit comprises an inductor of inductance 2 henries, a 10 Ohm resistor, a capacitor of capacitance 0.01 farads, and a 40 Volt voltage source. What is the differential equation that models this circuit?

1. a

2. b

3. b

4. c

5. a

6. d

7. a

8. d

9. b

10. a

11. c

12. 0.003032 grams

13. $\dfrac{dx}{dt} = kx(5001 - x)$

14. $\dfrac{d^2y}{dt^2} = -32,\ \ y(0) = 6,\ \ y'(0) = 200.$

15. $\dfrac{dT}{dt} = k(T - 700),\ \ T(0) = 500,\ \ k$ is negative.

16. (a) $\dfrac{dP}{dt} = kP - h$, where $h > 0$ is the constant rate of harvest.
    (b) A constant solution is $P_c = h/k$.
    (c) The population will increase.
    (d) The population will decrease.

17. (a) $\dfrac{dP}{dt} = kP - rP^2$, where $r > 0$ is the constant rate of proportionality.
    (b) A nontrivial constant solution is $P_c = k/r$.
    (c) The population will decrease.
    (d) The population will increase.

18. (a) A nontrivial constant solution is $x_c = n + 1$.
    (b) The population will decrease.
    (c) The population will increase.

19. (a) Nontrivial constant solutions are $X_1 = \alpha$ and $X_2 = \beta$.
    (b) The amount X of chemical C will increase.
    (c) The amount X of chemical C will decrease.
    (d) The amount X of chemical C will increase.

20. (a) 2 million cells per hour

    (b) 20 million cells

21. (a) $Vx(t)$

    (b) $rx(t)$

    (c) $\dfrac{d}{dt}(Vx) = 0 - rx$

22. (a) $-kv\,|v|$ or $-k\dot{y}\,|y|$ where k is a positive constant of proportionality

    (b) $m\dfrac{d^2y}{dt^2} = -mg - k\dfrac{dy}{dt}\,|y|$

23. $2\dfrac{d^2q}{dt^2} + 10\dfrac{dq}{dt} + 100q = 40.$

2.1   Solution Curves without a Solution Subject Correlation Guide

1. 1st order DE – geometric interpretation of $f(x, y)$

2. 1st order DE – geometric interpretation of $f(x, y) < 0$

3. 1st order DE – geometric interpretation of $f(x, y) > 0$

4. 1st order DE – geometric interpretation of $f(x, y) = 0$

5. 1st order DE – geometric interpretation of $f(x, y) = c$

6. 1st order DE – geometric interpretation of $f(x, y) = c$

7. 1st order DE – geometric interpretation of $f(x, y) = c$

8. 1st order autonomous DE – concepts

9. 1st order autonomous DE – concepts

10. 1st order autonomous DE – equilibrium solution

11. 1st order autonomous DE – equilibrium solution

12. 1st order autonomous DE – concepts

13. 1st order autonomous DE – stability of equilibrium solution

14. 1st order autonomous DE – stability of equilibrium solution

15. 1st order autonomous DE – equilibrium solution

16. 1st order autonomous DE – stability of equilibrium solution

17. 1st order autonomous DE – stability of equilibrium solution

18. 1st order autonomous DE – stability of equilibrium solution

19. 1st order autonomous DE – stability of equilibrium solution

20. 1st order DE – finding slopes of solutions, isoclines, and equilibrium solutions

21. 1st order DE – finding slopes of solutions, isoclines, and equilibrium solutions

22. 1st order DE – finding slopes of solutions, isoclines, and equilibrium solutions

23. 1st order DE – finding slopes of solutions, isoclines, and equilibrium solutions

24. 1st order DE – finding slopes of solutions, isoclines, and equilibrium solutions

25. 1st order DE – finding slopes of solutions, isoclines, and equilibrium solutions

26. 1st order DE – finding slopes of solutions, isoclines, and equilibrium solutions

27. 1st order autonomous DE – critical points and stability

28. 1st order autonomous DE – critical points and stability

29. 1st order autonomous DE – critical points and stability

30. 1st order autonomous DE – critical points and stability

31. 1st order autonomous DE – critical points and stability

32. 1st order autonomous DE – critical points and stability

33. 1st order autonomous DE – critical points and stability

1. In the differential equation $y' = f(x, y)$, the value of $f(x, y)$ at a point (x, y) gives

   (a) the slope of the solution through point (x, y).
   (b) the value of the solution through point (x, y).
   (c) the curvature of the solution through point (x, y).
   (d) the isoclines of the solution through point (x, y).

2. In the differential equation $y' = f(x, y)$, if $f(x, y) < 0$ at a point (x, y) in the interval of definition, then

   (a) nothing much can be said about the solution through point (x, y).
   (b) the solution through point (x, y) is increasing.
   (c) the solution through point (x, y) is decreasing.
   (d) the solution through point (x, y) is negative.

3. In the differential equation $y' = f(x, y)$, if $f(x, y) > 0$ at a point (x, y) in the interval of definition, then

   (a) nothing much can be said about the solution through point (x, y).
   (b) the solution through point (x, y) is increasing.
   (c) the solution through point (x, y) is decreasing.
   (d) the solution through point (x, y) is positive.

4. In the differential equation $y' = f(x, y)$, if $f(x, y) = 0$ at a point (x, y) in the interval of definition, then

   (a) nothing much can be said about the solution through point (x, y).
   (b) the solution through point (x, y) is increasing.
   (c) the solution through point (x, y) is decreasing.
   (d) the solution through point (x, y) is stationary.

5. In the differential equation $y' = f(x, y)$, if $f(x, y) = c$ (where c is a constant) along a curve in the xy plane, then that curve is called

   (a) a critical curve.
   (b) an isobar.
   (c) an isocline.
   (d) an isotherm.

6. In the differential equation $y' = f(x, y)$, suppose that $f(x, y) = 4$ at all points on the curve $y = x^3$. What can be said about the solution of the differential equation at point $(2, 8)$?

   (a) The solution contains the point $(2, 4)$.
   (b) The solution has slope 4.
   (c) The solution has slope 8.
   (d) Nothing can be said.

7. In the differential equation $y' = f(x, y)$, suppose that $f(x, y) = 4$ at all points on the curve $y = x^3$. What can be said about the solution of the differential equation at point $(2, 12)$?

    (a) The solution contains the point $(2, 4)$.

    (b) The solution has slope 4.

    (c) The solution has slope 8.

    (d) Nothing can be said.

8. The differential equation $y' = f(y)$

    (a) may have no equilibrium solution.

    (b) always has one equilibrium solution.

    (c) always has at least one equilibrium solution.

    (d) always has infinitely many equilibrium solutions.

9. A differential equation of the form $y' = f(y)$ is called

    (a) nonhomogeneous

    (b) homogeneous

    (c) nonautonomous

    (d) autonomous

10. A constant solution of an autonomous differential equation is called

    (a) an isocline.

    (b) an equilibrium solution.

    (c) a trivial solution.

    (d) as critical solution.

11. Suppose that $f(c) = 0$ (c a constant) for the differential equation $y' = f(y)$. Then function $y = c$ is called

    (a) an isocline.

    (b) an equlibrium solution.

    (c) a trivial solution.

    (d) (a) and (c)

12. Which differential equation is autonomous?

    (a) $y' = f(x, y)$

    (b) $y' = f(x)$

    (c) $y' = f(y)$

    (d) $y' = f(x, y, y')$

13. Suppose $y(x)$ is a nonconstant solution of an autonomous differential equation. If $y(x)$ is bounded above by an equilibrium solution, then

    (a) $y(x)$ must approach the equilibrium solution from below as $x \to -\infty$ or as $x \to \infty$.

    (b) $y(x)$ must approach the equilibrium solution from above as $x \to -\infty$ or as $x \to \infty$.

    (c) $y(x)$ must approach the equilibrium solution from below as $x \to -\infty$ and as $x \to \infty$.

    (d) $y(x)$ must approach the equilibrium solution from above as $x \to -\infty$ and as $x \to \infty$.

14. Suppose $y(x)$ is a nonconstant solution of an autonomous differential equation. If $y(x)$ is bounded below by a critical point, then

   (a) $y(x)$ must approach the critical point from below as $x \to -\infty$ or as $x \to \infty$.
   (b) $y(x)$ must approach the critical point from above as $x \to -\infty$ or as $x \to \infty$.
   (c) $y(x)$ must approach the critical point from below as $x \to -\infty$ and as $x \to \infty$.
   (d) $y(x)$ must approach the critical point from above as $x \to -\infty$ and as $x \to \infty$.

15. Graphically, an equilibrium solution of an autonomous differential equation is a

   (a) point in the xy plane.
   (b) curve in the xy plane.
   (c) vertical line in the xy plane.
   (d) horizontal line in the xy plane.

16. Suppose $y = c$ is an equilibrium solution of an autonomous differential equation. Let $y(x)$ denote nonconstant solutions immediately above and below the equilibrium solution. If $y(x)$ converges to $y = c$ as $x \to \infty$, then the equilibrium solution is called

   (a) an attractor.
   (b) a repellor.
   (c) a semi-attractor.
   (d) a semi-repeller.

17. Suppose $y = c$ is an equilibrium solution of an autonomous differential equation. Let $y(x)$ denote nonconstant solutions immediately above and below the equilibrium solution. If $y(x)$ converges to $y = c$ as $x \to \infty$, then the equilibrium solution is called

   (a) asymptotically stable.
   (b) unstable.
   (c) semi-stable.
   (d) periodically stable.

18. Suppose $y = c$ is an equilibrium solution of an autonomous differential equation. Let $y(x)$ denote nonconstant solutions immediately above and below the equilibrium solution. If $y(x)$ moves away from $y = c$ as $x \to \infty$, then the equilibrium solution is called

   (a) an attractor.
   (b) a repellor.
   (c) a semi-attractor.
   (d) a semi-repeller.

19. Suppose $y = c$ is an equilibrium solution of an autonomous differential equation. If nonconstant solutions $y(x)$ immediately above the equilibrium solution converge to $y = c$ as $x \to \infty$ while nonconstant solutions $y(x)$ immediately below the equilibrium solution move away from $y = c$ as $x \to \infty$, then the equilibrium solution is called

   (a) asymptotically stable.
   (b) unstable.
   (c) semi-stable.
   (d) periodically stable.

20. Consider the differential equation $\quad y' = y - x^2$.

    (a) Find the slope of the tangent line to the solution that contains the point $(1, 3)$.

    (b) Find the slope of the tangent line to the solution that contains the point $(2, 3)$.

    (c) Describe the isocline $f(x, y) = 0$ of the DE.

    (d) Describe the isocline $f(x, y) = -4$ of the DE.

    (e) Describe the isoclines $f(x, y) = c$ of the DE.

    (f) Does the DE have any constant solutions?

21. Consider the differential equation $\quad y' = x^2 + y^2$.

    (a) Find the slope of the tangent line to the solution that contains the point $(3, -4)$.

    (b) Find the slope of the tangent line to the solution that contains the point $(-3, 4)$.

    (c) Describe the isocline $f(x, y) = 0$ of the DE.

    (d) Describe the isocline $f(x, y) = -4$ of the DE.

    (e) Describe the isocline $f(x, y) = 4$ of the DE.

    (f) Describe the isoclines $f(x, y) = c$ of the DE.

    (g) What can be said of all solutions of the DE?

    (h) Does the DE have any constant solutions?

22. Consider the differential equation $\quad y' = x^2 - y^2$.

    (a) Find the slope of the tangent line to the solution that contains the point $(3, -4)$.

    (b) Find the slope of the tangent line to the solution that contains the point $(-4, 3)$.

    (c) Describe the isocline $f(x, y) = 0$ of the DE.

    (d) Describe the isocline $f(x, y) = -4$ of the DE.

    (e) Describe the isocline $f(x, y) = 4$ of the DE.

    (f) Describe the isoclines $f(x, y) = c$ of the DE.

    (g) Does the DE have any constant solutions?

23. Consider the differential equation $\quad y' = \cos x - y$.

    (a) Find the slope of the tangent line to the solution that contains the point $(0, -4)$.

    (b) Find the slope of the tangent line to the solution that contains the point $(\pi, 2)$.

    (c) Describe the isocline $f(x, y) = 0$ of the DE.

    (d) Describe the isocline $f(x, y) = 4$ of the DE.

    (e) Describe the isoclines $f(x, y) = c$ of the DE.

    (f) Does the DE have any constant solutions?

24. Consider the differential equation $y' = xy$.

    (a) Find the slope of the tangent line to the solution that contains the point $(3, -2)$.

    (b) Find the slope of the tangent line to the solution that contains the point $(-3, 4)$.

    (c) Describe the isocline $f(x, y) = 0$ of the DE.

    (d) Describe the isocline $f(x, y) = -4$ of the DE.

    (e) Describe the isoclines $f(x, y) = c$ of the DE.

    (f) What can be said of solutions $y(x)$ of the DE in quadrant I?

    (g) What can be said of solutions $y(x)$ of the DE in quadrant II?

    (h) What can be said of solutions $y(x)$ of the DE in quadrant III?

    (i) What can be said of solutions $y(x)$ of the DE in quadrant IV?

    (j) Does the DE have any constant solutions?

25. Consider the differential equation $y' = e^x$.

    (a) Find the slope of the tangent line to the solution that contains the point $(0, -2)$.

    (b) Find the slope of the tangent line to the solution that contains the point $(2, 4)$.

    (c) Describe the isocline $f(x, y) = 0$ of the DE.

    (d) Describe the isocline $f(x, y) = 1$ of the DE.

    (e) Describe the isoclines $f(x, y) = c$ of the DE.

    (f) What can be said of all nonconstant solutions $y(x)$ of the DE in quadrant I?

    (g) What can be said of all nonconstant solutions $y(x)$ of the DE in quadrant II?

    (h) What can be said of all nonconstant solutions $y(x)$ of the DE in quadrant III?

    (i) What can be said of all nonconstant solutions $y(x)$ of the DE in quadrant IV?

    (j) Does the DE have any constant solutions?

26. Consider the differential equation $y' = e^{-y}$.

    (a) Find the slope of the tangent line to the solution that contains the point $(-2, 0)$.

    (b) Find the slope of the tangent line to the solution that contains the point $(2, 4)$.

    (c) Describe the isocline $f(x, y) = 0$ of the DE.

    (d) Describe the isocline $f(x, y) = 1$ of the DE.

    (e) Describe the isoclines $f(x, y) = c$ of the DE.

    (f) What can be said of all nonconstant solutions $y(x)$ of the DE in quadrants I and II?

    (g) What can be said of all nonconstant solutions $y(x)$ of the DE in quadrants III and IV?

    (h) Does the DE have any constant solutions?

27. Consider the differential equation $y' = \sqrt{y}$.

    (a) Find critical points of the DE.

    (b) Determine whether the critical point is asymptotically stable, unstable, or semi-stable.

28. Consider the differential equation $y' = \sqrt{y - 3}$.

    (a) Find critical points of the DE.

    (b) Determine whether the critical point is asymptotically stable, unstable, or semi-stable.

29. Consider the differential equation $y' = 4y - y^2$.

   (a) Find critical points of the DE.

   (b) Determine whether the critical point is asymptotically stable, unstable, or semi-stable.

30. Consider the differential equation $y' = 3(y-2)(4-y)$.

   (a) Find critical points of the DE.

   (b) Determine whether the critical point is asymptotically stable, unstable, or semi-stable.

31. Consider the differential equation $y' = 9y - 18 - y^2$.

   (a) Find critical points of the DE.

   (b) Determine whether the critical point is asymptotically stable, unstable, or semi-stable.

32. Consider the differential equation $y' = 9y^2 - 18y - y^3$.

   (a) Find critical points of the DE.

   (b) Determine whether the critical point is asymptotically stable, unstable, or semi-stable.

33. Consider the differential equation $y' = y(y-3)(7-y)$.

   (a) Find critical points of the DE.

   (b) Determine whether the critical point is asymptotically stable, unstable, or semi-stable.

1. a

2. c

3. b

4. d

5. c

6. b

7. d

8. a

9. d

10. b

11. b

12. c

13. a

14. b

15. b

16. a

17. a

18. b

19. c

20. (a) 2
    (b) -1
    (c) It is the parabola $y = x^2$ that opens upward with vertex at the origin.
    (d) It is the parabola $y = x^2 - 4$ that opens upward with vertex at the point $(0, -4)$.
    (e) They are parabolas $y = x^2 + c$ that open upward with vertex at the point $(0, c)$.
    (f) No.

21. (a) 25
    (b) 25
    (c) It is the origin $(0, 0)$.
    (d) The prescribed isocline does not exist.
    (e) It is circle of radius 2 centered at the origin.
    (f) They are circles $x^2 + y^2 = c$ if $c > 0$; otherwise if $c < 0$ there are no associated isoclines.
    (g) All solutions are increasing with x (because clearly $y' > 0$ at all points).
    (h) No.

22. (a) -7

    (b) 7

    (c) The lines $y = x$ and $y = -x$.

    (d) It is the hyperbola $x^2 - y^2 = -4$ that runs parallel to the y axis with domain $-\infty < x < \infty$ and range $y \leq -2,\ y \geq 2$.

    (e) It is the hyperbola $x^2 - y^2 = 4$ that runs parallel to the x axis with domain $x \leq -2,\ x \geq 2$ and range $-\infty < y < \infty$.

    (f) If $c < 0$, they are hyperbolas $x^2 - y^2 = c$ that run parallel to the y axis with domain $-\infty < x < \infty$ and range $y \leq -\sqrt{c},\ y \geq \sqrt{c}$. If $c > 0$, they are hyperbolas $x^2 - y^2 = c$ that run parallel to the x axis with domain $x \leq -\sqrt{c},\ x \geq \sqrt{c}$ and range $-\infty < y < \infty$.

    (g) No.

23. (a) 5

    (b) -3

    (c) It is the sinusoid $y = \cos x$.

    (d) It is the sinusoid $y = \cos x - 4$, which is the function $\cos x$ shifted down 4 units.

    (e) It is the sinusoid $y = \cos x - c$, which is the function $\cos x$ shifted down c units if $c > 0$ and shifted up c units if $c < 0$.

    (f) No.

24. (a) -6

    (b) -12

    (c) They are the lines $x = 0$ and $y = 0$.

    (d) It is the hyperbola $y = -4/x$.

    (e) They are hyperbolas $y = c/x$.

    (f) They are increasing functions of x.

    (g) They are decreasing functions of x.

    (h) They are increasing functions of x.

    (i) They are decreasing functions of x.

    (j) No.

25. (a) 1

    (b) e^2

    (c) The prescribed isocline does not exist.

    (d) It is the vertical line $x = 0$.

    (e) They are vertical lines $x = \ln c$ if $c > 0$; otherwise if $c < 0$ there are no isoclines.

    (f) They are rapidly increasing functions of x.

    (g) They are very slowly increasing functions of x.

    (h) They are very slowly increasing functions of x.

    (i) They are rapidly slowly increasing functions of x.

    (j) No.

26. (a) 1

    (b) e^4

    (c) The prescribed isocline does not exist.

    (d) It is the horizontal line $y = 0$.

    (e) They are horizontal lines $y = \ln c$ if $c > 0$; otherwise if $c < 0$ there are no isoclines.

    (f) They increase slowly as $y \to -\infty$.

    (g) They increase rapidly as $y \to -\infty$.

    (h) No.

27. (a) $y = 0$

    (b) unstable

28. (a) $y = 3$

    (b) unstable

29. (a) $y = 0$ and $y = 4$

    (b) The critical point $y = 0$ is unstable. The critical point $y = 4$ is asymptotically stable.

30. (a) $y = 2$ and $y = 4$

    (b) The critical point $y = 2$ is unstable. The critical point $y = 4$ is asymptotically stable.

31. (a) $y = 3$ and $y = 6$

    (b) The critical point $y = 3$ is unstable. The critical point $y = 6$ is semi-stable.

32. (a) $y = 0$, $y = 3$ and $y = 6$

    (b) The critical point $y = 0$ is asymptotically stable. The critical point $y = 3$ is unstable. The critical point $y = 6$ is asymptotically stable.

33. (a) $y = 0$, $y = 3$ and $y = 7$

    (b) The critical point $y = 0$ is asymptotically stable. The critical point $y = 3$ is unstable. The critical point $y = 3$ is asymptotically stable.

1. 1st order separable DE – definition

2. 1st order separable DE – solution process

3. 1st order separable DE – solution with arbitrary constant

4. 1st order separable DE – solution with arbitrary constant

5. 1st order separable DE – solution process

6. True/False – 1st order separable DE

7. True/False – 1st order separable DE

8. True/False – manipulating arbitrary constants

9. True/False – manipulating arbitrary constants

10. True/False – manipulating arbitrary constants

11. True/False – manipulating arbitrary constants

12. True/False – manipulating arbitrary constants

13. True/False – manipulating arbitrary constants

14. True/False – manipulating arbitrary constants

15. True/False – 1st order separable DE

16. Solve a separable DE

17. Apply an initial condition

18. Solve a separable DE

19. Apply an initial condition

20. Solve a separable DE

21. Apply an initial condition

22. Solve a separable DE

23. Apply an initial condition

24. Solve a separable DE

25. Apply an initial condition

26. Solve a separable DE

27. Apply an initial condition

28. Solve a separable DE

29. Apply an initial condition

30. Solve a separable DE

31. Apply an initial condition

32. Solve a separable DE

33. Apply an initial condition

34. Solve a separable DE

35. Apply an initial condition

36. Solve a separable DE

37. Apply an initial condition

38. Solve a separable DE

39. Solve a separable DE

40. Solve a separable DE

41. Apply an initial condition

42. Solve a separable DE

43. Apply an initial condition

44. Solve a separable DE

45. Solve a separable DE

46. Apply an initial condition

47. Solve a separable DE

48. Apply an initial condition

1. A general separable differential equation is a differential equation that can be written in the form

   (a) $f(x, y)\, dy = dx$.

   (b) $y' = f(x, y)$.

   (c) $f(x)\, dx = g(y)\, dy$.

   (d) $dy = g(y)\, dx$.

2. Once a differential equation is separated, we should be able to solve it in principle by

   (a) differentiating one side of the equation.

   (b) differentiating both sides of the equation.

   (c) integrating one side of the equation.

   (d) integrating both sides of the equation.

3. The solution of the separable differential equation $dy = e^{-x}\, dx$ is

   (a) $y = -e^{-x}$.

   (b) $y = -e^{-x} + c$.

   (c) $y = e^{-x}$.

   (d) $y = e^{-x} + c$.

4. The solution of the separable differential equation $dy = dx/x$ is

   (a) $y = \ln x$.

   (b) $y = \ln x + c$.

   (c) $y = \ln |x|$.

   (d) $y = \ln |x| + c$.

5. The differential equation $y' = y\, e^{x-y}$ separates into the form

   (a) $\dfrac{e^y}{y}\, dx = e^x\, dy$.

   (b) $y\, dy = e^x e^{-y}\, dx$.

   (c) $e^{-x}\, dy = y\, e^{-y}\, dx$.

   (d) $\dfrac{e^y}{y}\, dy = e^x\, dx$.

6. True or False: All 1st order differential equations are separable.

7. True or False: Solving a 1st order separable differential equation produces two distinctly different arbitrary constants.

8. True or False: If c_1 and c_2 are arbitrary constants, then $c_1 - c_2$ is another arbitrary constant.

9. True or False: If c is an arbitrary constant, then $2c$ is another arbitrary constant.

10. True or False: If c is an arbitrary constant, then $4 - c$ is another arbitrary constant.

11. True or False: If c is an arbitrary constant, then c^2 is another arbitrary constant.

12. True or False: If c is an arbitrary constant, then e^c is another arbitrary constant.

13. True or False: If c is an arbitrary constant, then $\ln c$ is another arbitrary constant.

14. True or False: If c is an arbitrary constant, then we may rewrite e^{x-c} as ce^x.

15. True or False: Solving a separable differential equation produces a 2-parameter family of solutions.

16. Solve the differential equation by separation of variables $\quad y' = e^{2x-y}$.

17. Obtain the solution if the differential equation in the previous problem is accompanied by an initial condition $\quad y(0) = 3$.

18. Solve the differential equation by separation of variables $\quad \dfrac{dy}{dx} = \cos 3x$.

19. Obtain the solution if the differential equation in the previous problem is accompanied by an initial condition $\quad y(\pi/2) = 2/3$.

20. Solve the differential equation by separation of variables $\quad \dfrac{dy}{dx} = \dfrac{2y}{x}$.

21. Obtain the solution if the differential equation in the previous problem is accompanied by an initial condition $\quad y(2) = 16$.

22. Solve the differential equation by separation of variables $\quad \dfrac{dy}{dx} = \sec 2y$.

23. Obtain the solution if the differential equation in the previous problem is accompanied by an initial condition $\quad y(1) = \pi/4$.

24. Solve the differential equation by separation of variables $\quad y\,y' = e^{y^2} \sin x$.

25. Obtain the solution if the differential equation in the previous problem is accompanied by an initial condition $\quad y(\pi) = 0$.

26. Solve the differential equation by separation of variables $\quad \dfrac{dy}{dx} = \dfrac{x - xy}{x^2 + 1}$.

27. Obtain the solution if the differential equation in the previous problem is accompanied by an initial condition $\quad y(0) = 2$.

28. Solve the differential equation by separation of variables $\quad y^2\,y' = xy^3 + x$.

29. Obtain the solution if the differential equation in the previous problem is accompanied by an initial condition $\quad y(2) = 0$.

30. Solve the differential equation by separation of variables $\quad (6e^{3y} + 1)(x + 1)\,dy - xe^y\,dx = 0$.

31. Obtain the solution if the differential equation in the previous problem is accompanied by an initial condition $\quad y(-2) = 0$.

32. Solve the differential equation by separation of variables $\quad (y + e^{-y})\,y' = \sin x$.

33. Obtain the solution if the differential equation in the previous problem is accompanied by an initial condition $\quad y(\pi) = 0$.

34. Solve the differential equation by separation of variables $\quad 4\,(xy + 2y)\,dy + xe^{y^2}\,dx = 0$.

35. Obtain the solution if the differential equation in the previous problem is accompanied by an initial condition $\quad y(-3) = 0$.

36. Solve the differential equation by separation of variables $(x + 3xy^2)\,dy + (1 - 4x^2)\,dx = 0$.

37. Obtain the solution if the differential equation in the previous problem is accompanied by an initial condition $y(1) = -2$.

38. Solve the differential equation by separation of variables $y\cos^2 x\,dy - (y^2 + 1)\,dx = 0$.

39. Solve the differential equation by separation of variables $x\,y^2\,dy - (x^2 + 1)(y^3 + 1)\,dx = 0$.

40. Solve the differential equation by separation of variables $y(1 + e^x)\,dx - (y\,e^x + e^x)\,dy = 0$.

41. Obtain the solution if the differential equation in the previous problem is accompanied by an initial condition $y(0) = 1$.

42. Solve the differential equation by separation of variables $(4x + xy)\,dx - (2 + x^2)\,dy = 0$.

43. Obtain the solution if the differential equation in the previous problem is accompanied by an initial condition $y(1) = -5$.

44. Solve the differential equation by separation of variables $(4x + xy^2)\,dx - y\,e^{x^2}\,dy = 0$.

45. Solve the differential equation by separation of variables $(1 + e^x)\,dy = y\,e^x\,dx$.

46. Obtain the solution if the differential equation in the previous problem is accompanied by an initial condition $y(0) = 6$.

47. Solve the differential equation by separation of variables $(xy - 3y + x - 3)\,dy = (xy + y - 2x - 2)\,dx$.

48. Obtain the solution if the differential equation in the previous problem is accompanied by an initial condition $y(4) = 1$.

1. c

2. d

3. b

4. d

5. d

6. False

7. False

8. True

9. True

10. True

11. False

12. False

13. True

14. True

15. False

16. $e^y = \dfrac{1}{2}e^{2x} + c$

17. $e^y = \dfrac{1}{2}e^{2x} + \dfrac{5}{2}$

18. $y = \dfrac{1}{3}\sin 3x + c$

19. $y = \dfrac{1}{3}\sin 3x + 1$

20. $y = 0$ and $\ln|y| = 2\ln|x| + c$ or $y = cx^2$

21. $y = 4x^2$

22. $\sin 2y = 2x + c$ or $y = \dfrac{1}{2}\sin^{-1}(2x + c)$

23. $\sin 2y = 2x - 1$ or $y = \dfrac{1}{2}\sin^{-1}(2x - 1)$

24. $-\dfrac{1}{2}e^{-y^2} = -\cos x + c$ or $e^{-y^2} = 2\cos x + c$

25. $-\dfrac{1}{2}e^{-y^2} = -\cos x - 3/2$ or $e^{-y^2} = 2\cos x + 3$

26. $y = 1$ and $-\ln|1 - y| = \dfrac{1}{2}\ln(x^2 + 1) + c$ or $(y-1)^2(x^2+1) = c$

27. $-\ln|1-y| = \dfrac{1}{2}\ln(x^2+1)$ or $(y-1)^2(x^2+1) = 1$

28. $y = -1$ and $2\ln|y^3+1| = 3x^2+c$

29. $2\ln|y^3+1| = 3x^2-12$

30. $3e^{2y}-e^{-y} = x-\ln|x+1|+c$

31. $3e^{2y}-e^{-y} = x-\ln|x+1|+4$

32. $y^2-2e^{-y} = -2\cos x+c$

33. $y^2-2e^{-y} = -2\cos x-4$

34. $-2e^{-y^2} = -x+2\ln|x+2|+c$

35. $-2e^{-y^2} = -x+2\ln|x+2|-5$

36. $y+y^3 = 2x^2-\ln|x|+c$

37. $y+y^3 = 2x^2-\ln|x|-12$

38. $\ln(y^2+1) = 2\tan x+c$ or $y^2 = ce^{2\tan x}-1$

39. $y = -1$ and $2\ln|y^3+1| = 3x^2+6\ln|x|+c$

40. $y = 0$ and $y+\ln|y| = x-e^{-x}+c$

41. $y+\ln|y| = x-e^{-x}+2$

42. $y = -4$ and $2\ln|y+4| = x^2+4\ln|x|+c$ or $\ln\dfrac{|y+4|}{x^2} = \dfrac{1}{2}x^2+c$

43. $2\ln|y+4| = x^2+4\ln|x|-1$ or $\ln\dfrac{|y+4|}{x^2} = \dfrac{1}{2}x^2-\dfrac{1}{2}$

44. $\ln(y^2+4) = -e^{-x^2}+c$

45. $\ln|y| = \ln(1+e^x)+c$ or $y = c(1+e^x)$

46. $\ln|y| = \ln(1+e^x)+\ln 3$ or $y = 3(1+e^x)$

47. $y = 2$ and $y+\ln|y-2| = x+4\ln|x-3|+c$

48. $y+\ln|y-2| = x+4\ln|x-3|-3$

1. Identifying DE as linear, separable, both, or neither

2. Identifying DE as linear, separable, both, or neither

3. Identifying DE as linear, separable, both, or neither

4. Identifying DE as linear, separable, both, or neither

5. Identifying DE as linear, separable, both, or neither

6. Identifying DE as linear, separable, both, or neither

7. Identifying DE as linear, separable, both, or neither

8. Identifying DE as linear, separable, both, or neither

9. Identifying DE as linear, separable, both, or neither

10. Identifying DE as linear, separable, both, or neither

11. Identifying DE as linear, separable, both, or neither

12. linear differential equation – concepts multiple choice

13. linear differential equation – concepts true or false

14. linear differential equation – concepts true or false

15. linear differential equation – concepts true or false

16. linear differential equation – concepts true or false

17. solve a linear DE by integrating factors, with an initial condition

18. solve a linear DE by integrating factors, with an initial condition

19. solve a linear DE by integrating factors

20. solve a linear DE by integrating factors

21. solve a linear DE by integrating factors, with an initial condition

22. solve a linear DE by integrating factors

23. solve a linear DE by integrating factors, with an initial condition

24. solve a linear DE by integrating factors, with an initial condition

25. solve a linear DE by integrating factors, with an initial condition

26. solve a linear DE by integrating factors

27. solve a linear DE by integrating factors

28. solve a linear DE by integrating factors

29. solve a linear DE by integrating factors, with an initial condition

30. solve a linear DE by integrating factors

31. solve a linear DE by integrating factors

32. solve a linear DE by integrating factors

33. solve a linear DE by integrating factors

1. Identify the differential equation $x^2 \dfrac{dy}{dx} + (3\,x^2 + 2)\,y = 6\,e^{-6x}$. Assume that y is a function of x.

   (a) linear
   (b) separable
   (c) (a) and (b)
   (d) none of the above

2. Identify the differential equation $y^2\,y' = xy^3 + x$. Assume that y is a function of x.

   (a) linear
   (b) separable
   (c) (a) and (b)
   (d) none of the above

3. Identify the differential equation $(6e^{3y} + 1)(x + 1)\,dy - xe^y\,dx = 0$. Assume that y is a function of x.

   (a) linear
   (b) separable
   (c) (a) and (b)
   (d) none of the above

4. Identify the differential equation $(y + e^{-y})\,y' = \sin x$. Assume that y is a function of x.

   (a) linear
   (b) separable
   (c) (a) and (b)
   (d) none of the above

5. Identify the differential equation $x^2 \dfrac{dy}{dx} + y\,\cos x = 4\,e^{-5x}$. Assume that y is a function of x.

   (a) linear
   (b) separable
   (c) (a) and (b)
   (d) none of the above

6. Identify the differential equation $y\,y' = e^{y^2} \sin x$. Assume that y is a function of x.

   (a) linear
   (b) separable
   (c) (a) and (b)
   (d) none of the above

7. Identify the differential equation $x^2\,y' + 15y^4 = 2xy$. Assume that y is a function of x.

   (a) linear
   (b) separable
   (c) (a) and (b)
   (d) none of the above

8. Identify the differential equation $x^3 y' + \ln x = 4 y e^{3x}$. Assume that y is a function of x.

    (a) linear

    (b) separable

    (c) (a) and (b)

    (d) none of the above

9. Identify the differential equation $x^2 y' = y^2 \sin x + 2xy$. Assume that y is a function of x.

    (a) linear

    (b) separable

    (c) (a) and (b)

    (d) none of the above

10. Identify the differential equation $\dfrac{dy}{dx} = 2xy^2 + 2xy$. Assume that y is a function of x.

    (a) linear

    (b) separable

    (c) (a) and (b)

    (d) none of the above

11. Identify the differential equation $\dfrac{dy}{dx} = \dfrac{x - xy}{x^2 + 1}$. Assume that y is a function of x.

    (a) linear

    (b) separable

    (c) (a) and (b)

    (d) none of the above

12. To solve a 1st order linear differential equation, we must evaluate

    (a) 1 integral.

    (b) 2 integrals.

    (c) 3 integrals.

    (d) It depends on the problem.

13. True or False: Separable differential equations are also linear.

14. True or False: Linear differential equations are also separable.

15. True or False: We may solve a separable differential equation by integrating factors.

16. True or False: We may solve a linear differential equation by integrating factors.

17. (a) Solve the differential equation $(x^2 + 4) \dfrac{dy}{dx} + 2xy = 0$.

    (b) Determine the solution if the initial condition is $y(0) = 2$.

18. (a) Solve the differential equation $(x^3 - 9) y' + 6 x^2 y = 0$.

    (b) Determine the solution if the initial condition is $y(2) = 3$.

19. Solve the differential equation $\dfrac{dy}{dx} + \left(3 + \dfrac{2}{x}\right) y = \dfrac{6}{x^2} e^{-6x}$.

20. Solve the differential equation $\quad x^3 y' + (3x^2 - x^3) y = 4 e^{3x}$.

21. (a) Solve the differential equation $\quad y' - y = e^x \cos 2x$.

    (b) Determine the solution if the initial condition is $y(0) = 4$.

22. Solve the differential equation $\quad x \dfrac{dy}{dx} + (3x + 2) y = \dfrac{4}{x} e^{-5x}$.

23. (a) Solve the differential equation $\quad x \dfrac{dy}{dx} + 2y = \dfrac{3}{x} \sec^2 x$.

    (b) Determine the solution if the initial condition is $y(\pi) = -2$.

24. (a) Solve the differential equation $\quad x^2 \dfrac{dy}{dx} + (x + 2x^3) y = 6 x^2$.

    (b) Determine the solution if the initial condition is $y(1) = -2$.

25. (a) Solve the differential equation $\quad \dfrac{dy}{dx} + \left(\dfrac{1 - 2x}{x} \right) y = \dfrac{6}{x}$.

    (b) Determine the solution if the initial condition is $y(1) = 3$.

26. Solve the differential equation $\quad x y' + 3y = \sin x^3$.

27. Solve the differential equation $\quad \dfrac{dy}{dx} + \dfrac{2}{x} y = 6 e^{-x^3}$.

28. Solve the differential equation $\quad x \dfrac{dy}{dx} + (3x + 1) y = 8 x^3 e^{-3x}$.

29. (a) Solve the differential equation $\quad y' + 2y = e^{-2x} \ln x$.

    (b) Determine the solution if the initial condition is $y(1) = 0$.

30. Solve the differential equation $\quad \dfrac{dy}{dx} + \left(2x + \dfrac{1}{x} \right) y = 4$.

31. Solve the differential equation $\quad x^2 \dfrac{dy}{dx} + (x - 3x^2) y = 2 x e^{-x}$.

32. Solve the differential equation $\quad \dfrac{dx}{dy} + \left(2y + \dfrac{1}{y} \right) x = 4$.

33. Solve the differential equation $\quad y^2 \dfrac{dx}{dy} + (y - 3y^2) x = 2 y e^{-y}$.

1. a

2. d

3. b

4. b

5. a

6. b

7. d

8. a

9. a

10. c

11. c

12. b

13. False

14. False

15. False

16. True

17. (a) $y = \dfrac{c}{x^2 + 4}$,   (b) $y = \dfrac{8}{x^2 + 4}$

18. (a) $y = \dfrac{c}{(x^3 - 9)^2}$,   (b) $y = \dfrac{3}{(x^3 - 9)^2}$

19. $y = -\dfrac{2}{x^2} e^{-6x} + \dfrac{c}{x^2} e^{-3x}$

20. $y = -\dfrac{2}{x^3} e^{3x} + \dfrac{c}{x^3} e^{x}$

21. (a) $y = e^x \left(c + \dfrac{1}{2} \sin 2x\right)$,   (b) $y = e^x \left(4 + \dfrac{1}{2} \sin 2x\right)$

22. $y = -\dfrac{2}{x^2} e^{-5x} + \dfrac{c}{x^2} e^{-3x}$

23. (a) $y = \dfrac{3 \tan x + c}{x^2}$,   (b) $y = \dfrac{3 \tan x - 2\pi^2}{x^2}$

24. (a) $y = \dfrac{3}{x} + \dfrac{c}{x} e^{-x^2}$,   (b) $y = \dfrac{3}{x} - \dfrac{5}{x} e^{1-x^2}$

25. (a) $y = -\dfrac{3}{x} + \dfrac{c}{x} e^{2x}$,   (b) $y = -\dfrac{3}{x} + \dfrac{6}{x} e^{2(x-1)}$

26. $y = -\dfrac{1}{3x^3}\cos x^3 + \dfrac{c}{x^3}$

27. $y = -\dfrac{2}{x^2}e^{-x^3} + \dfrac{c}{x^2}$

28. $y = 2x^3 e^{-3x} + \dfrac{c}{x}e^{-3x}$

29. (a) $y = e^{-2x}\left(x\ln x - x + c\right),$ (b) $y = e^{-2x}\left(x\ln x - x + 1\right)$

30. $y = \dfrac{2}{x} + \dfrac{c}{x}e^{-x^2}$

31. $y = -\dfrac{1}{2x}e^{-x} + \dfrac{c}{x}e^{3x}$

32. $x = \dfrac{2}{y} + \dfrac{c}{y}e^{-y^2}$

33. $x = -\dfrac{1}{2y}e^{-y} + \dfrac{c}{y}e^{3y}$

1. Identify DE as linear, separable, exact, or none.

2. Identify DE as linear, separable, exact, or none.

3. Identify DE as linear, separable, exact, or none.

4. Identify DE as linear, separable, exact, or none.

5. Identify DE as linear, separable, exact, or none.

6. Identify DE as linear, separable, exact, or none.

7. Identify DE as linear, separable, exact, or none.

8. Identify DE as linear, separable, exact, or none.

9. Find a constant so that the DE is exact.

10. Find a constant so that the DE is exact.

11. Find a constant so that the DE is exact.

12. True or False; Exact ODEs — concepts

13. True or False; Exact ODEs — concepts

14. True or False; Exact ODEs — concepts

15. True or False; Exact ODEs — concepts

16. Show exactness and solve; also includes initial condition

17. Show exactness and solve; also includes initial condition

18. Show exactness and solve;

19. Show exactness and solve; also includes initial condition

20. Show exactness and solve; also includes initial condition

21. Show exactness and solve; also includes initial condition

22. Show exactness and solve; also includes initial condition

23. Show exactness and solve; also includes initial condition

24. Show exactness and solve; also includes initial condition

25. Show exactness and solve; also includes initial condition

26. Show exactness and solve; also includes initial condition

27. Show exactness and solve; also includes initial condition

28. Show exactness and solve;

29. Show exactness and solve; also includes initial condition

30. Show exactness and solve; also includes initial condition

1. Identify the differential equation $y\,y' = e^{y^2}\sin x$. Assume that y is a function of x.

   (a) linear
   (b) separable
   (c) exact
   (d) none of the above

2. Identify the differential equation $(x^2 + 1)\,dy = (x^2 - xy)\,dx$. Assume that y is a function of x.

   (a) linear
   (b) separable
   (c) exact
   (d) none of the above

3. Identify the differential equation $y^2\,y' = xy^3 + x$. Assume that y is a function of x.

   (a) linear
   (b) separable
   (c) exact
   (d) none of the above

4. Identify the differential equation $2\,x\sin y\,dx - x^2\cos y\,dx = 0$. Assume that y is a function of x.

   (a) linear
   (b) separable
   (c) exact
   (d) none of the above

5. Identify the differential equation $y\cos 2x\,dx + (\sin 2x - y)\,dy = 0$. Assume that y is a function of x.

   (a) linear
   (b) separable
   (c) exact
   (d) none of the above

6. Identify the differential equation $x^3\,y' + (3x^2 - x^3)\,y = 4\,e^{3x}$. Assume that y is a function of x.

   (a) linear
   (b) separable
   (c) exact
   (d) none of the above

7. Identify the differential equation $\dfrac{dy}{dx} = 2xy^2 + 2xy$. Assume that y is a function of x.

   (a) linear
   (b) separable
   (c) exact
   (d) none of the above

8. Identify the differential equation $(y - x) y' = x + y$. Assume that y is a function of x.

    (a) linear

    (b) separable

    (c) exact

    (d) none of the above

9. For the differential equation $(e^{2y} \cos x - 2x) \, dx = k e^{2y} \sin x \, dy$ to be exact, the value of k must be

    (a) 1.

    (b) 2.

    (c) -1

    (d) -2

10. For the differential equation $xy^2 \, dy - k x^2 y \, dx = 0$ to be exact, the value of k must be

    (a) 1.

    (b) 2.

    (c) -1

    (d) -2

11. For the differential equation $(\cos 2y + x) \, dx + kx \sin 2y \, dy = 0$ to be exact, the value of k must be

    (a) 1.

    (b) 2.

    (c) -1

    (d) -2

12. True or False: Exact differential equations are also linear.

13. True or False: Exact differential equations are also separable.

14. True or False: We may solve an exact differential equation by integrating factors.

15. True or False: Solving a 1st order exact differential equation requires evaluating two integrals.

16. Show that the differential equation is exact, and then solve it accordingly.
$$xy^4 \, dx + 2x^2 y^3 \, dy = 0$$

What is the solution if the initial condition is $y(-1) = 2$?

17. Show that the differential equation is exact, and then solve it accordingly.
$$x e^{-2y} \, dx - x^2 e^{-2y} \, dy = 0$$

What is the solution if the initial condition is $y(-1) = 0$?

18. Show that the differential equation is exact, and then solve it accordingly.
$$\frac{y^2}{x} \, dx + y \ln x^2 \, dy = 0$$

45

19. Show that the differential equation is exact, and then solve it accordingly.
$$2x \cos 3y \, dx \; - \; 3x^2 \sin 3y \, dy \; = \; 0$$
What is the solution if the initial condition is $y(1) = 0$?

20. Show that the differential equation is exact, and then solve it accordingly.
$$(x \cos 2y + 12 \, x^2) \, dx \; + \; (4 \, y^3 - x^2 \sin 2y) \, dy \; = \; 0$$
What is the solution if the initial condition is $y(-1) = 0$?

21. Show that the differential equation is exact, and then solve it accordingly.
$$(y^2 \cos x - 2x) \, dx \; + \; (2y \sin x + 4e^{-y}) \, dy \; = \; 0$$
What is the solution if the initial condition is $y(0) = 0$?

22. Show that the differential equation is exact, and then solve it accordingly.
$$\left(\frac{1}{y} + 2 \, y \, e^{-x} \right) dy \; = \; \left(y^2 \, e^{-x} - 2x \cos x^2 \right) dx$$
What is the solution if the initial condition is $y(0) = -1$?

23. Show that the differential equation is exact, and then solve it accordingly.
$$(4xy^3 - \cos y - e^{-x}) \, dx \; + \; (6x^2 y^2 + x \sin y + 3) \, dy \; = \; 0$$
What is the solution if the initial condition is $y(0) = 0$?

24. Show that the differential equation is exact, and then solve it accordingly.
$$(6 \, x \, y^3 + \cos 2x) \, dx \; + \; (9 \, x^2 \, y^2 + e^{-y}) \, dy \; = \; 0$$
What is the solution if the initial condition is $y(0) = 0$?

25. Show that the differential equation is exact, and then solve it accordingly.
$$(4x^3 y^2 + 3/x) \, dx \; + \; (2x^4 y + \sin y) \, dy \; = \; 0$$
What is the solution if the initial condition is $y(-1) = 0$?

26. Show that the differential equation is exact, and then solve it accordingly.
$$(4x^3 y^2 - e^{-x}) \, dx \; + \; (2x^4 y + 1/y) \, dy \; = \; 0$$
What is the solution if the initial condition is $y(0) = -1$?

27. Show that the differential equation is exact, and then solve it accordingly.
$$(2x \sin y + e^x) \, dx \; + \; (x^2 \cos y + 2y) \, dy \; = \; 0$$
What is the solution if the initial condition is $y(0) = 0$?

28. Show that the differential equation is exact, and then solve it accordingly.
$$(4x^3 - y^2 \sin x) \, dx \; + \; (2y \cos x + 12 \, y^2) \, dy \; = \; 0$$
What is the solution if the initial condition is $y(0) = -2$?

29. Show that the differential equation is exact, and then solve it accordingly.
$$(6 \, x \, y^3 + \cos y - e^x) \, dx \; + \; (9 \, x^2 \, y^2 - x \, \sin y + 1/y) \, dy \; = \; 0$$

30. Show that the differential equation is exact, and then solve it accordingly.
$$\left(\frac{1}{x-2} - \frac{1}{y} \right) dx \; + \; \frac{x}{y^2} \, dy \; = \; 0$$
What is the solution if the initial condition is $y(1) = -1$?

1. b

2. a

3. b

4. d

5. d

6. a

7. b

8. c

9. d

10. c

11. d

12. False

13. False

14. False

15. True

16. $x^2 y^4 = c$, $x^2 y^4 = 4$

17. $x^2 e^{-2y} = c$, $x^2 e^{-2y} = 1$

18. $y^2 \ln x = c$

19. $x^2 \cos 3y = c$, $x^2 \cos 3y = 1$

20. $x^2 \cos 2y + 8x^3 + 2y^4 = c$, $x^2 \cos 2y + 8x^3 + 2y^4 = -7$

21. $y^2 \sin x - x^2 - 4e^{-y} = c$, $y^2 \sin x - x^2 - 4e^{-y} = -4$

22. $\sin x^2 + y^2 e^{-x} + \ln|y| = c$, $\sin x^2 + y^2 e^{-x} + \ln|y| = 1$

23. $2x^2 y^3 - x \cos y + e^{-x} + 3y = c$, $2x^2 y^3 - x \cos y + e^{-x} + 3y = 1$

24. $6x^2 y^3 + \sin 2x - 2e^{-y} = c$, $6x^2 y^3 + \sin 2x - 2e^{-y} = -2$

25. $x^4 y^2 + 3 \ln|x| - \cos y = c$, $x^4 y^2 + 3 \ln|x| - \cos y = -1$

26. $x^4 y^2 + e^{-x} + \ln|y| = c$, $x^4 y^2 + e^{-x} + \ln|y| = 1$

27. $x^2 \sin y + e^x + y^2 = c$, $x^2 \sin y + e^x + y^2 = 1$

28. $x^4 + y^2 \cos x + 4x^3 = c$, $x^4 + y^2 \cos x + 4x^3 = 4$

29. $3x^2 y^3 + x \cos y - e^x + \ln|y| = c$

30. $y \ln|x - 2| - x = cy$, $y \ln|x - 2| - x = y$

47

1. classify DE as separable, Bernoulli, homogeneous, or none

2. classify DE as separable, Bernoulli, homogeneous, or none

3. classify DE as separable, Bernoulli, homogeneous, or none

4. classify DE as separable, Bernoulli, homogeneous, or none

5. classify DE as separable, Bernoulli, homogeneous, or none

6. classify DE as separable, Bernoulli, homogeneous, or none

7. classify DE as separable, Bernoulli, homogeneous, or none

8. homogeneous DE – concepts

9. Bernoulli DE – concepts

10. identifying degree of homogeneity

11. identifying degree of homogeneity

12. identifying degree of homogeneity

13. true or false – concepts

14. true or false – concepts

15. true or false – concepts

16. Determine degree of homogeneity and solve a homogeneous DE

17. Determine degree of homogeneity and solve a homogeneous DE

18. Determine degree of homogeneity and solve a homogeneous DE

19. Determine degree of homogeneity and solve a homogeneous DE

20. Determine degree of homogeneity and solve a homogeneous DE

21. Determine degree of homogeneity and solve a homogeneous DE

22. Solve a Bernoulli DE

23. Solve a Bernoulli DE

24. Solve a Bernoulli DE

25. Solve a Bernoulli DE

26. Solve a Bernoulli DE

27. Solve by substitution

28. Solve by substitution

29. Solve by substitution

30. Solve by substitution

31. Solve by substitution

1. Identify the differential equation $y\,y' = e^{y^2}\sin x$

   (a) separable
   (b) Bernoulli
   (c) homogeneous
   (d) none of the above

2. Identify the differential equation $x^2\,y' = 2xy + 15y^4$

   (a) separable
   (b) Bernoulli
   (c) homogeneous
   (d) none of the above

3. Identify the differential equation $\dfrac{dy}{dx} = \dfrac{x - xy}{x^2 + 1}$

   (a) separable
   (b) Bernoulli
   (c) homogeneous
   (d) none of the above

4. Identify the differential equation $x^3\,y' = (3x - y)\,y^2$

   (a) separable
   (b) Bernoulli
   (c) homogeneous
   (d) none of the above

5. Identify the differential equation $(6e^{3y} + 1)(x + 1)\,dy - xe^y\,dx = 0$

   (a) separable
   (b) Bernoulli
   (c) homogeneous
   (d) none of the above

6. Identify the differential equation $(y + e^{-y})\,y' = \sin x$

   (a) separable
   (b) Bernoulli
   (c) homogeneous
   (d) none of the above

7. Identify the differential equation $y\,(x + y)\,dx = (x^2 + y^2)\,dy$

   (a) separable
   (b) Bernoulli
   (c) homogeneous
   (d) none of the above

8. We can always turn a homogeneous DE into a DE that is

   (a) separable

   (b) Bernoulli

   (c) linear

   (d) none of the above

9. We can always turn a Bernoulli differential equation into a DE that is

   (a) separable

   (b) linear

   (c) homogeneous

   (d) none of the above

10. The differential equation $(xy^2 + x^2 y)\,dx + x^3\,e^{y/x}\,dy = 0$

    (a) is homogeneous of degree 2.

    (b) is homogeneous of degree 3.

    (c) is homogeneous of degree 4.

    (d) is not homogeneous.

11. The differential equation $x^3 y y' = (x^2 y^2 - x y^3)\,e^{y/x}$

    (a) is homogeneous of degree 2.

    (b) is homogeneous of degree 3.

    (c) is homogeneous of degree 4.

    (d) is not homogeneous.

12. The differential equation $(x^2 + y^2)\,dx = x\,e^y\,dy$

    (a) is homogeneous of degree 2.

    (b) is homogeneous of degree 3.

    (c) is homogeneous of degree 4.

    (d) is not homogeneous.

13. True or False: It is possible for a homogeneous DE to also be exact.

14. True or False: It is impossible for a Bernoulli DE to be linear.

15. True or False: It is possible for a homogeneous DE to also be separable.

16. Verify that the differential equation is homogeneous and state its degree. Then solve it by using an appropriate substitution, and write the solution in explicit form. Then determine the solution that satisfies the initial condition.

$$2x^2\,dy = (2xy - y^2)\,dx, \qquad y(1) = 2$$

17. Verify that the differential equation is homogeneous and state its degree. Then solve it by using an appropriate substitution, and write the solution in explicit form. Then determine the solution that satisfies the initial condition.

$$xy^2\,dy = (y^3 - x^3)\,dx, \qquad y(1) = 3$$

18. Verify that the differential equation is homogeneous and state its degree. Then solve it by using an appropriate substitution. Then determine the solution that satisfies the initial condition.

$$(x^2 + 2y^2)\, dx \;-\; 2xy\, dy \;=\; 0\,, \qquad y(1) \;=\; 9$$

19. Verify that the differential equation is homogeneous and state its degree. Then solve it by using an appropriate substitution, and write the solution in explicit form. Then determine the solution that satisfies the initial condition.

$$x^2\, dy - (xy + y^2)\, dx \;=\; 0\,, \qquad y(-1) \;=\; 1$$

20. Verify that the differential equation is homogeneous and state its degree. Then solve it by using an appropriate substitution. Then determine the solution that satisfies the initial condition.

$$(x^2 + 2\, y^2)\, dy \;=\; xy\, dx\,, \qquad y(3) \;=\; -1$$

21. Verify that the differential equation is homogeneous and state its degree. Then solve it by using an appropriate substitution, and write the solution in explicit form. Then determine the solution that satisfies the initial condition.

$$x^2\, dy \;=\; (xy - y^2)\, dx\,, \qquad y(4) \;=\; -1$$

Problems 22-31: Solve the Bernoulli equation by using an appropriate substitution. Leave the solution in implicit form.

22. $\dfrac{dy}{dx} \;=\; 2xy^2 + 2xy$

23. $x^2\, y' \;=\; 2xy \,+\, 15y^4$

24. $2x^3\, \dfrac{dy}{dx} \;=\; 3x^2 y - y^3 \cos x$

25. $xy' + xy \;=\; -y^2\, e^x$

26. $x\, \dfrac{dy}{dx} \,-\, (1 + 2\, x^2)\, y \;=\; 4\, x\, y^2$

27. $y' \;=\; \cos^2(y - x)$

28. $y' \;=\; \sec^2(x - y)$

29. $y' \;=\; \dfrac{1}{y - x}$

30. $y' \;=\; \sqrt{y + 3x} - 3$

31. $y' \;=\; (x - y)^2$

1. a

2. b

3. a

4. c

5. a

6. a

7. c

8. a

9. b

10. b

11. c

12. d

13. True

14. False

15. True

16. homogeneous of degree 2. $y = 2x/(c + \ln|x|)$, $y = 2x/(1 + \ln|x|)$

17. homogeneous of degree 3. $y = x(c - 3\ln|x|)^{1/3}$, $y = x(27 - 3\ln|x|)^{1/3}$

18. homogeneous of degree 2. $y^2 = x^2(c + \ln|x|)$, $y^2 = x^2(81 + \ln|x|)$

19. homogeneous of degree 2. $y = x/(c - \ln|x|)$, $y = -x/(1 + \ln|x|)$

20. homogeneous of degree 2. $x = y(c + \ln y^2)$, $x = y(\ln y^2 - 3)$

21. homogeneous of degree 2. $y = x/(c + \ln|x|)$, $y = x/(\ln|x| - 4)$

22. $y = 1/(ce^{-x^2} - 1)$

23. $y^{-3} = -9/x + cx^{-6}$

24. $x^3 y^{-2} = \sin x + c$

25. $y^{-1} = e^x(c + \ln|x|)$

26. $x/y = ce^{-x^2} - 2$

27. $\cot(y - x) = x + c$

28. $y = \cot(x - y) + c$

29. $y + \ln|y - x - 1| = c$

30. $2\sqrt{y + 3x} = x + c$

31. $\dfrac{1 + x - y}{1 - x + y} = ce^{2x}$

1. Euler's method – how h relates to computational effort

2. Euler's method – how h relates to accuracy

3. Euler's method – concept about tangent line approximations

4. Euler's method – expressing the DE in the proper or "normal form"

5. Euler's method formula

6. True/False – Euler's method

7. True/False – Euler's method

8. True/False – RK4 method

9. True/False – Euler's method

10. True/False – Euler's method

11. True/False – RK4 method

12. Calculator not required. Use Euler's method to approximate the solution to an IVP at 2 points.

13. Calculator not required. Use Euler's method to approximate the solution to an IVP at 2 points.

14. Calculator not required. Use Euler's method to approximate the solution to an IVP at 2 points.

15. Calculator not required. Use Euler's method to approximate the solution to an IVP at 2 points.

16. Calculator not required. Use Euler's method to approximate the solution to an IVP at 2 points.

17. Calculator not required. Use Euler's method to approximate the solution to an IVP at 2 points.

18. Calculator not required. Use Euler's method to approximate the solution to an IVP at 2 points.

19. Calculator not required. Use Euler's method to approximate the solution to an IVP at 2 points.

20. Calculator required. Use Euler's method to approximate the solution to an IVP at 2 points.

21. Calculator required. Use Euler's method to approximate the solution to an IVP at 2 points.

22. Calculator required. Use Euler's method to approximate the solution to an IVP at 2 points.

23. Calculator required. Use Euler's method to approximate the solution to an IVP at 2 points.

24. Calculator required. Use Euler's method to approximate the solution to an IVP at 2 points.

25. Calculator required. Use Euler's method to approximate the solution to an IVP at 2 points.

26. Calculator required. Use Euler's method to approximate the solution to an IVP at 2 points.

1. When using Euler's method to approximate a solution to an IVP on an interval $[a, b]$, halving the stepsize h will increase the number of calculations by a factor of about

   (a) one.

   (b) two.

   (c) three.

   (d) four.

2. When using Euler's method to approximate a solution to an IVP on an interval $[a, b]$, halving the stepsize h will generally

   (a) increase the accuracy in the approximate results.

   (b) decrease the accuracy in the approximate results.

   (c) have little effect on the accuracy in the approximate results.

   (d) give the same accuracy in the approximate results.

3. Euler's method approximates the solution of an IVP $y' = f(x, y)$, $y(x_0) = y_0$ at a point (x_1, y_1) by

   (a) approximating function $f(x, y)$ by a tangent line at point (x_0, y_0).

   (b) approximating function $f(x, y)$ by a tangent line at point (x_1, y_1).

   (c) approximating the solution $y(x)$ by a tangent line at point (x_0, y_0).

   (d) approximating the solution $y(x)$ by a tangent line at point (x_1, y_1).

4. If we use Euler's method to approximate a solution to the IVP $\cos y \, dx = e^x \, dy$, $y(0) = 2$, we must first write the differential equation in the form

   (a) $y' = e^{-x} \sec y$.

   (b) $y' = e^x \cos y$.

   (c) $y' = e^x \sec y$.

   (d) $y' = e^{-x} \cos y$.

5. The formula for Euler's method to approximate the solution to an IVP at point (x_1, y_1) is

   (a) $y_1 = y_0 + h \, f(x_1, y_1)$

   (b) $y_1 = y_0 - h \, f(x_1, y_1)$

   (c) $y_1 = y_0 + h \, f(x_0, y_0)$

   (d) $y_1 = y_0 - h \, f(x_0, y_0)$

6. True or False: Euler's method for approximating a solution to an IVP is widely used.

7. True or False: Euler's method for approximating a solution to an IVP will always give reasonable results.

8. True or False: The RK4 method gives more accurate results than Euler's method when approximating a solution to an IVP.

9. True or False: When using Euler's method to approximate a solution to an IVP, we may increase the accuracy of our approximate results by decreasing the stepsize h.

10. True or False: Suppose we use Euler's method to approximate a solution to an IVP and we obtain points (x_1, y_1), (x_2, y_2), (x_3, y_3), and (x_4, y_4). Then those points are on the solution of the IVP.

11. True or False: Suppose we use the RK4 method to approximate a solution to an IVP and we obtain points (x_1, y_1), (x_2, y_2), (x_3, y_3), and (x_4, y_4). Then those points are on the solution of the IVP.

12. Use Euler's method with $h = 0.5$ to approximate the solution to the IVP $y' = 4xy + 2$, $y(0) = 1$, at $x = 0.5$ and $x = 1.0$.

13. Use Euler's method with $h = 0.5$ to approximate the solution to the IVP $y' = xy + 2$, $y(1) = 2$, at $x = 1.5$ and $x = 2.0$.

14. Use Euler's method with $h = 0.5$ to approximate the solution to the IVP $y' = x(y + 2)$, $y(0) = 2$, at $x = 0.5$ and $x = 1.0$.

15. Use Euler's method with $h = 1.0$ to approximate the solution to the IVP $y' = y\sqrt{x}$, $y(0) = 2$, at $x = 1$ and $x = 2$.

16. Use Euler's method with $h = 1.0$ to approximate the solution to the IVP $y' = x/y^2$, $y(0) = -1$, at $x = 1$ and $x = 2$.

17. Use Euler's method with $h = 1.0$ to approximate the solution to the IVP $y' = x^2 + y^3$, $y(0) = -1$, at $x = 1$ and $x = 2$.

18. Use Euler's method with $h = 1.0$ to approximate the solution to the IVP $y' = x^2 + y^3$, $y(2) = -1$, at $x = 3$ and $x = 4$.

19. Use Euler's method with $h = 1.0$ to approximate the solution to the IVP $y' = x + \ln y^2$, $y(0) = -1$, at $x = 1$ and $x = 2$.

20. Use Euler's method with $h = 0.5$ to approximate the solution to the IVP $y' = x + \ln y^2$, $y(0) = 2$, at $x = 0.5$ and $x = 1.0$.

21. Use Euler's method with $h = 0.5$ to approximate the solution to the IVP $y' = x + \ln y^2$, $y(1) = 2$, at $x = 1.5$ and $x = 2.0$.

22. Use Euler's method with $h = 0.5$ to approximate the solution to the IVP $y' = y e^{-x^2}$, $y(0) = 3$, at $x = 1.5$ and $x = 2.0$.

23. Use Euler's method with $h = 0.5$ to approximate the solution to the IVP $y' = y \cos \sqrt{x}$, $y(0) = 4$, at $x = 1.5$ and $x = 2.0$.

24. Use Euler's method with $h = 0.5$ to approximate the solution to the IVP $y' = x^2 + \ln y$, $y(1) = 4$, at $x = 1.5$ and $x = 2.0$.

25. Use Euler's method with $h = 0.5$ to approximate the solution to the IVP $y' = x + \cos 2y$, $y(0) = 3$, at $x = 0.5$ and $x = 1.0$.

26. Use Euler's method with $h = 0.5$ to approximate the solution to the IVP $y' = x + \cos 2y$, $y(1) = 2$, at $x = 1.5$ and $x = 2.0$.

1. b

2. a

3. c

4. d

5. c

6. False

7. False

8. True

9. True

10. False

11. False

12. $y_1 = 2$ at $x_1 = 0.5$ and $y_2 = 5$ at $x_2 = 1.0$

13. $y_1 = 4$ at $x_1 = 1.5$ and $y_2 = 8$ at $x_2 = 2.0$

14. $y_1 = 2$ at $x_1 = 0.5$ and $y_2 = 3$ at $x_2 = 1.0$

15. $y_1 = 2$ at $x_1 = 1$ and $y_2 = 4$ at $x_2 = 2$

16. $y_1 = -1$ at $x_1 = 1$ and $y_2 = 0$ at $x_2 = 2$

17. $y_1 = -2$ at $x_1 = 1$ and $y_2 = -9$ at $x_2 = 2$

18. $y_1 = 3$ at $x_1 = 2.0$ and $y_2 = 19$ at $x_2 = 3$

19. $y_1 = -1$ at $x_1 = 1$ and $y_2 = 0$ at $x_2 = 2$

20. $y_1 = 2.693147180$ at $x_1 = 0.5$ and $y_2 = 3.933857645$ at $x_2 = 1.0$

21. $y_1 = 3.193147180$ at $x_1 = 1.5$ and $y_2 = 5.104154187$ at $x_2 = 2.0$

22. $y_1 = 4.500000000$ at $x_1 = 0.5$ and $y_2 = 6.252301762$ at $x_2 = 1.0$

23. $y_1 = 6.000000000$ at $x_1 = 0.5$ and $y_2 = 8.280733792$ at $x_2 = 1.0$

24. $y_1 = 5.193147180$ at $x_1 = 1.5$ and $y_2 = 7.141817133$ at $x_2 = 2.0$

25. $y_1 = 3.480085143$ at $x_1 = 0.5$ and $y_2 = 4.119817646$ at $x_2 = 1.0$

26. $y_1 = 2.173178190$ at $x_1 = 1.5$ and $y_2 = 2.744221350$ at $x_2 = 2.0$

3.1 Linear Models

1. population growth
2. population growth
3. population growth
4. radioactive decay
5. radioactive decay
6. radioactive decay
7. population growth
8. radioactive decay
9. population growth
10. heating/colling
11. radioactive decay
12. radioactive decay
13. radioactive decay
14. radioactive decay
15. population growth
16. population growth
17. population growth
18. population growth
19. population growth
20. population growth
21. radioactive decay
22. radioactive decay
23. radioactive decay
24. radioactive decay
25. radioactive decay
26. radioactive decay
27. radioactive decay
28. radioactive decay
29. heating/cooling

30. radioactive decay

31. radioactive decay

32. drug metabolism

33. populations in a closed environment

34. populations in a closed environment

35. hydrostatic equation with constant density and constant gravitational acceleration

36. mixtures

37. mixtures

38. LR circuit

39. RC circuit

40. RC circuit with step down voltage source

1. Suppose a population grows at a rate that is proportional to the population present at time t. If the population doubles every 20 years and the present population is 5 million members, how long will it take for the population to reach 320 million members?

    (a) 16 years

    (b) 32 years

    (c) 64 years

    (d) 120 years

2. Suppose a population grows at a rate that is proportional to the population present at time t. If the population doubles every 40 years and the present population is 10 million members, what will the population be in 200 years?

    (a) 50 million

    (b) 160 million

    (c) 320 million

    (d) 640 million

3. Suppose a population grows at a rate that is proportional to the population present at time t. If the population triples every 60 years, how often does it take for the population to double?

    (a) $60 \ln(3/2)$ years

    (b) $60 \ln(2/3)$ years

    (c) $60 \dfrac{\ln 3}{\ln 2}$ years

    (d) $60 \dfrac{\ln 2}{\ln 3}$ years

4. Suppose a radioactive element has a half-life of 40 years. If 128 grams of the element are now present, how much will remain after 200 years?

    (a) 2 grams

    (b) 4 grams

    (c) 8 grams

    (d) 16 grams

5. Suppose a radioactive element has a half-life of 500 years. What percentage of the original amount remains after 1,500 years?

    (a) 12.5%

    (b) 25%

    (c) 33%

    (d) 75%

6. Suppose a radioactive substance has a half-life of 400 years. What percentage of the original amount has decayed after 800 years?

    (a) 25%

    (b) 33%

    (c) 50%

    (d) 75%

7. Suppose a population grows at a rate that is proportional to the population present at time t. If the population increases by a factor of 5 in 100 years, how often does it take for the population to double?

   (a) $100 \ln(2/5)$ years

   (b) $100 \ln(5/2)$ years

   (c) $100 \dfrac{\ln 5}{\ln 2}$ years

   (d) $100 \dfrac{\ln 2}{\ln 5}$ years

8. Suppose the amount x of a substance decays at a rate proportional to the amount present at time t. The differential equation that models this is (assume $k > 0$)

   (a) $dx/dt = -kt$

   (b) $dx/dt = kt$

   (c) $dx/dt = -kx$

   (d) $dx/dt = kx$

9. Suppose that a population x grows at a rate proportional to the population present at time t. The differential equation that models this is (assume $k > 0$)

   (a) $dx/dt = -kt$

   (b) $dx/dt = kt$

   (c) $dx/dt = -kx$

   (d) $dx/dt = kx$

10. If a cool object is placed in a hot oven that is maintained at a temperature of T_m, then the object's temperature $T(t)$ at time t varies according to the model (assume $k > 0$)

    (a) $\dfrac{dT}{dt} = k(T - T_m)$

    (b) $\dfrac{dT}{dt} = k(t - T_m)$

    (c) $\dfrac{dT}{dt} = k(T_m - T)$

    (d) $\dfrac{dT}{dt} = k(T_m - t)$

11. True or False: A radioactive element with a half-life of 1,000 years is more stable than a radioactive element with a half-life of 100 years.

12. True or False: The phrase *half-life* of a radioactive element refers to the time it takes for half of the amount originally present to decay.

13. True or False: The phrase *half-life* of a radioactive element refers to half the time it takes the total amount of material originally present to decay.

14. True or False: If the half-life of a radioactive element is 20 years, then 1/4 of the substance decays in 5 years.

15. Suppose a population grows at a rate that is proportional to the population present at time t. If the population doubles every 15 years and the present population is 5 million members, how long will it take for the population to reach 100 million members?

16. Suppose a population grows at a rate that is proportional to the population present at time t. If the population doubles every 40 years and the present population is 100 million members, what will the population be in 300 years?

17. Suppose a population grows at a rate that is proportional to the population present at time t. If the population doubles every 40 years and the present population is 100 million members, what will the population be in 20 years?

18. Suppose a population grows at a rate that is proportional to the population present at time t. If the population triples in 100 years, how long does it take for the population to double?

19. Suppose a population grows at a rate that is proportional to the population present at time t. If the population increases by a factor of 6 in 200 years, how often does it take for the population to double?

20. Suppose a bacteria culture grows at a rate that is proportional to the population present at time t. If the bacteria population (measured in μg) triples in 2 days and the initial population is 0.2 μg, what will the population be in 1 week?

21. Suppose a radioactive element has a half-life of 40 years. If 30 grams of the element are now present, how much will remain after 20 years?

22. Suppose a radioactive element has a half-life of 30 years. If 60 grams of the element are now present, how much will remain after 100 years?

23. Suppose a radioactive element has a half-life of 70 years. If 50 grams of the element are now present, how much will have decayed after 300 years?

24. Suppose a radioactive element has a half-life of 300 years. What percentage of the original amount remains after 2,000 years?

25. Suppose a radioactive substance has a half-life of 4,000 years. What percentage of the original amount remains after 250 years?

26. Suppose a radioactive substance has a half-life of 14,000 years. What percentage of the original amount will have decayed after 1,000 years?

27. Suppose the amount of a radioactive substance decreases to 30% the original amount in 10,000 years. What is the half-life of the substance?

28. Suppose the amount of a radioactive substance decreases by 30% in 10,000 years. What is the half-life of the substance?

29. A textbook is left overnight in the trunk of a car during winter, and it reaches a temperature of 10 °F. The book is then brought into a room that is at 72 °F, and after 10 minutes the book has reached a temperature of 40 °F. What is the book's temperature 1 hour after it was brought into the room?

30. A calculator at 74 °F is placed in a car trunk where the temperature is only 20 °F. The calculator's temperature decreases 2 °F after 1 minute. When will the calculator's temperature drop to 32 °F?

31. A calculator at 70 °F is placed inside an enclosed car where the temperature is 160 °F. The calculator's temperature increases 30 °F after 7 minutes. a) What will the calculator's temperature be 1 hour after it is placed in the car? b) If the calculator can sustain a maximum temperature of only 120 °F, when will the calculator be damaged by the heat?

32. A dose d of drug is given to a patient at time $t = 0$. The body metabolizes the drug so that the drug level y in the body decreases at a rate proportional to the drug level y in the body. Consequently, the drug level y in the body at time t is modelled by the initial value problem (IVP)

$$\frac{dy}{dt} = -ky, \qquad y(0) = d \tag{1}$$

where d is the dose given (a constant) at time $t = 0$, and the constant of proportionality k is the relative rate of metabolism of the drug.

(a) Solve the IVP (1) to obtain y explicitly in terms of t, d, and k.

(b) Plot the drug level $y(t)$ on time interval $0 \le t \le 20$ if the initial dose is 10 units and $k = 0.25$.

(c) Suppose the drug level becomes ineffective when it reaches level $y = 2$ units in the body. When does the drug level become ineffective in the case when $d = 10$ and $k = 0.25$? (Use algebra, not the plot, to answer this.)

33. Consider a species confined within a closed environment (an environment wherein nutrients are supplied but metabolic waste is not removed). Examples would include a petri dish where a biological culture is grown and then harvested; a specific example would be growing a flu vaccine inside an egg.

As the culture's population increases, more metabolic waste is produced. When the amount of waste reaches a critical level it becomes toxic to the culture, thus killing members of the population. Consequently, initially the culture's population increases, but when the waste starts becoming toxic, the population reaches a maximum value P_{max}. It is then that the culture should be harvested because thereafter the population decreases until eventually the population P is zero and there are no members remaining to be harvested.

It can be shown[1] that the population may be modeled by the governing equation

$$\frac{dP}{dr} = -k \frac{r}{r+1}, \tag{2}$$

where P is the population, r is a variable that represents the relative growth rate of the population, and k is a constant related to the sensitivity of the species to the toxin.

(a) Solve the above differential equation for population P as a function of r. The solution will also involve the toxicity constant k.

(b) Apply the initial condition $P(r_0) = P_0$ to the result in step (a) and rewrite the solution $P(r)$.

(c) We are interested in knowing when to harvest the culture, *i.e.*, in knowing when the population attains its maximum. This occurs when $r = 0$. Consequently, evaluate $P(0)$ in step (b) to determine the maximum population, P_{max}. Simplify the result.

(d) We know that $r_0 = (1 - P_0)/k$. Substitute this into your result from step (c) to obtain an alternative expression for P_{max}.

   The resulting formula enables us to approximate the maximum population of the culture provided the initial population P_0 and the toxicity constant k are known (k must be determined experimentally).

---

[1] Kevin G. TeBeest. Numerical and Analytical Solutions of Volterra's Population Model. SIAM Review, Vol. 39, No. 3, pp. 484-493, September 1997.

34. In reference to the previous problem, it can be shown[1] that the population also satisfies the governing initial value problem

$$k\,p' + p = 1 - x, \qquad p(0) = p_0,$$

where p is the population, x is a variable, and k is a constant related to the sensitivity of the species to the toxin.

(a) Solve the above DE for to obtain population p explicitly in terms of x, k, and p_0.

(b) We are interested in knowing when to harvest the culture, i.e., in knowing when the population attains its maximum; this occurs when $p'(x) = 0$. Consequently, determine the critical value x_c at which $p'(x) = 0$.

(c) Evaluate $p(x_c)$ to determine the maximum population, P_{max}.

35. The hydrostatic equation $\quad dP = -\rho g\, dz \quad$ models the pressure $P(z)$ of a static fluid at altitude z where ρ is the fluid density, and g is planet's gravitational acceleration at its surface. Assuming that ρ and g are constant, solve the above DE subject to the constraint $P(0) = P_0$ to obtain pressure P explicitly in terms of z, ρ, g, and P_0, where P_0 is the pressure at altitude $z = 0$.

36. Consider the mixing of two salt solutions in a large tank. Suppose the tank holds 1,000 liters of brine with 10 liters entering per minute. The concentration of the salt in the inflow is 0.6 kilograms per liter. The solution is well stirred and is pumped out at 10 liters per minute. Initially there are 50 kg of salt in the tank.

(a) Determine the amount of salt in the tank at time t.

(b) How much salt is in the tank after a long period of time?

(c) When does the amount of salt in the tank reach 550 kg?

37. Suppose in the previous problem the outflow of the mixed brine is only 8 liters per minute.

(a) Determine the amount of salt in the tank at time t.

(b) When will the tank contain 2,000 liters of brine?

38. A 220 volt electromotive force is applied to an LR circuit in which the inductance is 2 henries and the resistance is 10 ohms.

(a) Determine the current $i(t)$ if the initial current in the circuit is 0 amps.

(b) What is the steady state current in the circuit?

39. A 200 volt electromotive force is applied to an RC circuit in which the capacitance is 0.01 farads and the resistance is 10 ohms.

(a) Determine the charge $q(t)$ on the capacitor if the initial charge is 0 coulombs.

(b) What is the steady state charge on the capacitor?

40. An electromotive force

$$E(t) = \begin{cases} 200, & 0 \le t \le 5 \\ 0, & t > 5 \end{cases}$$

is applied to an RC circuit in which the capacitance is 0.1 farads and the resistance is 50 ohms.

(a) Determine the charge $q(t)$ on the capacitor if the initial charge is 0 coulombs.

(b) What is the charge on the capacitor at $t = 10$ seconds?

1. d

2. c

3. d

4. b

5. a

6. d

7. d

8. c

9. d

10. c

11. True

12. True

13. False

14. False

15. $t = 300/\ln 2 = 432.8$ years

16. $P = 100\, e^{7.5\ln 2} = 18.102$ billion

17. $P = 100\, e^{0.5\ln 2} = 141,421,356$

18. $t = 100\,\dfrac{\ln 2}{\ln 3} = 63.1$ years

19. $200\,\dfrac{\ln 2}{\ln 6} = 77.37$ years

20. $P = 0.2\, e^{3.5\ln 3} = 9.353\ \mu$g

21. $x = 30\, e^{-0.75\,\ln 2} = 17.838$ grams

22. $x = 60\, e^{-10/3\,\ln 2} = 5.953$ grams

23. $x = 50 - 50\, e^{-30/7\,\ln 2} = 47.44$ grams

24. $e^{-20/3\,\ln 2} \cdot 100\% = 0.984\ \%$

25. $e^{-1/16\,\ln 2} \cdot 100\% = 95.76\ \%$

26. $100 - e^{-1/14\,\ln 2} \cdot 100\% = 4.83\ \%$

27. $-10,000\,\dfrac{\ln 2}{\ln 0.3} = 5,757$ years

28. $-10,000\,\dfrac{\ln 2}{\ln 0.7} = 19,433.6$ years

29. $T = 70.83\,°F$

30. $t = 39.85$ minutes

31. a) $T = 157.2\,°F$.   b) After only $t = 14$ minutes

32. (a) $y(t) = d\,e^{-kt}$

    (c) The drug becomes ineffective after about 6.44 hours

33. (a) $P(r) = k\left(\ln|r+1| - r\right) + C$

    (b) $P(r) = P_0 - k(r - r_0) + k\ln\left|\dfrac{r+1}{r_0+1}\right|$

    (c) $P_{max} = P_0 + k\,r_0 - k\ln|r_0 + 1|$

    (d) $P_{max} = 1 + k\ln\left|\dfrac{k}{1 - P_0 + k}\right|$

34. (a) $p(x) = 1 - x + k - (1 - p_0 + k)\,e^{-x/k}$

    (b) $x_c = -k\ln\left(\dfrac{k}{1 - p_0 + k}\right)$

    (c) $p_{max} = p(x_c) = 1 + k\ln\left(\dfrac{k}{1 - p_0 + k}\right)$

35. $P(z) = P_0 - \rho\,g\,z$

36. (a) $A(t) = 600 - 550\,e^{-t/100}$ kg

    (b) 600 kg of salt in the tank as $t \to \infty$

    (c) after about $t = 100\ln 11 = 240$ minutes

37. (a) $A(t) = 600 + 1.2\,t - 3.4375 \times 10^{13}/(500 + t)^{-4}$ kg

    (b) after about $t = 1170$ minutes

38. (a) $i(t) = 22 - 22\,e^{-5t}$ amps

    (b) the steady state current is 22 amps.

39. (a) $q(t) = 2 - 2\,e^{-10t}$ coulombs

    (b) the steady state charge is 2 coulombs.

40. (a) $q(t) = \begin{cases} 20 - 20\,e^{-t/5}, & 0 \le t \le 5 \\ 12.6424112\,e^{-(t-5)/5}, & t > 5 \end{cases}$

    (b) $q(10) = 4.6508832$ coulombs.

1. definition of relative rate of change

2. identifying the logistic equation

3. classification of the logistic equation

4. classifying a term in the logistic equation

5. inflow and outflow

6. linear drag force

7. nonlinear drag force

8. Newton's law of cooling/heating

9. modelling concepts

10. distance travelled in rectlinear motion

11. rectlinear projectile motion without drag

12. velocity *vs.* time in rectlinear projectile motion with nonlinear drag

13. altitude *vs.* time in rectlinear projectile motion with nonlinear drag force

14. velocity *vs.* time in rectlinear projectile motion with nonlinear drag

15. altitude *vs.* time in rectlinear projectile motion with nonlinear drag force

16. geodesic on a cone

17. hydrostatic equation

18. hydrostatic equation with variable density

19. hydrostatic equation with variable density and variable gravity

20. solve the logistic equation subject to given data

21. equilibrium solutions of the logistic equation

22. equilibrium solutions of the logistic equation with harvesting

23. velocity in pipe flow

24. leaking tank without friction

25. leaking tank with friction

1. If quantity x is a function of time, then the relative rate of change of x is

    (a) $\dot{x}$.

    (b) $\dfrac{\dot{x}}{x}$.

    (c) $\dfrac{x}{\dot{x}}$.

    (d) $\dfrac{\dot{x}}{t}$.

2. If constants a and b are positive, the logistic model for population growth is

    (a) $\dfrac{dP}{dt} = aP - bP^2$.

    (b) $\dfrac{dP}{dt} = aP^2 - bP$.

    (c) $\dfrac{dP}{dt} = aP + bP^2$.

    (d) $\dfrac{dP}{dt} = aP^2 + bP$.

3. The logistic model for population growth is

    (a) a linear differential equation.
    (b) an exact differential equation.
    (c) a homogeneous differential equation.
    (d) a Bernoulli differential equation.

4. In population models, a term of the form kP^2 accounts for

    (a) growth rate from births.
    (b) death rate from aging.
    (c) competition among the members of the population.
    (d) net growth rate (birth rate minus death rate).

5. If a liquid is flowing into a container at rate r_i and flowing out at rate r_o, then the rate of change of volume of liquid in the container is

    (a) $\dfrac{dV}{dt} = r_i - r_o$.

    (b) $\dfrac{dV}{dt} = r_o - r_i$.

    (c) $\dfrac{1}{V} \cdot \dfrac{dV}{dt} = r_o - r_i$.

    (d) $\dfrac{1}{V} \cdot \dfrac{dV}{dt} = r_i - r_o$.

6. When an object moves in a medium it experiences drag, such as air resistance. If the drag force exerted on the object is proportional to the object's speed, then the drag force is

    (a) $F_d = k\,|v|$.
    (b) $F_d = -k\,|v|$.
    (c) $F_d = k\,v$.
    (d) $F_d = -k\,v$.

7. When an object moves in a medium it experiences drag, such as air resistance. If the drag force exerted on the object is proportional to the square of the object's speed, then the drag force is (k is a positive constant)

   (a) $F_d = k\,v^2$.

   (b) $F_d = -k\,v^2$.

   (c) $F_d = k\,v|v|$.

   (d) $F_d = -k\,v|v|$.

8. If an object is placed in a medium of constant temperature T_m, then we might expect that the object's temperature T would be modelled by the equation (k is a positive constant)

   (a) $\dfrac{dT}{dt} = k\,(T - T_m)$.

   (b) $\dfrac{dT}{dt} = -k\,(T - T_m)$.

   (c) $\dfrac{dT}{dt} = k/(T - T_m)$.

   (d) $\dfrac{dT}{dt} = -k/(T - T_m)$.

9. True or False: All nonlinear differential equations that are models for real physical processes may be solved by separating variables.

10. True or False: If an object is undergoing rectilinear motion and its velocity at time t is v, then its distance travelled between times t_o and t_1 is $\displaystyle\int_{t_0}^{t_1} v(t)\,dt$.

11. Reconsider the simple model for projectile motion given by $dv/dt = -g$ and $ds/dt = v$ where only gravitational force is considered — that is, air resistance (drag) is ignored. Here $s = s(t)$ and $v = v(t)$ represent altitude and velocity respectively at time t, and g is the local gravitational acceleration.

    (a) Determine velocity $v(t)$ and altitude $s(t)$ if the initial velocity is 400 ft/s and the initial altitude is 20 ft.

    (b) When does the projectile attain its maximum altitude?

    (c) What is projectile's maximum altitude?

    (d) When does the projectile strike the ground?

    (e) At what speed will the projectile strike the ground?

Problems 12-15: We consider the projectile problem with air resistance (drag) included, and we compare the results with those obtained when drag was ignored.

12. When a projectile is propelled or falls it is subject to air resistance (drag). This drag force is roughly proportional to the square of velocity v. From Newton's second law we find that the differential equation that governs the velocity $v(t)$ during the projectile's ascent is $m\frac{dv}{dt} = -m\,g - \beta\,v^2$, where β is a positive constant called the drag coefficient. (Note: We have defined up to be positive, so as the object ascends its velocity is always positive.) For simplicity we divide by mass m to obtain $\dfrac{dv}{dt} = -g - k\,v^2$, where we've set $k = \beta/m$ (which therefore has units of $[\text{length}]^{-1}$). Consider a case where $k = 0.0008$ and the projectile is propelled upward with an initial speed of 400 ft/s.

(a) Solve the governing differential equation for velocity $v(t)$.

(b) Determine when the projectile attains its maximum altitude, and compare it with the time of ascent obtained in problem 11 when drag was ignored.

13. Recall that the projectile's altitude $s(t)$ and velocity $v(t)$ are related by $ds/dt = v$.

(a) Using the velocity $v(t)$ from problem 12, solve this differential equation to obtain the altitude $s(t)$ if the initial altitude of the projectile is 20 ft.

(b) What is the maximum altitude attained by the projectile? Compare it with the maximum altitude attained in problem 11 when drag was ignored.

14. When an object falls it accelerates but also experiences a drag force such as air resistance. This drag force is roughly proportional to the square of velocity v. From Newton's second law we find that the differential equation that governs the velocity v is $m \frac{dv}{dt} = -mg + \beta v^2$, where β is a positive constant called the drag coefficient. (Note: We have defined up to be positive, so as the object falls its velocity is always negative.) For simplicity we divide by mass m to obtain $\frac{dv}{dt} = -g + k v^2$, where we've set $k = \beta/m$ (which therefore has units of $[\text{length}]^{-1}$).

(a) Solve the latter differential equation for velocity $v(t)$ subject to the condition that the initial velocity is 0.

(b) As the object falls it cannot accelerate indefinitely. That is, eventually the object attains its terminal speed, v_c. Determine the terminal speed v_c by evaluating $\lim_{t \to \infty} v(t)$.

(c) Do you see a simpler way to obtain v_c directly from the governing differential equation?

(d) Re-solve the DE subject to the initial condition $v(0) = 0$ if $g = 32 \text{ ft/s}^2$ and $k = 0.0008 \text{ ft}^{-1}$. What is the terminal speed? (express it in miles per hour)

15. Recall that the projectile's altitude $s(t)$ and velocity $v(t)$ are related by $ds/dt = v$.

(a) Using the velocity $v(t)$ from problem 14, solve this differential equation to obtain the altitude $s(t)$ if the initial altitude of the projectile is the maximum altitude you found in problem 13.

(b) Determine the projectile's time of descent, and compare it with the time of descent obtained in problem 11 when drag was ignored.

(c) Determine the speed at which the projectile will strike the ground, and compare it with that obtained in problem 11 when drag was ignored.

16. **Analytical Geometry:** A *geodesic* is the shortest path between two points on a surface. It is well known that the shortest path between two points in a plane is a straight line. Also, cartographers have long known that the shortest path between two points on the earth (a sphere) is a "great circle" — a circle centered at the earth's center. However, both of these known facts require advanced mathematics, called *calculus of variations*, to prove.

Here we will determine a geodesic on a right circular cone. Consider two points on a right circular cone. Recall from multivariate calculus that the equation of a cone in spherical coordinates is given by the simple equation $\phi = \alpha$ where α is a constant. By calculus of variations, the geodesic on the cone must satisfy the differential equation

$$\rho^2 \theta' \sin^2\alpha = k \sqrt{1 + \rho^2 \sin^2\alpha \, (\theta')^2} \,,$$

where k is an arbitrary constant (recall that α is a known constant). Here, θ' means $\dfrac{d\theta}{d\rho}$.

Solve the DE to obtain the solution ρ explicitly in terms of angle θ. The solution will also involve the constants k and α. The resulting curve is the geodesic between two points on the cone.

17. **Engineering/Atmospheric Sciences:** The *hydrostatic equation* models the pressure $P = P(z)$ of a static fluid at altitude z according to $dP = -\rho g\, dz$ subject to the constraint $P(0) = P_0$, where P_0 is the pressure at altitude $z = 0$, ρ is the fluid density, and g is gravitational acceleration. If altitude change is small, then density ρ and gravity g are treated as constants.

   Assuming that ρ and g are constant, solve the hydrostatic equation to obtain pressure P explicitly in terms of z, ρ, g, and P_0.

18. **Atmospheric Sciences:** Now we will solve the hydrostatic equation $dP = -\rho g\, dz$ in problem 17 in the case where density ρ is allowed to vary with altitude (this occurs if the altitude change is large such as in the troposphere).

   Within certain layers of the atmosphere, the density of the air ρ is not constant but depends on pressure and temperature according to the ideal gas equation $P = \rho RT$, where R is the gas constant for the atmosphere.

   (a) Solve the ideal gas equation for ρ, and substitute the result into the hydrostatic equation.

   (b) Furthermore, assume that the atmosphere's temperature varies linearly with altitude according to $T = T_0 - \gamma z$, where z is the altitude above sea level, T_0 is the temperature at sea level (where $z = 0$), and γ is the called the *lapse rate* (a constant). Substitute the expression for T into your result in step (a) to eliminate temperature T from the DE.

   (c) Solve the resulting DE in step (b) subject to the condition that the pressure at sea level is P_0 (i.e., $P(0) = P_0$). Simplify the solution to obtain P explicitly in terms of R, g, z, γ, T_0, and P_0.

19. In problem 18, suppose we also allow for a decrease in the gravitational acceleration as altitude z increases. We may apply Newton's law of gravitation to show that the gravitational acceleration is no longer constant g but is a function of altitude z: $g(z) = g\,r^2/(z+r)^2$, where r is the earth's radius.

   (a) Now set up the hydrostatic equation $dP = -\rho\, g(z)\, dz$ with the atmospheric density decreasing with altitude as described in problem 18.

   (b) Solve the resulting DE in step (a) by separating variables, and apply the condition that the pressure at sea level is P_0 (i.e., $P(0) = P_0$). Simplify the solution to obtain P explicitly in terms of R, r, g, z, γ, T_0, and P_0.

   (c) Since the earth's radius r is large, show that the result in (b) reduces to that in problem 18(c).

20. Reconsider the logistic equation for population growth, $dP/dt = aP - bP^2$, where $a > 0$ is the intrinsic net growth rate and $b > 0$ is the intraspecific competition coefficient.

   (a) Solve the initial value problem for population $P(t)$ by treating the DE as a Bernoulli equation. Denote the initial population by P_0.

   (b) The *carrying capacity* is the maximum population that can be sustained by the resources. This is the population attained as time becomes large. Determine the carrying capacity.

   (c) What is the solution if $a = 0.04$, $b = 0.00001$, and the initial population is 20 members? What is the carrying capacity?

   (d) Plot the poulation in (c) on the interval $0 \le t \le 300$.

21. Reconsider the logistic equation for population growth, $dP/dt = aP - bP^2$, where $a > 0$ is the intrinsic net growth rate and $b > 0$ is the intraspecific competition coefficient. Recall that a constant solution of a DE is one for which all derivatives are zero. Such solutions are called *equilibrium solutions.*

(a) Set $dP/dt = 0$ in the logistic equation and solve for P to obtain both equilibrium solutions. Denote the smaller by P_1 and the larger by P_2.

(b) Give an argument that shows that if P is between P_1 and P_2, then the population must increase.

(c) Give an argument that shows that if P exceeds P_2, then the population must decrease.

22. Reconsider the logistic equation where harvesting is included, $dP/dt = aP - bP^2 - h$, where $a > 0$ is the intrinsic net growth rate, $b > 0$ is the intraspecific competition coefficient, and $h > 0$ is the rate at which the population is harvested. Recall that a constant solution of a DE is one for which all derivatives are zero. Such solutions are called *equilibrium solutions*.

(a) Show that the DE has equilibrium solutions only if $h \leq a^2/4b$.

(b) Assuming that $h < a^2/4b$, find two distinct equilibrium solutions of the DE. Denote the smaller by P_1 and the larger by P_2.

(c) What happens to the population if $0 < P < P_1$?

(d) What happens to the population if $P_1 < P < P_2$?

(e) What happens to the population if $P > P_2$?

(f) Based on these results, what population range and what harvest rate ensures that the population will not decay to zero?

23. Consider fluid flow in a cylindrical pipe of length L and radius a. We shall assume that the pressure P_i at the pipe inlet is greater than that at the outlet P_o — it is this pressure drop that drives the flow. Define the z axis along the centerline of the pipe. In fully developed flow the fluid velocity does not change in the z direction. However, within any circular cross section that is perpendicular to the z axis, the flow velocity v varies with distance r from the pipe's center, namely $v = v(r)$. From fluid mechanics we may show that the differential equation that governs the flow velocity is given by

$$\frac{1}{r} \frac{d}{dr} \left(r \frac{dv}{dr} \right) = k \,, \qquad \frac{dv}{dr}(0) = 0, \quad v(a) = 0 \,,$$

where $k = (P_o - P_i)/\mu L$ is a constant and μ is the fluid viscosity. The derivative boundary condition at the center is called a symmetry condition, while the boundary condition $v(a) = 0$ is called the *no-slip* boundary condition, which states that the flow velocity at the pipe wall is zero.

(a) Solve the differential equation for its general solution $v(r)$.

(b) Apply the first boundary condition to $v(r)$. What does it say about one of the constants of integration? Explain clearly.

(c) Apply the second boundary condition to $v(r)$ to determine the other constant of integration, and then rewrite the velocity function $v(r)$.

24. Consider a cylindrical tank standing on end that leaks fluid through a hole in the bottom. A model that governs the fluid depth h at time t is

$$\frac{dh}{dt} = -\frac{A_h}{A_f} \sqrt{2gh} \,,$$

where A_f and A_h are respectively the cross sectional areas of the tank and hole. Suppose the tank has a radius of 9 feet and the hole has a radius of 6 inches. If the fluid depth is initially 36 feet,

(a) solve the differential equation to obtain the fluid depth $h(t)$, and

(b) determine when the tank has emptied.

71

25. Reconsider problem 24 but now include friction. The model that governs the fluid depth h at time t is

$$\frac{dh}{dt} = -c\frac{A_h}{A_f}\sqrt{2gh},$$

where $0 < c < 1$ is a friction coefficient. With $c = 3/4$, use the data given in problem 24 to

(a) solve the differential equation to obtain the fluid depth $h(t)$, and

(b) determine when the tank has emptied.

1. b

2. a

3. d

4. c

5. a

6. d

7. d

8. b

9. False

10. False

11. (a) $v(t) = 400 - 32\,t$, $s(t) = 20 + 400\,t - 16\,t^2$

    (b) 12.5 ft/s

    (c) 2520 ft

    (d) after 25.05 s

    (e) 401.6 ft/s

12. (a) $v(t) = -200 \tan\left(\dfrac{4}{25}t - \arctan 2\right)$

    (b) $t = (25/4)\tan^{-1} 2 = 6.92$ seconds instead of $t = 12.5$ seconds

13. (a) $s(t) = 20 + 625\ln 5 + \ln\left[\cos\left(\dfrac{4}{25}t - \tan^{-1} 2\right)\right]$

    (b) 1025.9 feet instead of 2520 feet

14. (a) $v(t) = -\sqrt{g/k}\,\tanh(\sqrt{gk}\,t)$

    (b) $v_c = \sqrt{g/k} = \sqrt{mg/\beta}$

    (c) Hint: set $dv/dt = 0$ and solve for v

    (d) $v(t) = -200\tanh\left(\dfrac{4}{25}t\right)$; $v_c = 200$ ft/s $= 136.36$ mph

15. (a) $s(t) = 1025.9 - 1250\ln\left[\cosh\left(\dfrac{4}{25}t\right)\right]$

    (b) 9.1343 seconds after it begins its ascent; it is in the air a total of 16.05 seconds instead of 25.05 seconds.

    (c) 179.588 ft/s $= 122.45$ mph insted of 401.6 ft/s $= 273.8$ mph

16. $\rho = c_1\sec(\theta\sin\alpha + c_2)$, where c_1 and c_2 are arbitraty constants.

17. $P = P_0 = \rho\,g\,z$

18. (a) $dP = -\dfrac{Pg}{RT}\,dz$

    (b) $dP = -\dfrac{Pg}{R(T_0 - \gamma z)}\,dz$

    (c) $P(z) = P_0 \left| \dfrac{T_0 - \gamma z}{T_0} \right|^{g/\gamma R}$

19. (a) $dP = -\dfrac{Pgr^2}{R(T_0 - \gamma z)(z + r)^2}\,dz$

    (b) $P(z) = P_0 \left| \dfrac{T_0 - \gamma z}{T_0} \right|^k \cdot \left[\dfrac{r}{z + r} \right]^k \cdot \exp\left[-k\left(\dfrac{z}{z+r}\right)\left(\dfrac{T_0 + \gamma r}{\gamma r}\right) \right]$, where $k = \dfrac{\gamma g r^2}{R(T_0 + \gamma r)^2}$

    (c) Hint: let $r \to \infty$

20. (a) $P(t) = \dfrac{aP_0}{bP_0 + (a - bP_0)\,e^{-at}}$

    (b) a/b

    (c) $P(t) = \dfrac{4000}{1 + 199\,e^{-0.04t}}$, 4,000 members

21. (a) $P_1(t) = 0$ and $P_2(t) = a/b$

22. (b) $P_1 = \dfrac{a - \sqrt{a^2 - 4bh}}{2b}$ and $P_2 = \dfrac{a + \sqrt{a^2 - 4bh}}{2b}$

    (c) The population decays to 0.

    (d) The population increases to P_2.

    (e) The population decreases to P_2.

    (f) We should ensure that the population exceeds P_1 and that the harvest rate h remains below $a^2/4b$.

23. (a) $v(r) = \dfrac{k}{4}r^2 + c_1 \ln r + c_2$

    (b) $c_1 = 0$

    (c) $c_2 = -k\,a^2/4$

    (d) $v(r) = \dfrac{k}{4}(r^2 - a^2) = \dfrac{P_i - P_o}{4\mu L}(a^2 - r^2)$

24. (a) $h(t) = \left(6 - \dfrac{t}{81}\right)^2$

    (b) $t = 486$ seconds $= 8.1$ min

25. (a) $h(t) = \left(6 - \dfrac{t}{108}\right)^2$

    (b) $t = 648$ seconds $= 10.8$ min

1. salt mixing — concepts

2. salt mixing — concepts

3. salt mixing — concepts

4. electrical circuits — concepts

5. electrical circuits — concepts

6. electrical circuits — concepts

7. competition models — concepts

8. competition models — concepts

9. competition models — concepts

10. predator prey models — concepts

11. predator prey models — concepts

12. salt brine mixing governing system

13. salt brine mixing governing system

14. salt brine mixing governing system

15. lake pollution model

16. lake pollution model

17. lake pollution model

18. lake pollution model

19. predator-prey model

20. predator-prey model

21. predator-prey model

22. electrical circuit

23. electrical circuit

24. electrical circuit

1. If a tank contains x pounds of salt, V gallons of solution, and brine enters at a flow rate of r_1 gal/min and the perfectly mixed solution exits at r_2 gal/min, then the rate at which salt exits the tank is

   (a) $\dfrac{xr_2}{V}$.

   (b) $\dfrac{rV}{x}$.

   (c) $\dfrac{r_1 x}{V}$.

   (d) $\dfrac{V}{rx}$.

2. Brine enters a tank through two inlets at flow rates of 4 gal/min and 8 gal/min respectively. The perfectly mixed solution then discharges through three exits at 2 gal/min, 4 gal/min, and r gal/min. If the tank contains a constant 20 gallons of solution, then the flow rate r is

   (a) 4 gal/min.

   (b) 6 gal/min.

   (c) 12 gal/min.

   (d) 26 gal/min.

3. Brine enters a tank through two inlets at flow rates of 5 gal/min and 9 gal/min respectively. The perfectly mixed solution then discharges through three exits at 2 gal/min, 4 gal/min, and r gal/min. If the amount of brine in the tank decreases at 1 gal/min, then the flow rate r is

   (a) 7 gal/min.

   (b) 8 gal/min.

   (c) 9 gal/min.

   (d) 10 gal/min.

4. If a current i flows through a resistor with resistance R, the voltage drop across the resistor is

   (a) $R\,i$

   (b) R/i

   (c) $R\dfrac{di}{dt}$

   (d) $\dfrac{1}{R}\dfrac{di}{dt}$

5. If a current i flows through a inductor with inductance L, the voltage drop across the inductor is

   (a) $L\,i$

   (b) i/L

   (c) $L\dfrac{di}{dt}$

   (d) $\dfrac{1}{L}\dfrac{di}{dt}$

6. If a charge q is stored on a capacitor with capacitance C, the voltage drop across the capacitor is

   (a) $C\,q$

   (b) q/C

   (c) $C\,i$

   (d) i/C

7. In the system of DEs that models competition between two species for the same resources,

$$\frac{dx}{dt} = b_1\, x - c_{12}\, xy, \qquad \frac{dy}{dt} = b_2\, y - c_{21}\, xy,$$

the terms $c_{12}\, xy$ and $c_{21}\, xy$ are

   (a) linear and equal.
   (b) nonlinear and equal.
   (c) linear and different.
   (d) nonlinear and different.

8. In the system of DEs that models competition between two species for the same resources,

$$\frac{dx}{dt} = b_1\, x - c_{11}\, x^2 - c_{12}\, xy, \qquad \frac{dy}{dt} = b_2\, y - c_{22}\, y^2 - c_{21}\, xy,$$

the term $c_{21}\, xy$ represents

   (a) the impact on population x due to competition with members from population y.
   (b) the impact on population y due to competition with members from population x.
   (c) the impact on population x due to competition among its own members.
   (d) the impact on population y due to competition among its own members.

9. In the system of DEs that models competition between two species for the same resources,

$$\frac{dx}{dt} = b_1\, x - c_{11}\, x^2 - c_{12}\, xy, \qquad \frac{dy}{dt} = b_2\, y - c_{22}\, y^2 - c_{21}\, xy,$$

the term $c_{22}\, y^2$ represents

   (a) the impact on population x due to competition with members from population y.
   (b) the impact on population y due to competition with members from population x.
   (c) the impact on population x due to competition among its own members.
   (d) the impact on population y due to competition among its own members.

10. In the Lotka-Volterra system of DEs that models a predator-prey ecosystem,

$$\frac{dx}{dt} = b_1\, x - c_{11}\, x^2 - c_{12}\, xy, \qquad \frac{dy}{dt} = -b_2\, y - c_{22}\, y^2 + c_{21}\, xy,$$

the term $c_{21}\, xy$ represents

   (a) the impact on population x due to predation from population y.
   (b) the impact on population y due to predation from population x.
   (c) the impact on population x due to predation upon population y.
   (d) the impact on population y due to predation upon population x.

11. In the Lotka-Volterra system of DEs that models a predator-prey ecosystem,

$$\frac{dx}{dt} = b_1\, x - c_{11}\, x^2 - c_{12}\, xy, \qquad \frac{dy}{dt} = -b_2\, y - c_{22}\, y^2 + c_{21}\, xy,$$

the term $c_{12}\, xy$ represents

   (a) the impact on population x due to predation from population y.
   (b) the impact on population y due to predation from population x.
   (c) the impact on population x due to predation upon population y.
   (d) the impact on population y due to predation upon population x.

12. Tank A contains 300 liters of brine solution in which 50 kg of salt is dissolved. Tank B contains 200 liters of brine solution in which 20 kg of salt is dissolved. Pure water flows into tank A at 10 liters per minute, and solution flows from tank A into tank B at 14 liters per minute. Some of the solution from tank B is pumped back into tank A at 4 liters per minute and the remaining solution is discharged from tank B at 10 liters per minute. Let $x_a(t)$ and $x_b(t)$ denote the amount of salt (in kg) in tanks A and B respectively. Suppose the solutions in both tanks are well mixed.

    Determine the equations governing the amount of salt in each tank at time t.

13. Tank A contains 100 liters of brine solution in which 50 kg of salt is dissolved. Tank B contains 160 liters of brine solution in which 40 kg of salt is dissolved. Tank C contains 100 liters of brine solution in which 30 kg of salt is dissolved. Pure water flows into tank A at 10 liters per minute, and solution flows from tank A into tank B at 14 liters per minute. Some of the solution from tank B is pumped back into tank A at 4 liters per minute and the remaining solution is discharged from tank B into tank C at 16 liters per minute. Some of the solution from tank C is pumped back to tank B at 6 liters per minute and the remaining solution is discharged from tank C at 10 liters per minute.

    Let $x_a(t)$, $x_b(t)$, and $x_c(t)$ denote the amount of salt (in kg) in tanks A, B, and C respectively. Suppose the solutions in all tanks are well mixed.

    Determine the equations governing the amount of salt in each tank at time t.

14. Tank A contains 100 gallons of brine solution in which 50 pounds of salt is dissolved. Tank B contains 210 gallons of brine solution in which 30 pounds of salt is dissolved. Tank C contains 140 gallons of brine solution in which 25 pounds of salt is dissolved. Pure water flows into tank A at 4 gallons per minute, and solution flows from tank A into tank B at 8 gallons per minute. Some of the solution from tank B is pumped back into tank A at 3 gallons per minute and the remaining solution is discharged from tank B into tank C at 7 gallons per minute. Some of the solution from tank C is pumped back to tank B at 2 gallons per minute, and some of the solution from tank C is pumped back to tank A at 1 gallons per minute, and the remaining solution is discharged from tank C at 4 gallons per minute.

    Let $x_a(t)$, $x_b(t)$, and $x_c(t)$ denote the amount of salt (in kg) in tanks A, B, and C respectively. Suppose the solutions in all tanks are well mixed.

    Determine the equations governing the amount of salt in each tank at time t.

15. In many wetlands water from one lake may discharge into several other lakes. Likewise, one lake may receive water from several other lakes. This occurs, for example, in the boundary waters around the Canadian–Minnesotan border. Consider 4 lakes in the following state: Lake A discharges into Lakes B and C at rates r_1 and r_2 respectively; Lake B discharges into Lake D at the same rate at which it receives water from Lake A; Lake C discharges into Lake D at the same rate at which it receives water from Lake A; Lake D discharges via a river at rate r. Suppose Lake A is polluted but it now receives fresh (unpolluted) water from an underground spring at rate r. Let $x_a(t)$ denote the amount of pollution (in tons) in Lake A and V_a its volume, let $x_b(t)$ denote the amount of pollution in Lake B and V_b its volume, *etc.* Suppose all lake volumes remain constant and that the water and pollutants within each lake are well mixed.

    Determine the equations governing the amount of pollution x in each lake A, B, C, and D at time t.

16. Reconsider problem 15, but suppose now that Lake B discharges into Lakes C and D rates r_3 and r_4 respectively.

    Determine the equations governing the amount of pollution x in each lake A, B, C, and D at time t.

17. Reconsider problem 16, but suppose now that Lake A also discharges at rate r_5 into the rivulet that runs from Lake B to Lake C.

Determine the equations governing the amount of pollution x in each lake A, B, C, and D at time t.

18. In the preceding lake pollution problems suppose we are in a dry season where the lake volumes decrease due to evaporation. Suppose Lake A evaporates at rate u_a (volume per unit time), Lake B evaporates at rate u_b, etc.

   (a) Determine the equations governing the amount of pollution x in each lake A, B, C, and D at time t in problem 15.

   (b) Determine the equations governing the amount of pollution x in each lake A, B, C, and D at time t in problem 16.

   (c) Determine the equations governing the amount of pollution x in each lake A, B, C, and D at time t in problem 17.

19. Consider an ecosystem comprising mice, owls, and foxes. The mice have an ample food supply but are preyed upon by both the owls and the foxes. Let $x(t)$, $y(t)$, and $z(t)$, denote respectively the mouse, owl, and fox populations at time t. Obtain the system of differential equations that governs the population dynamics of each species if the mice compete among themselves for food, the owls compete among themselves and with the foxes for mice, and the foxes compete among themselves and with the owls foxes for mice. Describe all coefficients.

20. Suppose in problem 19 the owls are territorial and dispersed enough that they do not compete for mice among themselves. Likewise, suppose the foxes are territorial and dispersed enough that they do not compete for mice among themselves. Obtain the system of differential equations that governs the population dynamics of each species under these new assumptions. Describe all coefficients.

21. What is the model in problem 20 if bald eagles are in the ecosystem? Bald eagles will prey on mice, owls, and foxes. Let $w(t)$ denote the eagle population at time t, and assume that the eagles are territorial and dispersed enough that they do not compete for any of the prey among themselves. Obtain the system of differential equations that governs the population dynamics of each species under these new assumptions. Describe all coefficients.

22. A closed circuit comprises two loops. Clockwise the corners of the outer loop are $ABCD$. Between points AB is a branch point J_1, while between points CD is a branch point J_2. The circuit contains the following components:

   - Segment DA contains voltage source E.
   - Segment AJ_1 contains resistor R_1.
   - Segment BC contains inductor L.
   - Segment CJ_2 contains resistor R_2,
   - Segment J_1J_2 contains capacitor C.

Denote the current through J_2DAJ_1 by i_1, that through segment J_1J_2 by i_2, and that through segment J_1BCJ_2 by i_3. Determine differential equations for currents i_1 and i_3.

23. A closed circuit comprises two loops. Clockwise the corners of the outer loop are $ABCD$. Between points AB is a branch point J_1, while between points CD is a branch point J_2. The circuit contains the following components:

- Segment DA contains voltage source E.
- Segment AJ_1 contains resistor R_1.
- Segment BC contains inductor L.
- Segment J_2D contains resistor R_2,
- Segment J_1J_2 contains capacitor C.

Denote the current through J_2DAJ_1 by i_1, that through segment J_1J_2 by i_2, and that through segment J_1BCJ_2 by i_3. Determine differential equations for currents i_1 and i_3.

24. A closed circuit comprises two loops. Clockwise the corners of the outer loop are $ABCD$. Between points AB is a branch point J_1, while between points CD is a branch point J_2. The circuit contains the following components:

- Segment DA contains voltage source E.
- Segment AJ_1 contains resistor R_1.
- Segment BC contains inductor L_2.
- Segment CJ_2 contains resistor R_2,
- Segment J_1J_2 contains inductor L_1.

Denote the current through J_2DAJ_1 by i_1, that through segment J_1J_2 by i_2, and that through segment J_1BCJ_2 by i_3. Determine differential equations for currents i_2 and i_3.

1. a

2. b

3. c

4. a

5. c

6. b

7. d

8. b

9. d

10. d

11. a

12.

$$\frac{dx_a}{dt} = \frac{x_b}{50} - \frac{7x_a}{150}, \qquad x_a(0) = 50,$$

$$\frac{dx_b}{dt} = \frac{7x_a}{150} - \frac{7x_b}{100}, \qquad x_b(0) = 20.$$

13.

$$\frac{dx_a}{dt} = \frac{x_b}{40} - \frac{7x_a}{50}, \qquad x_a(0) = 50,$$

$$\frac{dx_b}{dt} = \frac{7x_a}{50} + \frac{3x_c}{50} - \frac{x_b}{8}, \qquad x_b(0) = 40,$$

$$\frac{dx_c}{dt} = \frac{x_b}{10} - \frac{4x_c}{24}, \qquad x_c(0) = 30.$$

14.

$$\frac{dx_a}{dt} = \frac{x_b}{70} + \frac{x_c}{140} - \frac{2x_a}{25}, \qquad x_a(0) = 50,$$

$$\frac{dx_b}{dt} = \frac{2x_a}{50} + \frac{x_c}{70} - \frac{x_b}{21}, \qquad x_b(0) = 30,$$

$$\frac{dx_c}{dt} = \frac{x_b}{30} - \frac{x_c}{20}, \qquad x_c(0) = 25.$$

15. With $r = r_1 + r_2$,

$$\frac{dx_a}{dt} = -r\frac{x_a}{V_a}, \qquad\qquad \frac{dx_c}{dt} = r_2\frac{x_a}{V_a} - r_2\frac{x_c}{V_c},$$

$$\frac{dx_b}{dt} = r_1\frac{x_a}{V_a} - r_1\frac{x_b}{V_b}, \qquad \frac{dx_d}{dt} = r_1\frac{x_b}{V_b} + r_2\frac{x_c}{V_c} - r\frac{x_d}{V_d}$$

16. With $r = r_1 + r_2$,

$$\frac{dx_a}{dt} = -r\frac{x_a}{V_a}, \qquad\qquad \frac{dx_c}{dt} = r_2\frac{x_a}{V_a} + r_3\frac{x_b}{V_b} - (r_2 + r_3)\frac{x_c}{V_c},$$

$$\frac{dx_b}{dt} = r_1\frac{x_a}{V_a} - r_1\frac{x_b}{V_b}, \qquad \frac{dx_d}{dt} = (r_2 + r_3)\frac{x_c}{V_c} + r_4\frac{x_b}{V_b} - r\frac{x_d}{V_d}$$

17. With $r = r_1 + r_2 + r_5$,

$$\frac{dx_a}{dt} = -r\frac{x_a}{V_a}, \qquad\qquad \frac{dx_c}{dt} = (r_2 + r_5)\frac{x_a}{V_a} + r_3\frac{x_b}{V_b} - (r_2 + r_3 + r_5)\frac{x_c}{V_c},$$

$$\frac{dx_b}{dt} = r_1\frac{x_a}{V_a} - r_1\frac{x_b}{V_b}, \qquad \frac{dx_d}{dt} = r_4\frac{x_b}{V_b} + (r_2 + r_3 + r_5)\frac{x_c}{V_c} - r\frac{x_d}{V_d}$$

18. (a) With $r = r_1 + r_2$,

$$\frac{dx_a}{dt} = -\frac{r\,x_a}{V_a - u_a\,t}, \qquad\qquad \frac{dx_c}{dt} = \frac{r_2\,x_a}{V_a - u_a\,t} - \frac{r_2\,x_c}{V_c - u_c\,t},$$

$$\frac{dx_b}{dt} = \frac{r_1\,x_a}{V_a - u_a\,t} - \frac{r_1\,x_b}{V_b - u_b\,t}, \qquad \frac{dx_d}{dt} = \frac{r_1\,x_b}{V_b - u_b\,t} + \frac{r_2\,x_c}{V_c - u_c\,t} - \frac{r\,x_d}{V_d - u_d\,t}$$

(b) With $r = r_1 + r_2$,

$$\frac{dx_a}{dt} = -\frac{r\,x_a}{V_a - u_a\,t}, \qquad\qquad \frac{dx_c}{dt} = \frac{r_2\,x_a}{V_a - u_a\,t} + \frac{r_3\,x_b}{V_b - u_b\,t} - \frac{(r_2 + r_3)\,x_c}{V_c - u_c\,t},$$

$$\frac{dx_b}{dt} = \frac{r_1\,x_a}{V_a - u_a\,t} - \frac{r_1\,x_b}{V_b - u_b\,t}, \qquad \frac{dx_d}{dt} = \frac{(r_2 + r_3)\,x_c}{V_c - u_c\,t} + \frac{r_4\,x_b}{V_b - u_b\,t} - \frac{r\,x_d}{V_d - u_d\,t}$$

(c) With $r = r_1 + r_2 + r_5$,

$$\frac{dx_a}{dt} = -\frac{r\,x_a}{V_a - u_a\,t}, \qquad\qquad \frac{dx_c}{dt} = \frac{(r_2 + r_5)\,x_a}{V_a - u_a\,t} + \frac{r_3\,x_b}{V_b - u_b\,t} - \frac{(r_2 + r_3 + r_5)\,x_c}{V_c - u_c\,t},$$

$$\frac{dx_b}{dt} = \frac{r_1\,x_a}{V_a - u_a\,t} - \frac{r_1\,x_b}{V_b - u_b\,t}, \qquad \frac{dx_d}{dt} = \frac{r_4\,x_b}{V_b - u_a\,t} + \frac{(r_2 + r_3 + r_5)\,x_c}{V_c - u_b\,t} - \frac{r\,x_d}{V_d - u_d\,t}$$

19.

$$\text{Species 1, Mice:} \quad \frac{dx}{dt} = b_1\,x - c_{11}\,x^2 - d_{12}\,xy - d_{13}\,xz,$$

$$\text{Species 2, Owls:} \quad \frac{dy}{dt} = -b_2\,y - c_{22}\,y^2 + p_{21}\,xy - c_{23}\,yz,$$

$$\text{Species 3, Foxes:} \quad \frac{dz}{dt} = -b_3\,z - c_{33}\,z^2 + p_{31}\,xz - c_{32}\,yz,$$

where b_i denotes the intrinsic net relative growth rate of species i, c_{ij} denotes the competition coefficient of species i with species j for mice, d_{ij} denotes the relative death rate of species i due to predation from species j, and p_{ij} denotes the relative rate of increase of species i due to preying upon species j.

20. See solution 19 for descriptions of the coefficents.

$$\text{Species 1, Mice:} \quad \frac{dx}{dt} = b_1\,x - c_{11}\,x^2 - d_{12}\,xy - d_{13}\,xz,$$

$$\text{Species 2, Owls:} \quad \frac{dy}{dt} = -b_2\,y + p_{21}\,xy - c_{23}\,yz,$$

$$\text{Species 3, Foxes:} \quad \frac{dz}{dt} = -b_3\,z + p_{31}\,xz - c_{32}\,yz$$

21. See solution 19 for descriptions of the coefficents.

$$\text{Species 1, Mice:} \quad \frac{dx}{dt} = b_1\,x - c_{11}\,x^2 - d_{12}\,xy - d_{13}\,xz - d_{14}\,xw,$$

$$\text{Species 2, Owls:} \quad \frac{dy}{dt} = -b_2\,y + p_{21}\,xy - c_{23}\,yz - c_{24}\,yw - d_{24}\,yw,$$

$$\text{Species 3, Foxes:} \quad \frac{dz}{dt} = -b_3\,z + p_{31}\,xz - c_{32}\,yz - c_{34}\,zw - d_{34}\,zw,$$

$$\text{Species 4, Eagles:} \quad \frac{dw}{dt} = -b_4\,w + p_{41}\,xw + p_{42}\,yw + p_{43}\,zw - c_{42}\,yw - c_{43}\,zw$$

22. $L\dfrac{di_3}{dt} + R_1\,i_1 + R_2\,i_3 = E, \qquad R_1\,C\dfrac{di_1}{dt} + i_1 - i_3 = 0$

23. $L\dfrac{di_3}{dt} + (R_1 + R_2)\,i_1 = E, \qquad (R_1 + R_2)\,C\dfrac{di_1}{dt} + i_1 - i_3 = 0$

24. $L_1\dfrac{di_2}{dt} + R_1\,i_2 + R_1\,i_3 = E, \qquad L_2\dfrac{di_3}{dt} + R_1\,i_2 + (R_1 + R_2)\,i_3 = E$

4.1 Linear Differential Equations – Basic Theory   Subject Correlation Guide

1. existence-uniqueness of solutions of homogeneous DEs

2. homogeneous DE – fundamental set of solutions and linear independence

3. homogeneous DE – general solution and linear independence

4. homogeneous DE – fundamental set of solutions and Wronskian

5. homogeneous DE – general solution and Wronskian

6. homogeneous DE – general solution and linear dependence

7. nonhomogeneous DE – general solution and linear dependence

8. True/False: trivial solution of a homogeneous DE

9. True/False: trivial solution of a nonhomogeneous DE

10. True/False: linear combinations of solutions of a homogeneous DE

11. True/False: linear combinations of solutions of a nonhomogeneous DE

12. True/False: existence-uniqueness of solutions of BVPs

13. True/False: existence-uniqueness of solutions of BVPs

14. True/False: existence-uniqueness of solutions of homogeneous ODEs

15. True/False: existence-uniqueness of solutions of nonhomogeneous ODEs

16. Applying initial conditions to a 2-parameter family of functions

17. Applying initial conditions to a 2-parameter family of functions

18. Applying initial conditions to a 2-parameter family of functions

19. Applying initial conditions to a 2-parameter family of functions

20. Applying initial conditions to a 2-parameter family of functions

21. Applying initial conditions to a 2-parameter family of functions

22. Applying initial conditions to a 2-parameter family of functions

23. Applying boundary conditions to a 2-parameter family of functions

24. Applying boundary conditions to a 2-parameter family of functions

25. Applying boundary conditions to a 2-parameter family of functions

26. Applying boundary conditions to a 2-parameter family of functions

27. Assessing linear dependence or independence of 3 functions

28. Assessing linear dependence or independence of 3 functions

29. Assessing linear dependence or independence of 3 functions

30. Assessing linear dependence or independence of 3 functions

31-36. Show that 2 functions form a fundamental set of solutions of a given DE.

37-40. Show that a given function is a 2-parameter family of solutions of a given DE.

1. The initial value problem $\quad y'' + 9y = 0, y(0) = 0, y'(0) = 0$

   (a) has a unique solution.

   (b) may have no solution.

   (c) may have many solutions.

   (d) (b) and (c) are possible.

2. A fundamental set of solutions of a homogeneous linear nth-order differential equation comprises

   (a) any set of solutions.

   (b) any set of n solutions.

   (c) any set of n linearly independent solutions.

   (d) any set of n homogeneous linearly independent solutions.

3. To obtain the general solution of a homogeneous linear nth-order differential equation, we must construct a linear combination of

   (a) any set of solutions.

   (b) any set of n solutions.

   (c) any set of n linearly independent solutions.

   (d) any set of n homogeneous linearly independent solutions.

4. If functions $y_1(x)$, $y_2(x)$, $\ldots, y_n(x)$ form a fundamental set of solutions of a homogeneous linear nth-order differential equation on interval I, then the Wronskian $W(y_1, y_2, \ldots, y_n)$

   (a) is zero at every x on I.

   (b) may be zero at finitely many x on I.

   (c) is not at any x on I.

   (d) is not at any x on I except possibly at $x = 0$.

5. If function $y = c_1 y_1(x) + c_2 y_2(x) + \cdots + c_n y_n(x)$ is the general solution of a homogeneous linear nth-order differential equation on interval I, then the Wronskian $W(y_1, y_2, \ldots, y_n)$

   (a) is zero at every x on I.

   (b) may be zero at finitely many x on I.

   (c) is not at any x on I.

   (d) is not at any x on I except possibly at $x = 0$.

6. If function $y = c_1 y_1(x) + c_2 y_2(x) + c_3 y_3(x)$ is a solution of a homogeneous linear 2nd-order differential equation on interval I, then the functions $y_1(x)$, $y_2(x)$, $y_3(x)$

   (a) form a fundamental set of solutions of the differential equation on I.

   (b) are linearly dependent on I.

   (c) are linearly independent on I.

   (d) need not all be solutions of the differential equation on I.

7. If function $y = c_1 y_1(x) + c_2 y_2(x) + y_p(x)$ is a solution of a nonhomogeneous linear 2nd-order differential equation on interval I, then the functions $y_1(x)$, $y_2(x)$, $y_p(x)$

   (a) form a fundamental set of solutions of the differential equation on I.

   (b) are linearly independent on I.

   (c) are linearly dependent on I.

   (d) need not all be solutions of the differential equation on I.

8. True or False: A homogeneous linear differential equation always possesses the trivial solution $y(x) = 0$.

9. True or False: A nonhomogeneous linear differential equation always possesses the trivial solution $y(x) = 0$.

10. True or False: If functions $y_1(x)$ and $y_2(x)$ are solutions of a homogeneous linear differential equation, then the function $y = c_1 y_1(x) + c_2 y_2(x)$ is also a solution.

11. True or False: If functions $y_1(x)$ and $y_2(x)$ are solutions of a nonhomogeneous linear differential equation, then the function $y = c_1 y_1(x) + c_2 y_2(x)$ is also a solution.

12. True or False: Boundary value problems have unique solutions.

13. True or False: A boundary value problem may have no solution.

14. True or False: Every nth-order homogeneous linear differential equation has at least one solution.

15. True or False: Every nth-order nonhomogeneous linear differential equation has at least one solution.

16. Given the 2-parameter family of functions $y = c_1 e^{-x} + c_2 e^{3x}$, find the member of the family that satisfies the conditions $y(0) = 1$ and $y'(0) = -5$.

17. Given the 2-parameter family of functions $y = c_1 x e^{2x} + c_2 e^{2x}$, find the member of the family that satisfies the conditions $y(0) = -3$ and $y'(0) = 0$.

18. Given the 2-parameter family of functions $y = c_1 x^2 + c_2 x$, find the member of the family that satisfies the conditions $y(0) = 0$ and $y'(0) = -3$.

19. Given the 2-parameter family of functions $y = c_1 \sin x + c_2 \cos x$, find the member of the family that satisfies the conditions $y(0) = -2$ and $y'(0) = 3$.

20. Given the 2-parameter family of functions $y = c_1 \cos 2x + c_2 \sin 2x$, find the member of the family that satisfies the conditions $y(0) = 4$ and $y'(0) = 6$.

21. Given the 2-parameter family of functions $y = c_1 e^{-x} \cos 2x + c_2 e^{-x} \sin 2x$, find the member of the family that satisfies the conditions $y(0) = 0$ and $y'(0) = 3$.

22. Given the 2-parameter family of functions $y = c_1 x^2 + c_2 x + c_3$, find the member of the family that satisfies the conditions $y(0) = 3$, $y'(0) = -6$, and $y''(0) = 8$.

23. Given the 2-parameter family of functions $y = c_1 x \ln x + c_2 x$, find the member of the family that satisfies the conditions $y(1) = -2$ and $y'(1) = 2$.

24. Given the 2-parameter family of functions $y = c_1 \cos 2x + c_2 \sin 2x$, find the member of the family that satisfies the conditions $y(0) = 4$ and $y'(\pi/2) = -6$.

25. Given the 2-parameter family of functions $y = c_1 \cos 2x + c_2 \sin 2x$, find, if possible, the member of the family that satisfies the conditions $y(0) = 4$ and $y'(\pi/2) = -8$.

26. Given the 2-parameter family of functions $y = c_1 \cos 2x + c_2 \sin 2x$, find, if possible, the member of the family that satisfies the conditions $y(0) = 4$ and $y'(\pi/2) = 2$.

27. Determine whether the set of functions $f_1 = 3$, $f_2 = e^x$, $f_3 = e^{-x}$ is linearly dependent or linearly independent on the interval $(-\infty, \infty)$.

28. Determine whether the set of functions $f_1 = 3$, $f_2 = x - 4$, $f_3 = 7 - 2x$ is linearly dependent or linearly independent on the interval $(-\infty, \infty)$.

29. Determine whether the set of functions $f_1 = \cos^2 3x$, $f_2 = \sin^2 3x$, $f_3 = 7$ is linearly dependent or linearly independent on the interval $(-\infty, \infty)$.

30. Determine whether the set of functions $f_1 = \sin^2 2x$, $f_2 = \cos 4x$, $f_3 = 7$, is linearly dependent or linearly independent on the interval $(-\infty, \infty)$.

31. Verify that the functions $y_1 = e^{2x}$ and $y_2 = e^{-3x}$ form a fundamental set of solutions of the differential equation $y'' + y' - 6y = 0$ on the interval $(-\infty, \infty)$.

32. Verify that the functions $y_1 = 1$ and $y_2 = e^{-x}$ form a fundamental set of solutions of the differential equation $y'' + y' = 0$ on the interval $(-\infty, \infty)$.

33. Verify that the functions $y_1 = \cos 3x$ and $y_2 = \sin 3x$ form a fundamental set of solutions of the differential equation $y'' + 9y = 0$ on the interval $(-\infty, \infty)$.

34. Verify that the functions $y_1 = e^{-2x} \cos 3x$ and $y_2 = e^{-2x} \sin 3x$ form a fundamental set of solutions of the differential equation $y'' + 4y' + 13y = 0$ on the interval $(-\infty, \infty)$.

35. Verify that the functions $y_1 = x^2$ and $y_2 = x^{-3}$ form a fundamental set of solutions of the differential equation $x^2 y'' + 2xy' - 6y = 0$ on the interval $(0, \infty)$.

36. Verify that the functions $y_1 = x^{1/2}$ and $y_2 = x^{-1/2}$ form a fundamental set of solutions of the differential equation $4x^2 y'' + 4xy' - y = 0$ on the interval $(0, \infty)$.

37. Verify that the two-parameter family of functions $y = c_1 e^{2x} + c_2 e^{-3x} - 2e^{-x}$ is the general solution of the nonhomogeneous differential equation $y'' + y' - 6y = 12e^{-x}$ on the interval $(-\infty, \infty)$.

38. Verify that the two-parameter family of functions $y = c_1 e^{-x} + c_2 e^{2x} + 2 - 4x$ is the general solution of the nonhomogeneous differential equation $y'' - y' - 2y = 8x$ on the interval $(-\infty, \infty)$.

39. Verify that the two-parameter family of functions $y = c_1 \cos 2x + c_2 \sin 2x + 6 - 2e^{-2x}$ is the general solution of the nonhomogeneous differential equation $y'' + 4y = 24 - 16e^{-2x}$ on the interval $(-\infty, \infty)$.

40. Verify that the two-parameter family of functions $y = c_1 \cos 3x + c_2 \sin 3x - 2x \cos 3x$ is the general solution of the nonhomogeneous differential equation $y'' + 9y = 12 \sin 3x$ on the interval $(-\infty, \infty)$.

1. a

2. c

3. c

4. c

5. c

6. b

7. d

8. True

9. False

10. True

11. False

12. False

13. True

14. True

15. False

16. $y = 2e^{-x} - e^{3x}$

17. $y = 6xe^{2x} - 3e^{2x}$

18. $y = 4x^2 + -3x$

19. $y = 3\cos x - 2\sin x$

20. $y = 4\cos 2x + 3\sin 2x$

21. $y = 3e^{-x}\sin 2x$

22. $y = 4x^2 - 6x + 3$

23. $y = 4x\ln x - 2x$

24. $y = 4\cos 2x + 3\sin 2x$

25. $y = 4\cos 2x + c_2\sin 2x$ where c_2 is arbitrary

26. no soution exists

27. linearly independent

28. linearly dependent

29. linearly dependent

30. linearly dependent

31-36. Each pair of functions forms a fundamental set of solutions of the given DE.

37-40. The given function is a 2-parameter family of solutions of the given DE.

1. concept — linear independence

2. reduction of order — obtain a second solution (exponential)

3. reduction of order — obtain a second solution (exponential)

4. reduction of order — obtain a second solution (exponential)

5. reduction of order — obtain a second solution (exponential)

6. reduction of order — obtain a second solution (exponential)

7. reduction of order — obtain a second solution (power)

8. reduction of order — obtain a second solution (power)

9. reduction of order — obtain a second solution (power)

10. reduction of order — obtain a second solution (power)

11. reduction of order — obtain a second solution (power)

12. reduction of order — obtain a second solution (exponential)

13. reduction of order — obtain a second solution (exponential)

14. reduction of order — obtain a second solution (exponential)

15. reduction of order — obtain a second solution (exponential)

16. reduction of order — obtain a second solution (exponential)

17. reduction of order — obtain a second solution (trigonometric)

18. reduction of order — obtain a second solution (power)

19. reduction of order — obtain a second solution (power)

20. reduction of order — obtain a second solution (power)

21. reduction of order — obtain a second solution (power)

22. reduction of order — obtain a second solution (power×trig)

23. reduction of order — obtain a second solution (power×trig)

1. If $y_1(x)$ and $y_2(x)$ are two linearly independent solutions of the same 2nd-order differential equation, then the ratio y_1/y_2

    (a) is a function of x.

    (b) is a constant.

    (c) could be (a) or (b)

    (d) none of the above

2. If $y_1 = e^{2x}$ is a solution of the given differential equation, use reduction of order to find a second solution y_2. $y'' - 5y' + 6y = 0$.

    (a) $y_2 = e^{-2x}$

    (b) $y_2 = xe^{2x}$

    (c) $y_2 = e^{-3x}$

    (d) $y_2 = e^{3x}$

3. If $y_1 = e^{-2x}$ is a solution of the given differential equation, use reduction of order to find a second solution y_2. $y'' - 3y' - 10y = 0$.

    (a) $y_2 = e^{2x}$

    (b) $y_2 = xe^{-2x}$

    (c) $y_2 = e^{5x}$

    (d) $y_2 = e^{-5x}$

4. If $y_1 = 1$ is a solution of the given differential equation, use reduction of order to find a second solution y_2. $y'' - 4y' = 0$.

    (a) $y_2 = e^{2x}$

    (b) $y_2 = e^{-2x}$

    (c) $y_2 = e^{4x}$

    (d) $y_2 = e^{-4x}$

5. If $y_1 = e^{4x}$ is a solution of the given differential equation, use reduction of order to find a second solution y_2. $y'' - 16y = 0$.

    (a) $y_2 = xe^{4x}$

    (b) $y_2 = e^{-4x}$

    (c) $y_2 = xe^{-4x}$

    (d) $y_2 = x^2 e^{4x}$

6. If $y_1 = e^{-x}$ is a solution of the given differential equation, use reduction of order to find a second solution y_2. $y'' - 2y' - 3y = 0$.

    (a) $y_2 = xe^{-x}$

    (b) $y_2 = e^{-3x}$

    (c) $y_2 = xe^{-3x}$

    (d) $y_2 = e^{3x}$

7. If $y_1 = x^3$ is a solution of the given differential equation, use reduction of order to find a second solution y_2. $x^2y'' - xy' - 3y = 0$.

(a) $y_2 = x^3 \ln x$

(b) $y_2 = x^{-1}$

(c) $y_2 = x^{-1} \ln x$

(d) $y_2 = x^4$

8. If $y_1 = x^2$ is a solution of the given differential equation, use reduction of order to find a second solution y_2. $x^2y'' - 7xy' + 12y = 0$.

(a) $y_2 = x^2 \ln x$

(b) $y_2 = x^4$

(c) $y_2 = x^3$

(d) $y_2 = x^6$

9. If $y_1 = x^2$ is a solution of the given differential equation, use reduction of order to find a second solution y_2. $x^2y'' - 3xy' + 4y = 0$.

(a) $y_2 = x^{-2}$

(b) $y_2 = x^{-2} \ln x$

(c) $y_2 = x^2$

(d) $y_2 = x^2 \ln x$

10. If $y_1 = x^3$ is a solution of the given differential equation, use reduction of order to find a second solution y_2. $x^2y'' + xy' - 9y = 0$.

(a) $y_2 = x^{-3}$

(b) $y_2 = x^3 \ln x$

(c) $y_2 = x^{-3} \ln x$

(d) $y_2 = x^2$

11. If $y_1 = x^{-2}$ is a solution of the given differential equation, use reduction of order to find a second solution y_2. $x^2y'' - 6y = 0$.

(a) $y_2 = x^2$

(b) $y_2 = x^{-2} \ln x$

(c) $y_2 = x^{-3}$

(d) $y_2 = x^3 \ln x$

12. If $y_1 = e^{2x}$ is a solution of the given differential equation, use reduction of order to find a second solution y_2. $y'' + y' - 6y = 0$.

13. If $y_1 = e^{3x}$ is a solution of the given differential equation, use reduction of order to find a second solution y_2. $y'' - 2y' - 3y = 0$.

14. If $y_1 = e^{5x}$ is a solution of the given differential equation, use reduction of order to find a second solution y_2. $y'' - 25y = 0$.

15. If $y_1 = e^{4x}$ is a solution of the given differential equation, use reduction of order to find a second solution y_2. $2y'' - 5y' - 12y = 0$.

16. If $y_1 = e^{-3x}$ is a solution of the given differential equation, use reduction of order to find a second solution y_2. $y'' + 6y' + 9y = 0$.

17. If $y_1 = \cos 4x$ is a solution of the given differential equation, use reduction of order to find a second solution y_2. $y'' + 16y = 0$.

18. If $y_1 = x^3$ is a solution of the given differential equation, use reduction of order to find a second solution y_2. $x^2 y'' + xy' - 9y = 0$.

19. If $y_1 = x^2$ is a solution of the given differential equation, use reduction of order to find a second solution y_2. $x^2 y'' + 3xy' - 8y = 0$.

20. If $y_1 = x^3$ is a solution of the given differential equation, use reduction of order to find a second solution y_2. $x^2 y'' + 3xy' - 15y = 0$.

21. If $y_1 = x \ln x$ is a solution of the given differential equation, use reduction of order to find a second solution y_2. $x^2 y'' - xy' + y = 0$.

22. If $y_1 = x^3 \cos(\ln x)$ is a solution of the given differential equation, use reduction of order to find a second solution y_2. $x^2 y'' - 5xy' + 10y = 0$.

23. If $y_1 = x^{-2} \cos(\ln x)$ is a solution of the given differential equation, use reduction of order to find a second solution y_2. $x^2 y'' + 5xy' + 5y = 0$.

1. a

2. d

3. c

4. c

5. b

6. d

7. b

8. d

9. d

10. a

11. c

12. $y_2 = e^{-3x}$

13. $y_2 = e^{-x}$

14. $y_2 = e^{-5x}$

15. $y_2 = e^{-3x/2}$

16. $y_2 = xe^{-3x}$

17. $y_2 = \sin 4x$

18. $y_2 = x^{-3}$

19. $y_2 = x^{-4}$

20. $y_2 = x^{-5}$

21. $y_2 = x$

22. $y_2 = x^3 \sin(\ln x)$

23. $y_2 = x^{-2} \sin(\ln x)$

1. number of initial conditions accompanying a DE

2. solution of the DE from a repeating root

3. solution of the DE from a repeating root

4. complex roots of auxiliary equations

5. solutions of the DE from roots of auxiliary equations

6. complex roots of auxiliary equations

7. degree of auxiliary equation

8. order of the general solution

9. number of linearly independent solutions

10. pairing of trigonometric solutions

11. possible number of complex root

12. Solve a 2nd-order linear homogeneous DE — distinct real roots

13. Solve a 2nd-order linear homogeneous DE — distinct real roots

14. Solve a 2nd-order linear homogeneous DE — distinct real roots

15. Solve a 2nd-order linear homogeneous DE — distinct real roots

16. Solve a 2nd-order linear homogeneous DE — distinct real roots

17. Solve a 2nd-order linear homogeneous DE — two repeating real roots

18. Solve a 2nd-order linear homogeneous DE — purely imaginary roots

19. Solve a 2nd-order linear homogeneous DE — complex roots

20. Solve a 2nd-order linear homogeneous DE — complex roots

21. Solve a 2nd-order linear homogeneous DE — complex roots

22. Solve a 3rd-order linear homogeneous DE — a double real root and a third disctinct root

23. Solve a 3rd-order linear homogeneous DE — 3 distinct real roots

24. Solve a 4th-order linear homogeneous DE — a double real root and 2 other distinct roots

25. Solve a 5th-order linear homogeneous DE — a triple real root and a repeating complex root

26. Solve a 5th-order linear homogeneous DE — a triple real root and a repeating complex root

27. Solve a 4th-order linear homogeneous DE — a repeating purely imaginary root and a repeating complex root

28. Given 9 roots of an auxiliary equation, write the general solution.

1. If an initial value problem comprises a 4th-order linear homogeneous differential equation, we would expect it to have

    (a) one initial condition.

    (b) two initial conditions.

    (c) four initial conditions.

    (d) eight initial conditions.

2. If $y = xe^{-3x}$ is a solution of a linear homogeneous differential equation, then another solution must be

    (a) $y = x$.

    (b) $y = e^{-3x}$.

    (c) $y = xe^{3x}$.

    (d) $y = x^2 e^{-3x}$.

3. If $y = x \cos 2x$ is a solution of a linear homogeneous differential equation, then another solution must be

    (a) $y = \cos 2x$.

    (b) $y = x \sin 2x$.

    (c) $y = \sin 2x$.

    (d) all of the above

4. If one root of the auxiliary equation to a linear homogeneous differential equation is $3 + 7i$, then another root must be

    (a) $3 + 7i$.

    (b) $-3 + 7i$.

    (c) $3 - 7i$.

    (d) $-3 - 7i$.

5. If the auxiliary equation of a linear homogeneous differential equation has a factor $(m - 4)^3$, then solutions of the DE must include

    (a) $y = e^{4x}$.

    (b) $y = e^{4x}$ and $y = xe^{4x}$.

    (c) $y = xe^{4x}$ and $y = x^2 e^{4x}$.

    (d) $y = e^{4x}$, $y = xe^{4x}$, and $y = x^2 e^{4x}$.

6. It is possible for the auxiliary equation of a 3rd-order linear homogeneous differential equation to have

    (a) two real roots and one complex root.

    (b) one real root and two complex roots.

    (c) three complex roots.

    (d) (a) or (c)

7. True or False: The auxiliary equation of a 3rd-order linear homogeneous differential equation is always a 3rd degree polynomial.

8. True or False: A 4th-order linear homogeneous differential equation always has a 4-parameter family of solutions.

9. True or False: A 5th-order linear homogeneous differential equation always has five linearly independent solutions.

10. True or False: If $\sin 3x$ is a solution of a linear homogeneous differential equation, then $\cos 3x$ must also be a solution.

11. True or False: It is possible for the auxiliary equation of a linear homogeneous differential equation to have 5 complex roots.

12. Find the general solution of the differential equation $y'' + y' - 6y = 0$.

13. Find the general solution of the differential equation $y'' - 5y' + 6y = 0$.

14. Find the general solution of the differential equation $y'' - 2y' - 3y = 0$.

15. Find the general solution of the differential equation $y'' - 25y = 0$.

16. Find the general solution of the differential equation $2y'' - 5y' - 12y = 0$.

17. Find the general solution of the differential equation $y'' + 6y' + 9y = 0$.

18. Find the general solution of the differential equation $y'' + 16y = 0$.

19. Find the general solution of the differential equation $y'' + 6y' + 13y = 0$.

20. Find the general solution of the differential equation $y'' + 2y' + 17y = 0$.

21. Find the general solution of the differential equation $y'' + 4y' + 40y = 0$.

22. Find the general solution of the differential equation $y''' + 4y'' + 4y' = 0$.

23. Find the general solution of the differential equation $y''' - 4y'' - 5y' = 0$.

24. Find the general solution of the differential equation $y^{(4)} - 8y''' + 15y'' = 0$.

25. Find the general solution of the differential equation $y^{(5)} + 6y^{(4)} + 10y^{(3)} = 0$.

26. Find the general solution of the differential equation $y^{(5)} + 4y^{(4)} + 20y^{(3)} = 0$.

27. Find the general solution of the differential equation $y^{(4)} - 8y'' + 16y = 0$.

28. A certain linear homogeneous DE with constant coefficients has an auxiliary equation whose roots are $m = 0, 0, 0, -2, -2, \pm 3i, \pm 3i$. Write the general solution of the DE.

1. c

2. b

3. d

4. c

5. d

6. b

7. True

8. True

9. True

10. True

11. False

12. $y = c_1 e^{2x} + c_2 e^{-3x}$

13. $y = c_1 e^{2x} + c_2 e^{3x}$

14. $y = c_1 e^{-x} + c_2 e^{3x}$

15. $y = c_1 e^{-5x} + c_2 e^{5x}$

16. $y = c_1 e^{4x} + c_2 e^{-3x/2}$

17. $y = c_1 e^{-3x} + c_2 x e^{-3x}$

18. $y = c_1 \cos 4x + c_2 \sin 4x$

19. $y = c_1 e^{-3x} \cos 2x + c_2 e^{-3x} \sin 2x$

20. $y = c_1 e^{-x} \cos 4x + c_2 e^{-x} \sin 4x$

21. $y = c_1 e^{2x} \cos 6x + c_2 e^{2x} \sin 6x$

22. $y = c_1 + c_2 e^{-2x} + c_3 x e^{-2x}$

23. $y = c_1 + c_2 e^{-x} + c_3 e^{5x}$

24. $y = c_1 + c_2 x + c_3 e^{3x} + c_4 e^{5x}$

25. $y = c_1 + c_2 x + c_3 x^2 + c_4 e^{-3x} \cos x + c_5 e^{-3x} \sin x$

26. $y = c_1 + c_2 x + c_3 x^2 + c_4 e^{-2x} \cos 3x + c_5 e^{-2x} \sin 3x$

27. $y = c_1 \cos 2x + c_2 \sin 2x + c_3 x \cos 2x + c_4 x \sin 2x$

28. $y = c_1 + c_2 x + c_3 x^2 + c_4 e^{-2x} + c_5 x e^{-2x} + c_6 \cos 3x + c_7 \sin 3x + c_8 x \cos 3x + c_9 x \sin 3x$

1. input function inappropriate for undetermined coefficients

2. input function inappropriate for undetermined coefficients

3. input function inappropriate for undetermined coefficients

4. input function inappropriate for undetermined coefficients

5. identifying proper trial particular solution

6. identifying proper trial particular solution

7. identifying proper trial particular solution

8. identifying proper trial particular solution

9. identifying proper trial particular solution

10. identifying proper trial particular solution

11. identifying proper trial particular solution

12. identifying proper trial particular solution

13. find the general solution by undetermined coefficients — 2nd-order; no repeating terms; exponential input

14. find the general solution by undetermined coefficients — 2nd-order; no repeating terms; trig input

15. find the general solution by undetermined coefficients — 2nd-order; no repeating terms; polynomial input

16. find the general solution by undetermined coefficients — 2nd-order; repeating exponential term; exponential & trig input

17. find the general solution by undetermined coefficients — 2nd-order; repeating exponential term; exponential & polynomial input

18. find the general solution by undetermined coefficients — 2nd-order; repeating exponential term; exponential & trig input

19. find the general solution by undetermined coefficients — 2nd-order; repeating exponential term; exponential & trig input

20. find the general solution by undetermined coefficients — 2nd-order; repeating exponential term; exponential & polynomial input

21. find the general solution by undetermined coefficients — 2nd-order; repeating exponential term; exponential & trig input

22. find the general solution by undetermined coefficients — 2nd-order; repeating exponential term; exponential & trig input

23. find the general solution by undetermined coefficients — 2nd-order; repeating exponential term; exponential & trig input

24. find the general solution by undetermined coefficients — 2nd-order; repeating exponential term; exponential & polynomial input

25. find the general solution by undetermined coefficients — 2nd-order; repeating exponential term; exponential & trig input

26. find the general solution by undetermined coefficients — 2nd-order; repeating exponential term; exponential & trig input

27. find the general solution by undetermined coefficients — 2nd-order; repeating exponential term; exponential & polynomial input

28. find the general solution by undetermined coefficients — 2nd-order; repeating exponential term; exponential & trig input

29. find the general solution by undetermined coefficients — 3rd-order; no repeating terms; trig input

30. find the general solution by undetermined coefficients — 3rd-order; repeating power terms; polynomial & trig input

31. find the general solution by undetermined coefficients — 4th-order; repeating terms; constant input

1. Undetermined coefficients cannot be used if the input function contains what term?

   (a) e^{3x}

   (b) $\ln 4x$

   (c) x^2

   (d) $x \cos 5x$

2. Undetermined coefficients cannot be used if the input function contains what term?

   (a) $x^4 e^{-2x}$

   (b) x^2

   (c) x^{-2}

   (d) $x^3 \sin 4x$

3. Undetermined coefficients cannot be used if the input function contains what term?

   (a) $\sqrt{x}$

   (b) $x^2 e^{-3x}$

   (c) $x^2 \cos 2x$

   (d) $x^3 \sin 4x$

4. Undetermined coefficients cannot be used if the input function contains what term?

   (a) $x^2 e^{-3x} \cos 4x$

   (b) $x^{-3} \cos 2x$

   (c) $e^{-3x} \sin 4x$

   (d) $e^{-2x} \sin^2 4x$

5. Without solving the differential equation, apply undetermined coefficients to determine the simplest form of a particular solution to the DE $y'' - 16y = \sin 4x$

   (a) $y_p = ae^{4x} + be^{4x}$

   (b) $y_p = a \sin 4x$

   (c) $y_p = a \cos 4x$

   (d) $y_p = a \cos 4x + b \sin 4x$

6. Without solving the differential equation, apply undetermined coefficients to determine the simplest form of a particular solution to the DE $y'' + 4y = e^{2x}$

   (a) $y_p = ae^{2x}$

   (b) $y_p = axe^{2x}$

   (c) $y_p = a \sin 4x$

   (d) $y_p = a \cos 4x$

7. Without solving the differential equation, apply undetermined coefficients to determine the simplest form of a particular solution to the DE $y'' - 16y = e^{4x}$

   (a) $y_p = ae^{2x}$

   (b) $y_p = axe^{2x}$

   (c) $y_p = a \sin 4x$

   (d) $y_p = a \cos 4x$

8. Without solving the differential equation, apply undetermined coefficients to determine the simplest form of a particular solution to the DE $y'' + 9y = 10x^2$

   (a) $y_p = ax^2$

   (b) $y_p = ax^2 + bx$

   (c) $y_p = ax^2 + bx + c$

   (d) $y_p = a \cos 3x + b \sin 3x$

9. Without solving the differential equation, apply undetermined coefficients to determine the simplest form of a particular solution to the DE $y'' + 9y = 4 \cos 3x$

   (a) $y_p = a \cos 3x + b \sin 3x$

   (b) $y_p = ax \cos 3x + b \sin 3x$

   (c) $y_p = a \cos 3x + bx \sin 3x$

   (d) $y_p = ax \cos 3x + bx \sin 3x$

10. Without solving the differential equation, apply undetermined coefficients to determine the simplest form of a particular solution to the DE $y'' + 9y' = \cos 3x$

    (a) $y_p = a \cos 3x + b \sin 3x$

    (b) $y_p = ax \cos 3x + b \sin 3x$

    (c) $y_p = a \cos 3x + bx \sin 3x$

    (d) $y_p = ax \cos 3x + bx \sin 3x$

11. Without solving the differential equation, apply undetermined coefficients to determine the simplest form of a particular solution to the DE $y'' + 4y' = 4x$

    (a) $y_p = ax$

    (b) $y_p = ax + b$

    (c) $y_p = ax^2 + bx$

    (d) $y_p = ax^2 + bx + c$

12. Without solving the differential equation, apply undetermined coefficients to determine the simplest form of a particular solution to the DE $y'' - 2y' - 8y = 12e^{4x}$

    (a) $y_p = ae^{4x}$

    (b) $y_p = axe^{4x}$

    (c) $y_p = ae^{-2x}$

    (d) $y_p = axe^{-2x}$

Problems 13-31: Use undetermined coefficients to obtain the general solution of the given differential equation.

13. $y'' + y' - 2y = 8e^{2x}$.

14. $y'' + 3y' - 4y = 100\cos 2x$.

15. $y'' - 6y' + 8y = 64x^2$.

16. $y'' + y' - 2y = 18e^x - 30\cos x$.

17. $y'' - 4y = 6 - 12x^2 + 4e^{2x}$

18. $y'' - 4y = 16e^{2x} + 5\cos x$

19. $y'' - y = 5\sin 2x + 4e^x$

20. $y'' - 2y' - 8y = 18e^{4x} + 32x^2$

21. $y'' + 2y' = 16\cos 2x + 6e^{-2x}$

22. $y'' + 2y' = 15\cos x + 4e^{-2x}$

23. $y'' - 2y' - 3y = 16e^{-x} + 30\sin 3x$

24. $y'' + y' - 2y = 18e^x + 4x$

25. $y'' + 2y' = 15\cos x + 12e^{-2x}$

26. $y'' - 9y = 10\cos x + 12e^{-3x}$

27. $y'' - 4y = 12x + 4e^{2x}$

28. $y'' + y' - 6y = 50xe^{2x} + 100\sin x$

29. $y''' + 4y' = 9\cos x$

30. $y''' - 4y' = 24x^2 + 16\cos 2x$

31. $y^{(4)} - 16y'' = 64$

1. b

2. c

3. a

4. b

5. d

6. a

7. b

8. c

9. d

10. a

11. d

12. b

13. $y = c_1 e^x + c_2 e^{-2x} + 2e^{2x}$

14. $y = c_1 e^x + c_2 e^{-4x} + 6\sin 2x - 8\cos 2x$

15. $y = c_1 e^{2x} + c_2 e^{4x} + 8x^2 + 12x + 7$

16. $y = c_1 e^x + c_2 e^{-2x} + 6xe^x + 9\cos x - 3\sin x$

17. $y = c_1 e^{2x} + c_2 e^{-2x} + xe^{2x} + 3x^2$

18. $y = c_1 e^{2x} + c_2 e^{-2x} + 4xe^{2x} - \cos x$

19. $y = c_1 e^x + c_2 e^{-x} + 2xe^x - \sin 2x$

20. $y = c_1 e^{-2x} + c_2 e^{4x} + 3xe^{4x} - 4x^2 - 3/2$

21. $y = c_1 + c_2 e^{-2x} + 2\sin 2x - 2\cos 2x - 3xe^{-2x}$

22. $y = c_1 + c_2 e^{-2x} + 6\sin x - 3\cos x - 2xe^{-2x}$

23. $y = c_1 e^{-x} + c_2 e^{3x} + \cos 3x - 2\sin 3x - 4xe^{-x}$

24. $y = c_1 e^x + c_2 e^{-2x} + 6xe^x - 2x - 1$

25. $y = c_1 + c_2 e^{-2x} + 6\sin x - 3\cos x - 6xe^{-2x}$

26. $y = c_1 e^{3x} + c_2 e^{-3x} - \cos x - 2xe^{-3x}$

27. $y = c_1 e^{2x} + c_2 e^{-2x} + xe^{2x} - 3x$

28. $y = c_1 e^{2x} + c_2 e^{-3x} + \frac{1}{2}x^2 e^{2x} - \frac{1}{5}xe^{2x} - 2\cos x - 14\sin x$

29. $y = c_1 + c_2 \cos 2x + c_3 \sin 2x + 3\sin x$

30. $y = c_1 + c_2 e^{2x} + c_2 e^{-2x} - 2x^3 - 3x - \sin 2x$

31. $y = c_1 + c_2 e^{4x} + c_3 e^{-4x} + c_4 x - 2x^2$

1. identify the operator of lowest order that annihilates given function

2. identify the operator of lowest order that annihilates given function

3. identify the operator of lowest order that annihilates given function

4. identify the operator of lowest order that annihilates given function

5. identify the operator of lowest order that annihilates given function

6. identify the operator of lowest order that annihilates given function

7. identify the operator of lowest order that annihilates given function

8. identify the operator of lowest order that annihilates given function

9. identify the operator of lowest order that annihilates given function

10. identify the operator of lowest order that annihilates given function

11. identify the operator of lowest order that annihilates given function

12. write given expression in operator form

13. write given expression in operator form

14. write given expression in operator form

15. find the general solution by undetermined coefficients — 2nd-order; no repeating terms; exponential input

16. find the general solution by undetermined coefficients — 2nd-order; no repeating terms; trig input

17. find the general solution by undetermined coefficients — 2nd-order; no repeating terms; polynomial input

18. find the general solution by undetermined coefficients — 2nd-order; repeating exponential term; exponential & trig input

19. find the general solution by undetermined coefficients — 2nd-order; repeating exponential term; exponential & polynomial input

20. find the general solution by undetermined coefficients — 2nd-order; repeating exponential term; exponential & trig input

21. find the general solution by undetermined coefficients — 2nd-order; repeating exponential term; exponential & trig input

22. find the general solution by undetermined coefficients — 2nd-order; repeating exponential term; exponential & polynomial input

23. find the general solution by undetermined coefficients — 2nd-order; repeating exponential term; exponential & trig input

24. find the general solution by undetermined coefficients — 2nd-order; repeating exponential term; exponential & trig input

25. find the general solution by undetermined coefficients — 2nd-order; repeating exponential term; exponential & trig input

26. find the general solution by undetermined coefficients — 2nd-order; repeating exponential term; exponential & polynomial input

27. find the general solution by undetermined coefficients — 2nd-order; repeating exponential term; exponential & trig input

28. find the general solution by undetermined coefficients — 2nd-order; repeating exponential term; exponential & trig input

29. find the general solution by undetermined coefficients — 2nd-order; repeating exponential term; exponential & polynomial input

30. find the general solution by undetermined coefficients — 2nd-order; repeating exponential term; exponential & trig input

31. find the general solution by undetermined coefficients — 3rd-order; no repeating terms; trig input

32. find the general solution by undetermined coefficients — 3rd-order; repeating power terms; polynomial & trig input

33. find the general solution by undetermined coefficients — 4th-order; repeating terms; constant input

1. What operator annihilates the function e^{3x}?

   (a) D

   (b) $D + 3$

   (c) $D - 3$

   (d) $D^2 + 9$

2. What operator annihilates the function e^{-2x}?

   (a) D

   (b) $D + 2$

   (c) $D - 2$

   (d) $D^2 + 4$

3. What operator annihilates the function $\sin 2x$?

   (a) $D + 2$

   (b) $D - 2$

   (c) $D^2 + 4$

   (d) $D^2 - 4$

4. What operator of lowest possible order annihilates the function x^2?

   (a) $D + 2$

   (b) $D - 2$

   (c) D^2

   (d) D^3

5. What operator of lowest possible order annihilates the function xe^{2x}?

   (a) $D^2 - 4D + 4$

   (b) $D^2 + 4D + 4$

   (c) $(D^2 - 4D + 4)^2$

   (d) $(D^2 + 4D + 4)^2$

6. What operator of lowest possible order annihilates the function xe^{-3x}?

   (a) $D^2 - 6D + 9$

   (b) $D^2 + 6D + 9$

   (c) $(D^2 - 6D + 9)^2$

   (d) $(D^2 + 6D + 9)^2$

7. What operator of lowest possible order annihilates the function $e^x \sin 2x$?

   (a) $D^2 - 2D + 5$

   (b) $D^2 + 2D + 5$

   (c) $D^2 - D + 4$

   (d) $D^2 + D + 4$

8. What operator of lowest possible order annihilates the function $e^{-2x}\cos 4x$?

   (a) $D^2 - 2D + 16$

   (b) $D^2 + 2D + 16$

   (c) $D^2 - 4D + 20$

   (d) $D^2 + 4D + 20$

9. What operator of lowest possible order annihilates the function $4x + e^{2x}$?

   (a) $D(D - 2)$

   (b) $D(D + 2)$

   (c) $D^2(D - 2)$

   (d) $D^2(D + 2)$

10. What operator of lowest possible order annihilates the function $2e^{-x}\cos 3x - 4e^{-x}\sin 3x$?

    (a) $D^2 + 2D + 10$

    (b) $D^2 - 2D + 10$

    (c) $D^2 + D + 9$

    (d) $D^2 - D + 9$

11. What operator of lowest possible order annihilates the function $8x^2 + e^{-3x}$?

    (a) $D^2(D - 3)$

    (b) $D^2(D + 3)$

    (c) $D^3(D - 3)$

    (d) $D^3(D + 3)$

12. In lowest order, we may write the expression $y'' + 4y' - 4y$ as

    (a) $(D^2 - 4D + 4)\, y.$

    (b) $(D^2 + 4D - 4)\, y.$

    (c) $(D^3 - 4D^2 + 4D)\, y.$

    (d) $(D^3 + 4D^2 - 4D)\, y.$

13. In lowest order, we may write the expression $y'' + 6y'$ as

    (a) $D(D + 6)\, y.$

    (b) $(D + 6)\, y.$

    (c) $D^2(D + 6)\, y.$

    (d) $D^2(D + 6D)\, y.$

14. In lowest order, we may write the expression $y'' + 4y$ as

    (a) $(D^2 + 4)\, y.$

    (b) $(D^2 + 4D)\, y.$

    (c) $(D + 2)^2\, y.$

    (d) $(D - 2)^2\, y.$

Problems 15-33: Use undetermined coefficients (the annihilator approach) to obtain the general solution of the given differential equation.

15. $y'' + y' - 2y = 8e^{2x}$.

16. $y'' + 3y' - 4y = 100\cos 2x$.

17. $y'' - 6y' + 8y = 64x^2$.

18. $y'' + y' - 2y = 18e^x - 30\cos x$.

19. $y'' - 4y = 6 - 12x^2 + 4e^{2x}$

20. $y'' - 4y = 16e^{2x} + 5\cos x$

21. $y'' - y = 5\sin 2x + 4e^x$

22. $y'' - 2y' - 8y = 18e^{4x} + 32x^2$

23. $y'' + 2y' = 16\cos 2x + 6e^{-2x}$

24. $y'' + 2y' = 15\cos x + 4e^{-2x}$

25. $y'' - 2y' - 3y = 16e^{-x} + 30\sin 3x$

26. $y'' + y' - 2y = 18e^x + 4x$

27. $y'' + 2y' = 15\cos x + 12e^{-2x}$

28. $y'' - 9y = 10\cos x + 12e^{-3x}$

29. $y'' - 4y = 12x + 4e^{2x}$

30. $y'' + y' - 6y = 50xe^{2x} + 100\sin x$

31. $y''' + 4y' = 9\cos x$

32. $y''' - 4y' = 24x^2 + 16\cos 2x$

33. $y^{(4)} - 16y'' = 64$

108

1. c

2. b

3. c

4. d

5. a

6. b

7. a

8. d

9. c

10. a

11. d

12. b

13. a

14. a

15. $y = c_1 e^x + c_2 e^{-2x} + 2e^{2x}$

16. $y = c_1 e^x + c_2 e^{-4x} + 6\sin 2x - 8\cos 2x$

17. $y = c_1 e^{2x} + c_2 e^{4x} + 8x^2 + 12x + 7$

18. $y = c_1 e^x + c_2 e^{-2x} + 6xe^x + 9\cos x - 3\sin x$

19. $y = c_1 e^{2x} + c_2 e^{-2x} + xe^{2x} + 3x^2$

20. $y = c_1 e^{2x} + c_2 e^{-2x} + 4xe^{2x} - \cos x$

21. $y = c_1 e^x + c_2 e^{-x} + 2xe^x - \sin 2x$

22. $y = c_1 e^{-2x} + c_2 e^{4x} + 3xe^{4x} - 4x^2 - 3/2$

23. $y = c_1 + c_2 e^{-2x} + 2\sin 2x - 2\cos 2x - 3xe^{-2x}$

24. $y = c_1 + c_2 e^{-2x} + 6\sin x - 3\cos x - 2xe^{-2x}$

25. $y = c_1 e^{-x} + c_2 e^{3x} + \cos 3x - 2\sin 3x - 4xe^{-x}$

26. $y = c_1 e^x + c_2 e^{-2x} + 6xe^x - 2x - 1$

27. $y = c_1 + c_2 e^{-2x} + 6\sin x - 3\cos x - 6xe^{-2x}$

28. $y = c_1 e^{3x} + c_2 e^{-3x} - \cos x - 2xe^{-3x}$

29. $y = c_1 e^{2x} + c_2 e^{-2x} + xe^{2x} - 3x$

30. $y = c_1 e^{2x} + c_2 e^{-3x} + \dfrac{1}{2}x^2 e^{2x} - \dfrac{1}{5}xe^{2x} - 2\cos x - 14\sin x$

31. $y = c_1 + c_2 \cos 2x + c_3 \sin 2x + 3 \sin x$

32. $y = c_1 + c_2 e^{2x} + c_2 e^{-2x} - 2x^3 - 3x - \sin 2x$

33. $y = c_1 + c_2 e^{4x} + c_3 e^{-4x} + c_4 x - 2x^2$

1. role of Wronskian in linear independence

2. role of Wronskian in linear independence

3. size of determinant in calculating the Wronskian

4. size of determinant in calculating the Wronskian

5. purpose of variation of parameters

6. number of integrals to evaluate when using variation of parameters

7. number of integrals to evaluate when using variation of parameters

8. when we may use variation of parameters

9. when we may use variation of parameters

10. purpose of variation of parameters

11. purpose of variation of parameters

12. purpose of variation of parameters

13. relationship between solution obtained by variation of parameters and complementary solution

Problems 14–36: Use variation of parameters to obtain the general solution of a 2nd-order linear DE.

1. If functions y_1 and y_2 are solutions of a 2nd-order linear differential equation on interval I, then

   (a) the Wronskian $W(y_1, y_2)$ is 0 everywhere on I.

   (b) the Wronskian $W(y_1, y_2)$ might be 0 at some points on I.

   (c) the Wronskian $W(y_1, y_2)$ cannot be 0 anywhere on I.

   (d) Nothing can be said with certainty without more information.

2. If functions y_1 and y_2 are linearly independent solutions of a 2nd-order linear differential equation on interval I, then

   (a) the Wronskian $W(y_1, y_2)$ is 0 everywhere on I.

   (b) the Wronskian $W(y_1, y_2)$ might be 0 at some pints on I.

   (c) the Wronskian $W(y_1, y_2)$ cannot be 0 anywhere on I.

   (d) Nothing can be said with certainty without more information.

3. If functions y_1 and y_2 are linearly independent solutions of a 2nd-order linear differential equation on interval I, then the Wronskian $W(y_1, y_2)$ may be found by evaluating a

   (a) 2×2 determinant.

   (b) 3×3 determinant.

   (c) 4×4 determinant.

   (d) 5×5 determinant.

4. If functions y_1, y_2, and y_3 are linearly independent solutions of a 3rd-order linear differential equation on interval I, then the Wronskian $W(y_1, y_2, y_3)$ may be found by evaluating a

   (a) 2×2 determinant.

   (b) 3×3 determinant.

   (c) 4×4 determinant.

   (d) 5×5 determinant.

5. We use variation of parameters to obtain

   (a) the complementary solution of a linear differential equation.

   (b) a particular solution of a linear differential equation.

   (c) both (a) and (b).

   (d) neither (a) nor (b).

6. When using variation of parameters to solve a 2nd-order linear differential equation, we must evaluate

   (a) 1 integral.

   (b) 2 integrals.

   (c) 3 integrals.

   (d) 4 integrals.

7. When using variation of parameters to solve a 3rd-order linear differential equation, we must evaluate

   (a) 1 integral.

   (b) 2 integrals.

   (c) 3 integrals.

   (d) 6 integrals.

8. True or False: We may use variation of parameters only to solve linear differential equations that have constant coefficients.

9. True or False: We may use variation of parameters only to solve 2nd-order linear differential equations.

10. True or False: To use variation of parameters to solve a linear differential equation, we must first find the complementary solution.

11. True or False: Variation of parameters is a method for finding a particular solution of a linear differential equation.

12. True or False: Variation of parameters is a method for finding a complementary solution of a linear differential equation.

13. True or False: When using variation of parameters, the resulting particular solution will always be linearly independent of the complementary solution.

Problems 14-36: Use variation of parameters to obtain the general solution of the given differential equation.

14. $y'' + y' - 2y = 8e^{2x}$.

15. $y'' - 6y' + 8y = 64x^2$.

16. $y'' - 4y = 6 - 12x^2 + 4e^{2x}$

17. $y'' - 4y = 16e^{2x} + 5\cos x$

18. $y'' - y = 5\sin 2x + 4e^x$

19. $y'' - 2y' - 8y = 18e^{4x}$

20. $y'' + 2y' = 6e^{-2x}$

21. $y'' - 2y' - 3y = 16e^{-x}$

22. $y'' + y' - 2y = 18e^x + 4x$

23. $y'' - 9y = 12e^{-3x}$

24. $y'' - 4y = 12x + 4e^{2x}$

25. $y'' + y' - 6y = 50xe^{2x}$

26. $y'' - 2y' + y = \dfrac{e^x}{1 + x^2}$

27. $y'' - y = 6e^{2x} - 4e^x$

28. $y'' - y' - 2y = 12 + 9e^{2x}$

29. $y'' - 3y' + 2y = 8 + e^{2x}$

30. $y'' - y' - 6y = 12e^{-x} + 10e^{3x}$

31. $y'' - 4y' + 3y = 8e^{3x}$

32. $y'' - 2y' - 3y = 16e^{-x}$

33. $y'' + y = \csc^2 x$

34. $y'' + y = \sin^2 x$

35. $y'' + y = 4\cos x$

36. $y'' + 4y = 8\cos x$

1. d

2. c

3. a

4. b

5. c

6. b

7. c

8. False

9. False

10. True

11. True

12. False

13. True

14. $y = c_1 e^x + c_2 e^{-2x} + 2e^{2x}$

15. $y = c_1 e^{2x} + c_2 e^{4x} + 8x^2 + 12x + 7$

16. $y = c_1 e^{2x} + c_2 e^{-2x} + xe^{2x} + 3x^2$

17. $y = c_1 e^{2x} + c_2 e^{-2x} + 4xe^{2x} - \cos x$

18. $y = c_1 e^x + c_2 e^{-x} + 2xe^x - \sin 2x$

19. $y = c_1 e^{-2x} + c_2 e^{4x} + 3xe^{4x}$

20. $y = c_1 + c_2 e^{-2x} - 3xe^{-2x}$

21. $y = c_1 e^{-x} + c_2 e^{3x} - 4xe^{-x}$

22. $y = c_1 e^x + c_2 e^{-2x} + 6xe^x - 2x - 1$

23. $y = c_1 e^{3x} + c_2 e^{-3x} - 2xe^{-3x}$

24. $y = c_1 e^{2x} + c_2 e^{-2x} + xe^{2x} - 3x$

25. $y = c_1 e^{2x} + c_2 e^{-3x} + \frac{1}{2}x^2 e^{2x} - \frac{1}{5}xe^{2x}$

26. $y = c_1 e^x + c_2\, x\, e^x + \frac{1}{2}\, e^x\, \ln(1 + x^2) + 2x\tan^{-1} x$

27. $y = c_1 e^x + c_2 e^{-x} + 2e^{2x} - 2xe^x$

28. $y = c_1 e^{2x} + c_2 e^{-x} + 3xe^{2x} - 6$

29. $y = c_1 e^x + c_2 e^{2x} + xe^{2x} + 4$

115

30. $y = c_1 e^{-2x} + c_2 e^{3x} + 2xe^{3x} - 3e^{-x}$

31. $y = c_1 e^x + c_2 e^{3x} + 4xe^{3x}$

32. $y = c_1 e^{3x} + c_2 e^{-x} - 4xe^{-x}$

33. $y = c_1 \cos x + c_2 \sin x - 1 - \cos x \ln|\csc x - \cot x|$

34. $y = c_1 \cos x + c_2 \sin x + \cos x (6\cos x - 2\cos^3 x) + 2\sin^4 x = c_1 \cos x + c_2 \sin x + 2 + 2\cos^2 x$

35. $y = c_1 \cos x + c_2 \sin x + \cos x (2\cos 2x) + \sin x (2x + \sin 2x) = c_1 \cos x + c_2 \sin x + 2x \sin x$

36. $y = c_1 \cos 2x + c_2 \sin 2x + 2\cos 2x \ln|\cos 2x| + 4x \sin 2x$

1. Function substitution needed to solve a Cauchy-Euler DE

2. Variable substitution needed to solve a Cauchy-Euler DE

3. Given the auxiliary equation of a Cauchy–Euler De, state the solutions

4. Given the auxiliary equation of a Cauchy–Euler De, state the solutions

5. Given the auxiliary equation of a Cauchy–Euler De, state the solutions

6. Given the auxiliary equation of a Cauchy–Euler De, state the solutions

7. Given the auxiliary equation of a Cauchy–Euler De, state the solutions

8. Given the auxiliary equation of a Cauchy–Euler De, state the solutions

9. Given the auxiliary equation of a Cauchy–Euler De, state the solutions

10. Domain of solution of a Cauchy–Euler DE

11. Substitution needed to obtain solution of a Cauchy–Euler DE on $(\infty, 0)$

12. Solve a 2nd-order homogeneous Cauchy-Euler DE; distinct real roots

13. Solve a 2nd-order homogeneous Cauchy-Euler DE; distinct real roots

14. Solve a 2nd-order homogeneous Cauchy-Euler DE; distinct real roots

15. Solve a 2nd-order homogeneous Cauchy-Euler DE; distinct real roots

16. Solve a 2nd-order homogeneous Cauchy-Euler DE; distinct real roots

17. Solve a 2nd-order homogeneous Cauchy-Euler DE; distinct real roots

18. Solve a 2nd-order homogeneous Cauchy-Euler DE; purely imaginary roots

19. Solve a 2nd-order homogeneous Cauchy-Euler DE; purely imaginary roots

20. Solve a 2nd-order homogeneous Cauchy-Euler DE; complex roots

21. Solve a 2nd-order homogeneous Cauchy-Euler DE; complex roots

22. Solve a 2nd-order homogeneous Cauchy-Euler DE; complex roots

23. Solve a 2nd-order homogeneous Cauchy-Euler DE; repeating real roots

24. Solve a 2nd-order homogeneous Cauchy-Euler DE; repeating real roots

25. Solve a 2nd-order homogeneous Cauchy-Euler DE; repeating real roots

26. Solve a 3rd-order homogeneous Cauchy-Euler DE; two repeating real roots & third distinct real root

27. Solve a 3rd-order homogeneous Cauchy-Euler DE; two repeating real roots & third distinct real root

28. Solve a 3rd-order homogeneous Cauchy-Euler DE; two repeating real roots & third distinct real root

29. Solve a 3rd-order homogeneous Cauchy-Euler DE; complex roots & one real root

30. Solve a 2nd-order nonhomogeneous Cauchy-Euler DE

31. Solve a 2nd-order nonhomogeneous Cauchy-Euler DE

32. Solve a 2nd-order nonhomogeneous Cauchy-Euler DE

33. Solve a 2nd-order nonhomogeneous Cauchy-Euler DE

34. Solve a 2nd-order nonhomogeneous Cauchy-Euler DE

1. Solving a Cauchy–Euler differential equation is equivalent to using the substitution

   (a) $y = m^x$.

   (b) $y = \ln x$.

   (c) $y = x^m$.

   (d) $y = e^{mx}$.

2. We may transform a Cauchy–Euler differential equation to a DE with constant coefficients by using the variable substitution

   (a) $x = e^t$.

   (b) $x = t^m$.

   (c) $t = e^x$.

   (d) $x = \ln t$.

3. If the auxiliary equation of a homogeneous Cauchy–Euler differential equation is $(m+2)(m-4) = 0$, then linearly independent solutions of the DE are

   (a) $y_1 = x^{-2}$ and $y_2 = x^4$

   (b) $y_1 = e^{-2x}$ and $y_2 = e^{4x}$

   (c) $y_1 = x^2$ and $y_2 = x^{-4}$

   (d) $y_1 = e^{2x}$ and $y_2 = e^{-4x}$

4. If the auxiliary equation of a homogeneous Cauchy–Euler differential equation is $(m-3)^2 = 0$, then linearly independent solutions of the DE are

   (a) $y_1 = x^3$ and $y_2 = x^4$

   (b) $y_1 = x^3$ and $y_2 = x^3 \ln x$

   (c) $y_1 = e^{3x}$ and $y_2 = xe^{3x}$

   (d) $y_1 = e^{3x}$ and $y_2 = e^{3x} \ln x$

5. If the auxiliary equation of a homogeneous Cauchy–Euler differential equation is $(m-4i)(m+4i) = 0$, then linearly independent solutions of the DE are

   (a) $y_1 = \cos(\ln 4x)$ and $y_2 = \sin(\ln 4x)$

   (b) $y_1 = \cos(4 \ln x)$ and $y_2 = \sin(4 \ln x)$

   (c) $y_1 = \ln(\cos 4x)$ and $y_2 = \ln(\sin 4x)$

   (d) $y_1 = \ln(4 \cos x)$ and $y_2 = \ln(4 \sin x)$

6. If the auxiliary equation of a homogeneous Cauchy–Euler differential equation is $(m - 3 + 2i)(m - 3 - 2i) = 0$, then linearly independent solutions of the DE are

   (a) $y_1 = x^3 \ln(\cos 2x)$ and $y_2 = x^3 \ln(\sin 2x)$

   (b) $y_1 = x^3 \ln(2 \cos x)$ and $y_2 = x^3 \ln(2 \sin x)$

   (c) $y_1 = x^3 \cos(\ln 2x)$ and $y_2 = x^3 \sin(\ln 2x)$

   (d) $y_1 = x^3 \cos(2 \ln x)$ and $y_2 = x^3 \sin(2 \ln x)$

7. If the auxiliary equation of a homogeneous Cauchy–Euler differential equation is $(m - 4 + 2i)(m - 4 - 2i) = 0$, then linearly independent solutions of the DE are

    (a) $y_1 = x^4 \cos(4 \ln x)$ and $y_2 = x^4 \sin(2 \ln x)$

    (b) $y_1 = x^4 \cos(\ln 2x)$ and $y_2 = x^4 \sin(\ln 2x)$

    (c) $y_1 = x^2 \ln(4 \cos x)$ and $y_2 = x^2 \ln(\sin 4x)$

    (d) $y_1 = x^2 \ln(\cos 4x)$ and $y_2 = x^2 \ln(4 \sin x)$

8. If the auxiliary equation of a homogeneous Cauchy–Euler differential equation is $m^2(m - 4) = 0$, then linearly independent solutions of the DE are

    (a) $y_1 = 1$, $y_2 = x$, and $y_3 = e^{4x}$

    (b) $y_1 = 1$, $y_2 = \ln x$, and $y_3 = e^{4x}$

    (c) $y_1 = 1$, $y_2 = x$, and $y_3 = x^4$

    (d) $y_1 = 1$, $y_2 = \ln x$, and $y_3 = x^4$

9. If the auxiliary equation of a homogeneous Cauchy–Euler differential equation is $m(m - 5)^2 = 0$, then linearly independent solutions of the DE are

    (a) $y_1 = 1$, $y_2 = \ln 5x$, and $y_3 = x \ln 5x$

    (b) $y_1 = 1$, $y_2 = e^{5x}$, and $y_3 = xe^{5x}$

    (c) $y_1 = 1$, $y_2 = x^5$, and $y_3 = x^5 \ln x$

    (d) $y_1 = 1$, $y_2 = e^{5x}$, and $y_3 = e^{5x} \ln x$

10. To obtain a solution of a Cauchy–Euler differential equation that is valid on the interval $(-\infty, 0)$, we must use the substitution

    (a) $x = \ln t$

    (b) $x = t^m$

    (c) $x = t^{-1}$

    (d) $x = -t$

11. The solution of a Cauchy–Euler differential equation is valid on the interval

    (a) $(-\infty, \infty)$

    (b) $(-\infty, 0)$

    (c) $(0, \infty)$

    (d) one cannot say without more information

Problems 12-34: Obtain the general solution of the given differential equation.

12. $x^2 y'' - 6y = 0$

13. $x^2 y'' + 2xy' - 6y = 0$

14. $4x^2 y'' + 4xy' - y = 0$

15. $x^2 y'' - xy' - 3y = 0$

16. $x^2 y'' + xy' - 9y = 0$

17. $x^2 y'' + 3xy' - 8y = 0$

18. $x^2 y'' + xy' + 9y = 0$

19. $x^2 y'' + xy' + 25y = 0$

20. $x^2 y'' - 5xy' + 10y = 0$

21. $x^2 y'' + 5xy' + 13y = 0$

22. $x^3 y''' - x^2 y' + 10xy' = 0$

23. $x^2 y'' - 3xy' + 4y = 0$

24. $x^2 y'' - xy' + y = 0$

25. $x^2 y'' + 5xy' + 4y = 0$

26. $x^3 y''' + 5x^2 y' + 3xy' = 0$

27. $x^3 y''' - 3x^2 y' + 4xy' = 0$

28. $x^3 y''' + 11x^2 y' + 25xy' = 0$

29. $x^3 y''' - x^2 y' + 10xy' = 0$

30. $x^2 y'' - 6y = 25x^3$

31. $x^2 y'' + xy' - 9y = 30x^2$

32. $x^2 y'' - xy' + y = 4x$

33. $x^2 y'' + 2xy' - 6y = \ln x$

34. $x^2 y'' - xy' - 3y = 9\ln x$

1. c

2. a

3. a

4. b

5. b

6. d

7. a

8. d

9. c

10. d

11. c

12. $y = c_1 x^{-2} + c_2 x^3$

13. $y = c_1 x^2 + c_2 x^{-3}$

14. $y = c_1 x^{1/2} + c_2 x^{-1/2}$

15. $y = c_1 x^3 + c_2 x^{-1}$

16. $y = c_1 x^3 + c_2 x^{-3}$

17. $y = c_1 x^2 + c_2 x^{-4}$

18. $y = c_1 \cos(3\ln x) + c_2 \sin(3\ln x)$

19. $y = c_1 \cos(5\ln x) + c_2 \sin(5\ln x)$

20. $y = c_1 x^3 \cos(\ln x) + c_2 x^3 \sin(\ln x)$

21. $y = c_1 x^{-2} \cos(3\ln x) + c_2 x^{-2} \sin(3\ln x)$

22. $y = c_1 + c_2 x^2 \cos(2\ln x) + c_3 x^2 \sin(2\ln x)$

23. $y = c_1 x^2 + c_2 x^2 \ln x$

24. $y = c_1 x + c_2 x \ln x$

25. $y = c_1 x^{-2} + c_2 x^{-2} \ln x$

26. $y = c_1 + c_2 \ln x + c_3 x^{-2}$

27. $y = c_1 + c_2 x^3 + c_3 x^3 \ln x$

28. $y = c_1 + c_2 x^{-4} + c_3 x^{-4} \ln x$

29. $y = c_1 + c_2 x^2 \cos(3\ln x) + c_3 x^2 \sin(3\ln x)$

30. $y = c_1 x^{-2} + c_2 x^3 + 5x^3 \ln x$

31. $y = c_1 x^3 + c_2 x^{-3} - 6x^2$

32. $y = c_1 x + c_2 x \ln x + 2x (\ln x)^2$

33. $y = c_1 x^2 + c_2 x^{-3} - 1 - 36 \ln x$

34. $y = c_1 x^3 + c_2 x^{-1} + 2 - 3 \ln x$

1. Solve a system of linear 1st-order homogeneous DEs

2. Solve a system of linear 1st-order homogeneous DEs

3. Solve a system of linear 1st-order homogeneous DEs

4. Solve a system of linear 1st-order homogeneous DEs

5. Solve a system of linear 1st-order homogeneous DEs

6. Solve a system of linear 1st-order homogeneous DEs

7. Solve a system of linear 1st-order homogeneous DEs

8. Solve a system of linear 1st-order nonhomogeneous DEs

9. Solve a system of linear 1st-order nonhomogeneous DEs

10. Solve a system of linear 1st-order nonhomogeneous DEs

11. Solve a system of linear 2nd-order homogeneous DEs

12. Solve a system of linear 2nd-order homogeneous DEs

13. Solve a system of linear 2nd-order homogeneous DEs

14. Solve a system of linear 2nd-order homogeneous DEs

15. Solve a system of linear 2nd-order homogeneous DEs

16. Solve a system of linear 2nd-order nonhomogeneous DEs

17. Solve a system of linear 2nd-order nonhomogeneous DEs

18. Solve a system of linear 2nd-order nonhomogeneous DEs

19. Solve a system of linear 2nd-order nonhomogeneous DEs

Problems 1-19: Solve the given system of differential equations by systematic elimination.

1. $\dfrac{dx}{dt} = 5x + 4y\,, \qquad \dfrac{dy}{dt} = -x$

2. $\dfrac{dx}{dt} = 2y\,, \qquad \dfrac{dy}{dt} = 2x + 3y$

3. $\dfrac{dx}{dt} = 6x - 2y\,, \qquad \dfrac{dy}{dt} = x + 3y$

4. $\dfrac{dx}{dt} = 8x + y\,, \qquad \dfrac{dy}{dt} = 7x + 2y$

5. $\dfrac{dx}{dt} = 8x + 3y\,, \qquad \dfrac{dy}{dt} = 5x + 6y$

6. $\dfrac{dx}{dt} = 3x - 2y\,, \qquad \dfrac{dy}{dt} = 2x - y$

7. $\dfrac{dx}{dt} = 5x + 4y\,, \qquad \dfrac{dy}{dt} = -x + y$

8. $\dfrac{dx}{dt} = 3y + 9t\,, \qquad \dfrac{dy}{dt} = x + 2y - 3$

9. $\dfrac{dx}{dt} = 3y + 5\,e^{2t}\,, \qquad \dfrac{dy}{dt} = 3x - 10\,e^{2t}$

10. $\dfrac{dx}{dt} = 2y + 6\,, \qquad \dfrac{dy}{dt} = 8x + 12\,e^{-2t}$

11. $\dfrac{d^2 x}{dt^2} + 2y = 0\,, \qquad \dfrac{d^2 y}{dt^2} + 8x = 0$

12. $\dfrac{d^2 x}{dt^2} + 16\dfrac{dy}{dt} + 9\,x = 0\,, \qquad \dfrac{dx}{dt} + 25\,y = 0$

13. $\dfrac{d^2 x}{dt^2} - 4x + 6y = 0\,, \qquad \dfrac{d^2 y}{dt^2} + 2x = 0$

14. $\dfrac{d^2 x}{dt^2} + \dfrac{dy}{dt} - 4x = 0\,, \qquad \dfrac{dy}{dt} - 8x = 0$

15. $D^2 y + 6\,Dx = 0\,, \qquad (D+1)x + (D-1)y = 0$

16. $D^2 y + 6\,Dx = 6\,e^{-t}\,, \qquad (D+1)\,x + (D-1)\,y = 12\,e^{-t}$

17. $D^2 x - 4\,Dy = 12\,, \qquad (D+2)\,x + (D+2)\,y = 8\,t$

18. $(D^2 + 9)\,x + 16\,Dy = 225\,t\,, \qquad Dx + 25\,y = 50$

19. $(D^2 + 9)\,x + 16\,Dy = 90\,\cos 5t\,, \qquad Dx + 25\,y = 50$

1. $x = c_1 e^t - 4c_2 e^{4t}$, $y = c_1 e^t + c_2 e^{4t}$

2. $x = c_1 e^{-t} + c_2 e^{4t}$, $y = -\dfrac{1}{2} c_1 e^{-t} + 2c_2 e^{4t}$

3. $x = c_1 e^{4t} + c_2 e^{5t}$, $y = c_1 e^{4t} + \dfrac{1}{2} c_2 e^{5t}$

4. $x = c_1 e^t + c_2 e^{9t}$, $y = -7 c_1 e^t + c_2 e^{9t}$

5. $x = c_1 e^{11t} + c_2 e^{3t}$, $y = c_1 e^{11t} - \dfrac{5}{3} c_2 e^{3t}$

6. $x = (c_1 + c_2 t) e^t$, $y = \dfrac{1}{2} (2c_1 - c_2 + 2c_2 t) e^t$

7. $x = (c_1 + c_2 t) e^{3t}$, $y = -\dfrac{1}{4} (2c_1 - c_2 + 2c_2 t) e^{3t}$

8. $x = c_1 e^{-t} + c_2 e^{3t} - 4 + 6t$, $y = -\dfrac{1}{3} c_1 e^{-t} + c_2 e^{3t} + 2 - 3t$

9. $x = c_1 e^{-3t} + c_2 e^{3t} + 4 e^{2t}$, $y = -c_1 e^{-3t} + c_2 e^{3t} + e^{2t}$

10. $x = c_1 e^{4t} + c_2 e^{-4t} - 2 e^{-2t}$, $y = 2 c_1 e^{4t} - 2 c_2 e^{-4t} + 2 e^{2t} - 3$

11. $x = c_1 e^{2t} + c_2 e^{-2t} + c_3 \cos 2t + c_4 \sin 2t$, $y = -2 c_1 e^{2t} - 2 c_2 e^{-2t} + 2 c_3 \cos 2t + 2 c_4 \sin 2t$

12. $x = c_1 \cos 5t + c_2 \sin 5t$, $y = -\dfrac{1}{5} c_2 \cos 5t + \dfrac{1}{5} c_1 \sin 5t$

13. $x = -3 c_1 e^{\sqrt{6}\,t} - 3 c_2 e^{-\sqrt{6}\,t} + c_3 \cos \sqrt{2}\,t + c_4 \sin \sqrt{2}\,t$,
    $y = c_1 e^{\sqrt{6}\,t} + c_2 e^{-\sqrt{6}\,t} + c_3 \cos \sqrt{2}\,t + c_4 \sin \sqrt{2}\,t$

14. $x = c_1 \cos 2t + c_2 \sin 2t$, $y = -4 c_2 \cos 2t + 4 c_1 \sin 2t + c_3$

15. $x = c_1 - \dfrac{1}{3} c_2 e^{2t} - \dfrac{1}{2} c_3 e^{3t}$, $y = c_1 + c_2 e^{2t} + c_3 e^{3t}$

16. $x = c_1 - \dfrac{1}{6} c_2 e^{2t} - \dfrac{1}{6} c_3 e^{3t} - 2 e^{-t}$, $y = c_1 + \dfrac{1}{2} c_2 e^{2t} + \dfrac{1}{3} c_3 e^{3t} - 6 e^{-t}$

17. $x = -c_1 - c_2 e^{-4t} - 2 c_3 e^{-2t} + 7t$, $y = c_1 + c_2 e^{-4t} + c_3 e^{-2t} - 2 - 3t$

18. $x = c_1 \cos 5t + c_2 \sin 5t + 25t$, $y = -\dfrac{1}{5} c_2 \cos 5t + \dfrac{1}{5} c_1 \sin 5t + 1$

19. $x = c_1 \cos 5t + c_2 \sin 5t + 25 t \sin 5t$, $y = -\dfrac{1}{5} c_2 \cos 5t + \dfrac{1}{5} c_1 \sin 5t - 5 t \cos 5t - \sin 5t + 2$

1. Nonlinear differential equations — concepts

2. Nonlinear differential equations — concepts

3. Nonlinear differential equations — concepts

4. Use the substitution $u = y'$ to solve a nonlinear 2nd-order differential equation.

5. Use the substitution $u = y'$ to solve a nonlinear 2nd-order differential equation.

6. Use the substitution $u = y'$ to solve a nonlinear 2nd-order differential equation.

7. Use the substitution $u = y'$ to solve a nonlinear 2nd-order differential equation.

8. Use the substitution $u = y'$ to solve a nonlinear 2nd-order differential equation.

9. Use the substitution $u = y'$ to solve a nonlinear 2nd-order differential equation.

10. Use the substitution $u = y'$ to solve a nonlinear 2nd-order differential equation.

11. Use the substitution $u = y'$ to solve a nonlinear 2nd-order differential equation.

12. Use the substitution $u = y'$ to solve a nonlinear 2nd-order differential equation.

13. Use the substitution $u = y'$ to solve a nonlinear 2nd-order differential equation.

14. Use the substitution $u = y'$ to solve a nonlinear 2nd-order differential equation.

15. Use the substitution $u = y'$ to solve a nonlinear 2nd-order differential equation.

16. Solve a nonlinear 2nd-order IVP by the Taylor series method.

17. Solve a nonlinear 2nd-order IVP by the Taylor series method.

18. Solve a nonlinear 2nd-order IVP by the Taylor series method.

19. Solve a nonlinear 2nd-order IVP by the Taylor series method.

20. Solve a nonlinear 2nd-order IVP by the Taylor series method.

21. Solve a nonlinear 3rd-order IVP by the Taylor series method.

1. True or False: If y_1 and y_2 are linearly independent solutions of a 2nd-order nonlinear DE, then the linear combination $y = c_1 y_1 + c_2 y_2$ is also a solution.

2. True or False: If $y = c_1 y_1 + c_2 y_2$ is a 2-parameter set of solutions of a nonlinear DE, then it is also the general solution of the DE.

3. True or False: A constant multiple of a solution of a nonlinear DE is also a solution.

Problems 4-15: Solve the given differential equations by using the substitution $u = y'$. Apply any given initial conditions.

4. $y'' - 2yy' = 0$, $y(0) = 0$, $y'(0) = 9$

5. $y'' = (y')^2$

6. $y'' = y'(1 + y)$, $y(0) = 1$, $y'(0) = 4$

7. $y'' = 4 + (y')^2$, $y(1) = 0$, $y'(1) = 0$

8. $(1 + y)^2 y'' + 2 = 0$, $y(0) = 3$, $y'(0) = 1$

9. $y'' - 4 \sec^2 y \tan y = 0$, $y(0) = 0$, $y'(0) = 2$

10. $y' y'' = (y')^2 + 1$, $y(0) = 1$, $y'(0) = 0$

11. $x^2 y'' = (y')^2$

12. $x y'' = y'$

13. $x y'' = y'(1 + x)$

14. $(1 + y') y'' = 4x$, $y(0) = 5$, $y'(0) = -1$

15. $(1 + y') y'' = x$

Problems 16-21: Solve the given initial value problems by constructing the first 6 nonzero terms of the Taylor series solution of $y(x)$, centered at 0.

16. $y'' = (y')^2$, $y(0) = 1$, $y'(0) = 2$

17. $y'' = 1 + y y'$, $y(0) = 1$, $y'(0) = -1$

18. $y'' = x^2 + y y'$, $y(0) = 1$, $y'(0) = -2$

19. $y'' = xy - (y')^2$, $y(0) = 1$, $y'(0) = -1$

20. $y'' = y^2 + xy'$, $y(0) = -1$, $y'(0) = 2$

21. $y''' = 2 + xy^3$, $y(0) = 6$, $y'(0) = 5$, $y''(0) = -2$

1. False

2. False

3. False

4. $y = 3 \tan 3x$

5. $y = -\ln(c_1 x + c_2)$

6. $y = \dfrac{1 + 2x}{1 - 2x}$

7. $2x - 2 - \tan^{-1}\sqrt{e^{2y} - 1} = 0 \quad$ or $\quad y = \dfrac{1}{2} \ln\left[1 + \tan 4(x - 1)^2\right]$

8. $3x + 8 = (1 + y)^{3/2} \quad$ or $\quad y = (3x + 8)^{2/3} - 1$

9. $y = \sin^{-1} 2x$

10. $x = \ln\left(y + \sqrt{y^2 - 1}\right) \quad$ or $\quad y = \cosh x$

11. $y = c_1 + c_2 x - c_2^2 \ln(x + c_2)$

12. $y = c_1 x^2 + c_2$

13. $y = c_1 + c_2\left(xe^x - e^x\right)$

14. $y = x^2 - x + 5$

15. $y = c_2 - x \pm \dfrac{1}{2} x \sqrt{x^2 + 2c_1 + 1} \pm \left(c_1 + \dfrac{1}{2}\right)\ln\left(x + \sqrt{x^2 + 2c_1 + 1}\right)$

16. $y = 1 + 2x + 2x^2 + \dfrac{8}{3} x^3 + 4x^4 + \dfrac{32}{5} x^5$

17. $y = 1 - x + \dfrac{1}{6} x^3 + \dfrac{1}{24} x^4 - \dfrac{1}{40} x^5$

18. $y = 1 - 2x - x^2 + \dfrac{1}{3} x^3 + \dfrac{2}{3} x^4 + \dfrac{1}{10} x^5$

19. $y = 1 - x - \dfrac{1}{2} x^2 - \dfrac{1}{6} x^3 - \dfrac{1}{4} x^4 - \dfrac{7}{40} x^5$

20. $y = -1 + 2x + \dfrac{1}{2} x^2 - \dfrac{1}{3} x^3 + \dfrac{1}{3} x^4 + \dfrac{1}{12} x^5$

21. $y = 6 + 5x - x^2 + \dfrac{1}{3} x^3 + 9x^4 + 9x^5$

5.1   Linear Models – Initial Value Problems   Subject Correlation Guide

1. Hooke's law, mass, weight

2. Hooke's law, mass, weight

3. Hooke's law, mass, weight

4. free *vs.* damped or forced motion

5. terminologies (governing equation)

6. terminologies (simple harmonic motion)

7. terminology — period of motion

8. terminologies (pure resonance)

9. classifying damped motion as underdamped, critically damped, or overdamped

10. classifying damped motion as underdamped, critically damped, or overdamped

11. behavior or critically damped motion

12. behavior or underdamped motion

13. spring-mass initial conditions

14. steady-state and transient terms

15. terminologies (underdamped motion)

16. damped *vs.* undamped or forced motion

17. using m, β and k to determine underdamped motion

18. using m, β and k to determine overdamped motion

19. using m, β and k to determine critically damped motion

20. using m and k to determine the β that produces critically damped motion

21. simple harmonic motion

22. simple harmonic motion, solving DE and applying initial conditions

23. simple harmonic motion, solving DE and applying initial conditions

24. simple harmonic motion, solving DE and applying initial conditions

25. unforced, critically damped LRC circuit

26. unforced, critically damped LRC circuit

27. unforced, overdamped LRC circuit

28. forced, undamped spring-mass without pure resonance

29. forced, undamped spring-mass with pure resonance

30. forced, undamped LRC circuit without pure resonance

31. forced, undamped LRC circuit with pure resonance

32. forced, damped LRC circuit, steady-state solution

33. forced, damped spring-mass, steady-state solution

1. A 64 lb weight stretches a spring 4 ft. The mass of the weight is

   (a) 16 slugs.
   (b) 16 kg.
   (c) 2 slugs.
   (d) 2 kg.

2. A 2 kg mass stretches a spring 0.4 m. The spring constant is

   (a) 0.2 kg/m.
   (b) 49 N/m.
   (c) 0.8 kg · m.
   (d) 160 N.

3. A 24 lb weight stretches a spring 3 in. The spring constant is

   (a) 8 lb/ft.
   (b) 76 lb/ft.
   (c) 6 lb/ft.
   (d) 96 lb/ft.

4. Free motion indicates the absence of

   (a) damping forces.
   (b) gravitational force.
   (c) external forces.
   (d) a and c

5. The differential equation that describes the behavior of a spring-mass apparatus is called the

   (a) governing equation.
   (b) equation of motion.
   (c) complementary function.
   (d) steady-state solution.

6. Simple harmonic motion is also called

   (a) free undamped motion.
   (b) pure resonant motion.
   (c) forced motion.
   (d) a and c

7. The period of the expression $\sin 4\pi t$ is

   (a) π s.
   (b) 2 s.
   (c) $1/4\pi$ s.
   (d) 0.5 s.

8. Pure resonance requires

    (a) the absence of damping.
    (b) that the frequency of the driving force equals the natural frequency of the apparatus.
    (c) the absence of a driving force.
    (d) a and b

9. Suppose an LRC circuit is critically damped. Increasing the resistance of the resistor will result in

    (a) underdamped motion.
    (b) overdamped motion.
    (c) pure resonant motion.
    (d) a and c

10. In free damped motion, quantities that remain constant are

    (a) amplitude and frequency.
    (b) amplitude and period.
    (c) period and frequency.
    (d) amplitude, period and frequency.

11. In a spring-mass apparatus that undergoes critically damped motion, the mass will cross the equilibrium position how many times?

    (a) once
    (b) at least once
    (c) at most once
    (d) infinitely many times

12. In a spring-mass apparatus that undergoes underdamped motion, the mass will cross the equilibrium position how many times?

    (a) once
    (b) at least once
    (c) at most once
    (d) infinitely many times

13. A mass is released from a point 0.5 m below equilibrium with an upward speed of 2 m/s. The initial conditions are

    (a) $x(0) = -0.5$ and $x'(0) = -2$.
    (b) $x(0) = -0.5$ and $x'(0) = +2$.
    (c) $x(0) = +0.5$ and $x'(0) = -2$.
    (d) $x(0) = +0.5$ and $x'(0) = +2$.

14. An LRC circuit will have both a steady-state solution and a transient solution when there is

    (a) a resistor and a simple harmonic voltage source.
    (b) no resistor and no voltage source.
    (c) no resistor and a simple harmonic voltage source.
    (d) a resistor and a decaying voltage source.

15. Underdamped motion may be described by

   (a) simple harmonic motion.

   (b) decaying oscillation.

   (c) growing oscillation.

   (d) constant amplitude oscillation.

16. An LRC circuit with a resistor but without a voltage source will exhibit

   (a) simple harmonic motion.

   (b) pure resonance.

   (c) damped motion.

   (d) forced motion.

17. A 3 kg mass is attached to a spring whose spring constant is 12 N/m. The surrounding medium offers a damping force that is numerically equal to 12 times the instantaneous velocity. The motion will be

   (a) overdamped.

   (b) underdamped.

   (c) critically damped.

   (d) purely resonant.

18. A 2 kg mass is attached to a spring whose spring constant is 12 N/m. The surrounding medium offers a damping force that is numerically equal to 10 times the instantaneous velocity. The motion will be

   (a) overdamped.

   (b) underdamped.

   (c) critically damped.

   (d) purely resonant.

19. A 1 kg mass is attached to a spring whose spring constant is 20 N/m. The surrounding medium offers a damping force that is numerically equal to 4 times the instantaneous velocity. The motion will be

   (a) overdamped.

   (b) underdamped.

   (c) critically damped.

   (d) purely resonant.

20. A 32 lb weight is attached to a spring whose spring constant is 16 lb/ft. The surrounding medium offers a damping force that is numerically equal to β times the instantaneous velocity. Determine the value(s) of β so that the motion is underdamped.

   (a) all $\beta < 8$

   (b) $\beta = 8$

   (c) all $\beta > 8$

   (d) $\beta = 2$

21. A 4 pound weight stretches a spring 6 inches. Assume there is no resistance and no external driving force and that the apparatus is set in motion.

   (a) What is the period of motion?
   (b) What is the frequency of motion?
   (c) How many cycles will have been completed after 2π seconds?

22. A 4 pound weight stretches a spring 6 inches. The mass is then released from an initial position of 4 feet below the equilibrium position with an initial upward velocity of 24 ft/s.

   (a) Determine the equation of motion.
   (b) What is the period of motion?
   (c) What is the amplitude of motion?
   (d) What is the frequency of motion?
   (e) Write the equation of motion in sine form.

23. A 2 kg mass is attached to a spring whose spring constant is 12 N/m. The mass is then released from an initial position of 3 m above the equilibrium position with an initial downward velocity of 8 m/s.

   (a) Determine the equation of motion.
   (b) What is the period of motion?
   (c) What is the amplitude of motion?
   (d) What is the frequency of motion?
   (e) Write the equation of motion in sine form.
   (f) Determine the first time the mass attains is maximum displacement.

24. A 2 kg mass is attached to a spring whose spring constant is 26 N/m. The surrounding medium offers a damping force numerically equal to 8 times the instantaneous velocity. The mass is then released from an initial position of 3 m below the equilibrium position with an initial upward velocity of 18 m/s.

   (a) Determine the equation of motion.
   (b) What is the period of motion?
   (c) What is the amplitude of motion?
   (d) What is the frequency of motion?
   (e) Write the equation of motion in sine form.
   (f) Determine the first time the mass crosses the equilibrium position.

25. An LRC circuit comprises a 1 h inductor, a 20 Ω resistor, and a 0.01 f capacitor. Initially there is a 25 C charge stored on the capacitor with an initial current of 0 amps in the circuit.

   (a) Determine the charge stored on the capacitor at time t.
   (b) Is the motion underdamped, critically damped, overdamped, or simple harmonic?
   (c) Is the charge on the capacitor ever zero? If so, when?

26. An LRC circuit comprises a 1 h inductor, a 10 Ω resistor, and a 0.04 f capacitor. Initially there is a $q(0) = -20$ C charge stored on the capacitor with an initial current of $i(0) = 110$ amps in the circuit.

   (a) Determine the charge stored on the capacitor at time t.

   (b) Is the motion underdamped, critically damped, overdamped, or simple harmonic?

   (c) Is the charge on the capacitor ever zero? If so, when?

27. An LRC circuit comprises a 1 h inductor, a 12 Ω resistor, and a 0.05 f capacitor. Initially there is an 8 C charge stored on the capacitor with an initial current of 0 amps in the circuit.

   (a) Determine the charge stored on the capacitor at time t.

   (b) Is the motion underdamped, critically damped, overdamped, or simple harmonic?

   (c) Is the charge on the capacitor ever zero? If so, when?

28. A 32 lb weight is attached to a spring whose spring constant is 4 lb/ft. There is no damping force, but there is a driving force of $10 \cos 3t$ lb present. The mass is released from an initial position of 1 ft below the equilibrium position with an initial upward velocity of 2 ft/s.

   (a) Determine the equation of motion.

   (b) What is the natural frequency of the apparatus?

   (c) Does the motion undergo pure resonance?

29. A 32 lb weight is attached to a spring whose spring constant is 4 lb/ft. There is no damping force, but there is a driving force of $16 \cos 2t$ lb present. The mass is released from an initial position of 1 ft below the equilibrium position with an initial upward velocity of 2 ft/s.

   (a) Determine the equation of motion.

   (b) What is the natural frequency of the apparatus?

   (c) Does the motion undergo pure resonance?

30. A circuit comprises a 1 h inductor and a 0.25 f capacitor. There is no resistor, but there is a $20 \sin 3t$ V voltage source present. Initially there is a charge of $q(0) = 5$ C stored on the capacitor but no initial current in the circuit.

   (a) Determine the charge stored on the capacitor at time t.

   (b) What is the natural frequency of the circuit?

   (c) Does the circuit undergo pure resonance?

31. A circuit comprises a 1 h inductor and a 0.25 f capacitor. There is no resistor, but there is a $16 \sin 2t$ V voltage source present. Initially there is a charge of $q(0) = 3$ C stored on the capacitor but no initial current in the circuit.

   (a) Determine the charge stored on the capacitor at time t.

   (b) What is the natural frequency of the circuit?

   (c) Does the circuit undergo pure resonance?

32. A circuit comprises a 1 h inductor, a 6 Ω resistor, a 1/13 f capacitor, and a $75 \sin 2t$ V voltage source. Initially there is a charge of $q(0) = -2$ C stored on the capacitor but no initial current in the circuit.

   (a) Determine the charge stored on the capacitor at time t.

   (b) State the transient charge.

   (c) State the steady state charge.

   (d) State the steady state amplitude.

   (e) State the steady state frequency.

33. A 1 kg mass is attached to a spring whose spring constant is 13 N/m. The surrounding medium offers a resistance that is numerically equal to 6 times the instantaneous velocity. An external driving force of $75 \sin 2t$ N is applied. The mass is released from rest from a point 2 m above the equilibrium position.

   (a) Determine the equation of motion.

   (b) State the transient solution.

   (c) State the steady state solution.

   (d) State the steady state amplitude.

   (e) State the steady state frequency.

1. c

2. b

3. d

4. d

5. a

6. a

7. d

8. d

9. b

10. c

11. c

12. d

13. c

14. a

15. b

16. c

17. b

18. a

19. c

20. a

21. (a) $\pi/4$ s
    (b) $4/\pi$ cyc/s
    (c) 8 cycles

22. (a) $x(t) = 4\cos 8t - 3\sin 8t$
    (b) $\pi/4$ s
    (c) 5 ft
    (d) $4/\pi$ cyc/s
    (e) $x(t) = 5\sin(8t + 2.214)$

23. (a) $x(t) = -3\cos 2t + 4\sin 2t$
    (b) π s
    (c) 5 m
    (d) $1/\pi$ cyc/s
    (e) $x(t) = 5\sin(2t - .6435)$
    (f) $t = 1.107$ s

24. (a) $x(t) = 3e^{-2t} \cos 3t - 4e^{-2t} \sin 3t$

    (b) $2\pi/3$ s

    (c) $5e^{-2t}$ m

    (d) $3/2\pi$ cyc/s

    (e) $x(t) = 5e^{-2t} \sin(2t + 2.498)$

    (f) $t = 0.2145$ s

25. (a) $q(t) = 25(1 + 10te^{-10t})$

    (b) critically damped

    (c) The charge stored on the capacitor is never zero.

26. (a) $q(t) = 10e^{-5t}(t - 2)$

    (b) critically damped

    (c) The charge stored on the capacitor is zero at $t = 2$ s.

27. (a) $q(t) = 2e^{-6t}(5e^{-4t} - e^{4t})$

    (b) overdamped

    (c) The charge stored on the capacitor is never zero.

28. (a) $x(t) = 3 \cos 2t - \sin 2t - 2 \cos 3t$

    (b) $1/\pi$ s

    (c) no

29. (a) $x(t) = \cos 2t - \sin 2t + 4t \sin 2t$

    (b) $1/\pi$ s

    (c) yes

30. (a) $q(t) = 5 \cos 2t + 6 \sin 2t - 4 \cos 3t$

    (b) $1/\pi$ s

    (c) no

31. (a) $q(t) = 3 \cos 2t + 2 \sin 2t - 4t \cos 2t$

    (b) $1/\pi$ s

    (c) yes

32. (a) $q(t) = 3 \sin 2t - 4 \cos 2t + 2e^{-3t} \cos 2t$

    (b) $2e^{-3t} \cos 2t$

    (c) $q_{ss}(t) = 3 \sin 2t - 4 \cos 2t$

    (d) $A_{ss} = 5$ C

    (e) $f_{ss} = 1/\pi$ Hz.

33. (a) $x(t) = 3 \sin 2t - 4 \cos 2t + 2e^{-3t} \cos 2t$

    (b) $2e^{-3t} \cos 2t$

    (c) $x_{ss}(t) = 3 \sin 2t - 4 \cos 2t$

    (d) $A_{ss} = 5$ m

    (e) $f_{ss} = 1/\pi$ Hz.

1. deflecting beam boundary conditions

2. deflecting beam boundary conditions

3. deflecting beam boundary conditions

4. deflecting beam governing equation

5. terminology — cantilever beam

6. buckling column governing equation

7. definition of eigenvalue

8. difference between DE for rotating string, cantilever beam, buckling column

9. definition of "Euler load"

10. critical loads of buckling column

11. critical loads of buckling column

12. deflecting beam with uniform load and embedded ends

13. deflecting beam with uniform load and one embedded and one free end

14. deflecting beam with nonuniform load and one embedded and one free end

15. deflecting beam with uniform load and simply supported ends

16. deflecting beam with nonuniform load and simply supported ends

17. heat transfer in long rod

18. eigenvalues and eigenfunctions

19. eigenvalues and eigenfunctions

20. eigenvalues and eigenfunctions

21. eigenvalues and eigenfunctions

22. eigenvalues and eigenfunctions

23. eigenvalues and eigenfunctions

24. eigenvalues and eigenfunctions

25. eigenvalues and eigenfunctions — Cauchy-Euler equation

26. eigenvalues and eigenfunctions — Cauchy-Euler equation

27. eigenvalues and eigenfunctions — mixed boundary conditions

28. eigenvalues and eigenfunctions — mixed boundary conditions

1. In the deflecting beam problem, what boundary conditions are associated with an embedded end?

   (a) $y = 0$ and $y' = 0$

   (b) $y = 0$ and $y'' = 0$

   (c) $y' = 0$ and $y'' = 0$

   (d) $y'' = 0$ and $y''' = 0$

2. In the deflecting beam problem, what boundary conditions are associated with a free end?

   (a) $y = 0$ and $y' = 0$

   (b) $y = 0$ and $y'' = 0$

   (c) $y' = 0$ and $y'' = 0$

   (d) $y'' = 0$ and $y''' = 0$

3. In the deflecting beam problem, what boundary conditions are associated with a simply supported end?

   (a) $y = 0$ and $y' = 0$

   (b) $y = 0$ and $y'' = 0$

   (c) $y' = 0$ and $y'' = 0$

   (d) $y'' = 0$ and $y''' = 0$

4. What is the order of the governing differential equation that models a deflecting beam?

   (a) one

   (b) two

   (c) three

   (d) four

5. An example of a cantilever beam is

   (a) a pendulum

   (b) a ladder rung

   (c) an airplane wing

   (d) a hanging wire

6. What is the order of the governing equation that models the buckling of a thin vertical column?

   (a) one

   (b) two

   (c) three

   (d) four

7. An eigenvalue of a boundary value problem (BVP) is a value of λ for which the BVP has

   (a) the trivial solution $y = 0$.

   (b) a nontrivial solution.

   (c) no solution.

   (d) a positive solution.

8. The differential equation $y'' + \lambda y = 0$ governs what apparatus(es)?

    (a) a rotating string

    (b) a cantilever beam

    (c) the buckling of a thin vertical column

    (d) a and c

9. The smallest critical load that will cause a thin vertical column to buckle is called the

    (a) Euler load.

    (b) Einstein load.

    (c) Newton load.

    (d) Bernoulli load.

10. If a thin vertical column has a restraint placed at its midpoint, then the critical load is the

    (a) first buckling load P_1.

    (b) second buckling load P_2.

    (c) third buckling load P_3.

    (d) fourth buckling load P_4.

11. If a thin vertical column has restraints placed at 1/3 and 2/3 its height, then the critical load is the

    (a) first buckling load P_1.

    (b) second buckling load P_2.

    (c) third buckling load P_3.

    (d) fourth buckling load P_4.

12. A beam of length 10 ft is embedded at both ends and a uniform load of 24 lb is applied. Determine the displacement $y(x)$.

13. A beam of length 10 ft is embedded at the left end and is free at the right end. A uniform load of 24 lb is applied. Determine the displacement $y(x)$.

14. A 10 meter flag pole is subject to a wind force of $w = 3x$ Newtons. Determine the displacement $y(x)$.

15. A 4 meter beam is simply supported at both ends. A uniform load of 4 Newtons is applied. Determine the displacement $y(x)$.

16. A beam of length L is simply supported at both ends. A nonuniform load of $\sin(\pi x/L)$ is applied. Determine the displacement $y(x)$.

17. A long rod of length L is used to transfer heat to help cool an object to which its ends are attached. Its ends are maintained at constant temperature T_o while the surrounding medium is at temperature zero. The temperature $T(x)$ inside the rod satisfies the governing DE

$$\frac{d^2T}{dx^2} = \frac{kc}{hA}T, \qquad 0 < x < L,$$

where k is the rod's thermal conductivity, c is its specific heat, A is its cross sectional area, and h is the convection coefficient of the surrounding medium.

(a) Let $\alpha^2 = kc/hA$, and solve the differential equation for $T(x)$.

(b) Under the conditions stated, the boundary conditions are

$$T(0) = T_o, \qquad T(L) = T_o.$$

Apply the boundary conditions to obtain the solution $T(x)$ in terms of x, α, T_o, and L.

18. Find the eigenvalues and eigenfunctions of the boundary value problem $y'' + \lambda y = 0$, $y'(0) = 0$, $y(\pi/2) = 0$.

19. Find the eigenvalues and eigenfunctions of the boundary value problem $y'' + \lambda y = 0$, $y'(0) = 0$, $y(\pi) = 0$.

20. Find the eigenvalues and eigenfunctions of the boundary value problem $y'' + \lambda y = 0$, $y(0) = 0$, $y'(1) = 0$.

21. Find the eigenvalues and eigenfunctions of the boundary value problem $y'' + \lambda y = 0$, $y'(-\pi) = 0$, $y'(\pi) = 0$.

22. Find the eigenvalues and eigenfunctions of the boundary value problem $y'' + (\lambda-1)\, y = 0$, $y'(0) = 0$, $y(\pi) = 0$.

23. Find the eigenvalues and eigenfunctions of the boundary value problem $y'' + (\lambda+4)\, y = 0$, $y'(0) = 0$, $y(\pi) = 0$.

24. Find the eigenvalues and eigenfunctions of the boundary value problem $y'' + (\lambda+4)\, y = 0$, $y(0) = 0$, $y(\pi/2) = 0$.

25. Find the eigenvalues and eigenfunctions of the boundary value problem $x^2\, y'' + x\, y' + \lambda\, y = 0$, $y(1) = 0$, $y(e^2) = 0$.

26. Find the eigenvalues and eigenfunctions of the boundary value problem $x^2\, y'' + x\, y' + \lambda\, y = 0$, $y'(1) = 0$, $y(e^\pi) = 0$.

27. Find the condition that must be satisfied by eigenvalues of the following boundary value problem. Take $\lambda = \alpha^2$ where $\alpha > 0$.

$$y'' + \lambda\, y = 0, \qquad 0 < x < L,$$
$$y(0) = 0, \qquad h\, y(L) + k\, y'(L) = 0.$$

28. Find the condition that must be satisfied by eigenvalues of the following boundary value problem. Take $\lambda = \alpha^2$ where $\alpha > 0$.

$$y'' + \lambda\, y = 0, \qquad 0 < x < L,$$
$$y'(0) = 0, \qquad h\, y(L) + k\, y'(L) = 0.$$

1. a

2. d

3. b

4. d

5. c

6. b

7. b

8. d

9. a

10. b

11. c

12. $y(x) = \dfrac{x^4 - 20\,x^3 + 100\,x^2}{EI} = \dfrac{x^2\,(x-10)^2}{EI}$

13. $y(x) = \dfrac{x^4 - 40\,x^3 + 600\,x^2}{EI}$

14. $y(x) = \dfrac{1}{EI}\left(\dfrac{1}{40}x^5 - 25\,x^3 + 500\,x^2\right)$

15. $y(x) = \dfrac{x^4 - 8\,x^3 + 4\,x^2}{EI}$

16. $y(x) = \dfrac{L^4}{\pi^4 EI}\sin(\pi x/L)$

17. (a) $T(x) = c_1\,e^{\alpha x} + c_2\,e^{-\alpha x}$ or $T(x) = c_1\cosh \alpha x + c_2 \sinh \alpha x$.

   (b) $T(x) = \dfrac{T_o}{e^{\alpha L} - e^{-\alpha L}}\left[(1 - e^{-\alpha L})\,e^{\alpha x} - (1 - e^{\alpha L})\,e^{-\alpha x}\right]$ or

   $T(x) = \dfrac{T_o}{\sinh \alpha L}\left[\sinh \alpha x + \sinh \alpha(L - x)\right]$

18. $\lambda_n = (2n-1)^2$, $y_n = \cos(2n-1)\,x$, $n = 1, 2, \ldots$

19. $\lambda_n = \dfrac{(2n-1)^2}{4}$, $y_n = \cos\left[\dfrac{(2n-1)}{2}\,x\right]$, $n = 1, 2, \ldots$

20. $\lambda_n = \dfrac{(2n-1)^2\pi^2}{4}$, $y_n = \sin\left[\dfrac{(2n-1)\pi}{2}\,x\right]$, $n = 1, 2, \ldots$

21. $\lambda_n = n$, $y_n = \cos(nx)$, $n = 1, 2, \ldots$

22. $\lambda_n = \dfrac{(2n-1)^2}{4} + 1$, $y_n = \cos\left(\dfrac{2n-1}{2}\right)x$, $n = 1, 2, \ldots$

23. $\lambda_n = \dfrac{(2n+3)(2n-5)}{4}$, $y_n = \sin\left(\dfrac{2n-1}{2}\right)x$, $n = 1, 2, \ldots$

24. $\lambda_n = 4(n^2 - 1)$, $\quad y_n = \sin 2nx$, $\quad n = 1, 2, \ldots$

25. $\lambda_n = \dfrac{n^2 \pi^2}{4}$, $\quad y_n = \sin\left(\dfrac{n\pi}{2} \ln x\right)$, $\quad n = 1, 2, \ldots$

26. $\lambda_n = \dfrac{(2n-1)^2}{4}$, $\quad y_n = \sin\left(\dfrac{2n-1}{2} \ln x\right)$, $\quad n = 1, 2, \ldots$

27. $k\,\alpha_n + h\,\tan(\alpha_n L) = 0$ $\quad$ or $\quad$ $k\sqrt{\lambda_n} + h\,\tan(L\sqrt{\lambda_n}) = 0$

28. $k\,\alpha_n - h\,\cot(\alpha_n L) = 0$ $\quad$ or $\quad$ $k\sqrt{\lambda_n} - h\,\cot(L\sqrt{\lambda_n}) = 0$

1. hard nonlinear spring

2. soft nonlinear spring

3. simple pendulum governing eqution

4. comparison of governing equations of simple pendulum, spring-mass apparatus, buckling column, deaflection of a beam

5. linearized pendulum

6. linearized pendulum

7. hanging wire

8. rocket governing equation

9. nonlinear damping force

10. Newton's 2nd law with variable mass

11. solving hard nonlinear spring-mass

12. solving soft nonlinear spring-mass

13. nonlinear pendulum — phase plane solution by substitution

14. rocket — phase plane solution by substitution

15. rocket — solution by linearization

16. inverse square force — phase plane solution by substitution

17. population in closed system — nonlinear integro-differential equation, phase plane solution by substitution 1

18. population in closed system — nonlinear integro-differential equation, phase plane solution by substitution 2

1. Which expression describes a force exerted by a hard nonlinear spring displaced by amount x?

   (a) $F(x) = x + x^2$
   (b) $F(x) = x - x^2$
   (c) $F(x) = x + x^3$
   (d) $F(x) = x - x^3$

2. Which expression describes a force exerted by a soft nonlinear spring displaced by amount x?

   (a) $F(x) = x + x^2$
   (b) $F(x) = x - x^2$
   (c) $F(x) = x + x^3$
   (d) $F(x) = x - x^3$

3. The differential equation governing a simple pendulum is

   (a) first order and linear.
   (b) second order and linear.
   (c) first order and nonlinear.
   (d) second order and nonlinear.

4. The differential equation governing a simple pendulum is the same as that governing what apparatus?

   (a) the undamped spring-mass apparatus
   (b) the buckling of a thin column
   (c) the deflection of a beam with a hinged end and a free end
   (d) none of the above

5. We linearized the differential equation that governs a simple pendulum by

   (a) expanding $\sin\theta$ as a first order Maclaurin series.
   (b) expanding $\sin\theta$ as a second order Maclaurin series.
   (c) expanding $\sin\theta$ as a third order Maclaurin series.
   (d) none of the above

6. The solution to the linearized differential equation that governs a simple pendulum is

   (a) simple harmonic.
   (b) underdamped.
   (c) overdamped.
   (d) critically damped.

7. The shape of a hanging wire is an arc of a

   (a) parabola.
   (b) catenary.
   (c) sinusoid.
   (d) circle.

8. The differential equation governing the motion of the rocket applies only

    (a) while the fuel continues to burn.

    (b) after the fuel has ceased to burn.

    (c) under the assumption that the amount of fuel is constant.

    (d) a and c.

9. What is the form of a damping (resistance) term that is proportional to the square of velocity?

    (a) $\left(\dfrac{dx}{dt}\right)^2$

    (b) $\left|\dfrac{dx}{dt}\right|^2$

    (c) $\left|\dfrac{d^2x}{dt^2}\right|$

    (d) $\left|\dfrac{dx}{dt}\right|\dfrac{dx}{dt}$

10. When mass is variable, Newton's second law is written as

    (a) $\dfrac{d}{dt}(mv) = F$

    (b) $m\dfrac{d}{dt}(v) = F$

    (c) $\dfrac{d}{dt}(mv) = a$

    (d) $m\dfrac{d}{dt}(v) = F$

11. A 1 kg mass is attached to a nonlinear spring. The motion is governed by the differential equation $x'' + 2\,x + 4\,x^3 = 0$.

    (a) Use the substitution $u = x'$ to separate the differential equation. Also, what is the physical meaning of u?

    (b) Solve the differential equation obtained in (a) to obtain an expression relating u and x.

    (c) Determine the solution if the mass is released from rest from a point 2 m below the equilibrium position.

    (d) What is the velocity of the mass when it is 1 m below the equilibrium position?

    (e) What is the velocity of the mass when it is crossing the equilibrium position?

12. A 1 kg mass is attached to a nonlinear spring. The motion is governed by the differential equation $x'' + 12\,x - 2\,x^3 = 0$.

    (a) Use the substitution $u = x'$ to separate the differential equation. Also, what is the physical meaning of u?

    (b) Solve the differential equation obtained in (a) to obtain an expression relating u and x.

    (c) Determine the solution if the mass is released from rest from a point 3 m below the equilibrium position.

    (d) What is the velocity of the mass when it is 1 m below the equilibrium position?

    (e) What is the velocity of the mass when it is crossing the equilibrium position?

13. Consider the differential equation governing the motion of a simple pendulum $\ell\theta'' + g\sin\theta = 0$.

    (a) Use the substitution $\omega = \theta'$ to separate the differential equation. Also, what is the physical meaning of ω?

    (b) Solve the differential equation obtained in (a) to obtain an expression relating ω and θ.

    (c) Determine the solution if the pendulum is released from rest from an angle of $\pi/3$ radians.

    (d) What is the value of ω at the instant the pendulum is passing the equilibrium position? Give a physical interpretation of your answer.

    (e) What is the velocity of the mass when the pendulum is passing the equilibrium position?

14. In the study of rocket motion, we obtained the differential equation

$$\frac{d^2y}{dt^2} = -\frac{gR^2}{y^2},$$

where y denotes the rocket's distance from the earth's center, t is time, R is the earth's radius, and g is the gravitational acceleration at the earth's surface.

    (a) Substitute $y' = e^u$ into the differential equation and separate variables to obtain a differential equation involving functions u and y.

    (b) Recall that the velocity is $v = y'$. Use this to rewrite the differential equation obtained in (a).

    (c) Now solve the differential equation obtained in (b) to obtain an expression for the general solution (an equation involving v and y).

    (d) Now apply the initial conditions $y(0) = R$ and $y'(0) = v_o$ to obtain the equation of motion (an equation involving v and y).

    (e) Now use the fact that when $y \to \infty$, the rocket's velocity is zero. Solve the resulting equation for v_o. This resulting expression for v_o is the planet's escape velocity.

15. In the study of rocket motion, we obtained the differential equation

$$\frac{d^2y}{dt^2} = -\frac{gR^2}{y^2},$$

where y denotes the rocket's distance from the earth's center, t is time, R is the earth's radius, and g is the gravitational acceleration at the earth's surface. We may approximate the solution by linearizing the differential equation.

    (a) Let s denote the rocket's distance above the earth's surface, so that $y = s + R$. Substitute this into the differential equation to obtain a differential equation involving only function s.

    (b) Now linearize the right side of the differential equation obtained in (a) by expanding it as a first order Maclaurin series (or by the binomial expansion). The term $\sqrt{2g/R}$ should appear; label it k.

    (c) Now solve the differential equation obtained in (b) for the general solution $s(t)$.

    (d) Now apply the initial conditions $s(0) = 0$ and $s'(0) = v_o$ to obtain the equation of motion $s(t)$.

16. Consider the planar motion of a mass m that is attracted to the origin O with a force that is inversely proportional to the square of distance r (with proportionality constant k). Let (r, θ) denote the position of the mass in polar coordinates with the coordinate system centered at O. The motion of the mass is governed by the nonlinear differential equation

$$\frac{d^2r}{d\theta^2} - \frac{2}{r}\left(\frac{dr}{d\theta}\right)^2 - r + \frac{k}{c^2m} = 0,$$

where c is the angular momentum (constant).

(a) Introduce a new function y by letting $r = y^{-1}$. Substitute this into the differential equation to obtain a differential equation involving only function y.

(b) Solve the differential equation obtained in (a) to obtain the general solution for $y(\theta)$. Write it in pure sine form.

(c) Write the general solution for $r(\theta)$.

17. The initial value problem

$$k \frac{du}{dt} = u - u^2 - u \int_0^t u(x)\, dx, \qquad u(0) = u_o,$$

models the population of a species in a closed system[2]. Here u is the population at time t, k is a constant, and u_o is the initial population. The problem has been scaled so that $0 < u < 1$. A problem of this type is called an integro–differential equation.

(a) Define a new function by $y = \ln u$. Determine y' and give its physical meaning.

(b) Substitute the items from (a) into the integro-differential equation to obtain an equation involving functions u and y or an equation involving function y only. Find the initial conditions $y(0)$ and $y'(0)$.

(c) Differentiate the equation obtained in (a) to eliminate the integral. If necessary, rewrite this result to obtain a pure second order differential equation for function $y(t)$.

(d) Now define a new function by $x = y'$. Use this substitution to separate the differential equation obtained in (c). Solve this to obtain the general solution in the form of an equation involving x and y.

(e) Apply the initial conditions on x and y to the general solution obtained in (d), and rewrite the solution.

(f) The population u is greatest when $x = 0$. Use this to determine the maximum population.

18. The initial value problem

$$k \frac{du}{dt} = u - u^2 - u \int_0^t u(x)\, dx, \qquad u(0) = u_o,$$

models the population of a species in a closed system[2]. Here u is the population at time t, k is a constant, and u_o is the initial population. The problem has been scaled so that $0 < u < 1$. A problem of this type is called an integro–differential equation.

(a) Define a new function by $y = \int_0^t u(x)\, dx$, and determine $\dfrac{dy}{dt}$. Also state initial condition $y(0)$.

(b) Substitute the results from (a) into the integro–differential equation above to obtain two, first order differential equation. Now combine them to obtain a single differential equation involving u and y.

(c) The differential equation obtained in (b) is first order and linear. Solve it to obtain the general solution for u explicitly in terms of y.

(d) Apply the initial condition to the general solution obtained in (c), and rewrite the solution u explicitly in terms of y.

(e) Determine the maximum population (the maximum value of u).

---

[2]Kevin G. TeBeest. Numerical and Analytical Solutions of Volterra's Population Model. SIAM Review, Vol. 39, No. 3, pp. 484-493, September 1997.

1. c

2. d

3. d

4. d

5. a

6. a

7. b

8. b

9. d

10. a

11. (a) $u \, du = -(4 \, x^3 + 2 \, x) \, dx$. u is the velocity of the mass.
    (b) $u^2 = -2 \, x^4 - 2 \, x^2 + c$.
    (c) $u^2 = -2 \, x^4 - 2 \, x^2 + 40$.
    (d) ± 6 m/s
    (e) $\pm \sqrt{40}$ m/s

12. (a) $u \, du = (2 \, x^3 - 12 \, x) \, dx$. u is the velocity of the mass.
    (b) $u^2 = x^4 - 12 \, x^2 + c$.
    (c) $u^2 = x^4 - 12 \, x^2 + 27$.
    (d) ± 4 m/s
    (e) $\pm \sqrt{27}$ m/s

13. (a) $\ell \, \omega \, d\omega = -g \, \sin \theta \, d\theta$. ω is the angular velocity of the pendulum.
    (b) $\ell \omega^2 = 2 \, g \, \cos \theta + c$.
    (c) $\ell \omega^2 = g \, (2 \, \cos \theta - 1)$.
    (d) $\pm \sqrt{g/\ell}$ rad/s. It is the angular velocity of the pendulum at the instant the pendulum is passing the equilibrium position.
    (e) $\pm \sqrt{g\ell}$

14. (a) $e^u \, d(e^u) = -\dfrac{gR^2}{y^2} \, dy$

    (b) $v \, dv = -\dfrac{gR^2}{y^2} \, dy$

    (c) $v^2 = \dfrac{2gR^2}{y} + c$

    (d) $v^2 = \dfrac{2gR^2}{y} + v_o^2 - 2gR$

    (e) $v_o = \sqrt{2gR}$

15. (a) $\dfrac{d^2 s}{dt^2} = -g\left(1 - \dfrac{2}{R}\,s\right)$

(b) $s(t) = c_1\, e^{kt} + c_2\, e^{-kt} + R/2$ or

$s(t) = c_1 \cosh kt + c_2 \sinh kt + R/2,$ where $k = \sqrt{2g/R}$.

(c) $s(t) = -\dfrac{1}{4}\, e^{kt}\left(R - \dfrac{2v_o}{k}\right) - \dfrac{1}{4}\, e^{-kt}\left(R + \dfrac{2v_o}{k}\right) + R/2$ or

$s(t) = \dfrac{v_o}{k} \sinh kt - \dfrac{R}{2} \cosh kt + R/2,$

16. (a) $\dfrac{d^2 y}{d\theta^2} + y = \dfrac{k}{c^2 m}$

(b) $y(\theta) = A\sin(\theta + \phi) + \dfrac{k}{c^2 m} = \dfrac{k}{c^2 m}\Big[1 + e\sin(\theta + \phi)\Big]$, where A, e, and ϕ are arbitrary constants.

(c) $r(\theta) = \dfrac{c^2 m/k}{1 + e\sin(\theta + \phi)}$, where e and ϕ are arbitrary constants.

Note that the solution describes elliptical orbits if $e < 1$, parabolic paths if $e = 1$, and hyperbolic paths if $e > 1$.

17. (a) $y' = u'/u$ is the relative rate of change of population u.

(b) $k\dfrac{dy}{dt} = 1 - u - \displaystyle\int_0^t u(x)\,dx$ or $k\dfrac{dy}{dt} = 1 - e^y - \displaystyle\int_0^t e^{y(x)}\,dx$
with $y(0) = \ln u_o$ and $y'(0) = (1 - u_o)/k$.

(c) $k\,y'' = y'\,e^y - e^y$ with initial conditions $y(0) = \ln u_o$ and $y'(0) = (1 - u_o)/k$.

(d) $\dfrac{dx}{du} = -\dfrac{x+1}{x}$, so the general solution is $u = -k\Big(x - \ln|x + 1|\Big) + c$.

(e) $c = 1 - k\ln|x_o + 1|$, and since $x_o = (1 - u_o)/k$, the solution is

$$u(x) \;=\; 1 \;-\; k\,x \;+\; k\ln|x + 1| \;+\; k\ln\left|\dfrac{1 + k - u_o}{k}\right|.$$

(f) $u_{max} = 1 - k\ln\left|\dfrac{1 + k - u_o}{k}\right|$

18. (a) $\dfrac{dy}{dt} = u(t),\ y(0) = 0.$

(b) $k\dfrac{du}{dt} = u - u^2 - uy$ and $\dfrac{dy}{dt} = u$. Combining them gives $k\dfrac{du}{dy} = 1 - u - y$.

(c) The general solution is $u(y) = c\,e^{-y/k} + 1 - k - y$.

(d) $c = u_o + k - 1$, so $u(y) = (u_o + k - 1)\,e^{-y/k} + 1 - k - y$.

(e) $u_{max} = 1 - k\ln\left|\dfrac{1 + k - u_o}{k}\right|$

6.1   Series Solutions about Ordinary Points   **Subject Correlation Guide**

1. Radius of convergence and interval of convergence

2. Radius of convergence and interval of convergence

3. Radius of convergence and interval of convergence

4. Shifting the summation index

5. Shifting the summation index

6. Shifting the summation index

7. Lower bound for radius of convergence

8. Lower bound for radius of convergence

9. Lower bound for radius of convergence

10. Finding two power series solutions of a linear 2nd-order differential equation

11. Finding two power series solutions of a linear 2nd-order differential equation

12. Finding two power series solutions of a linear 2nd-order differential equation

13. Finding two power series solutions of a linear 2nd-order differential equation

14. Finding two power series solutions of a linear 2nd-order differential equation

15. Finding two power series solutions of a linear 2nd-order differential equation

16. Finding two power series solutions of a linear 2nd-order differential equation

17. Finding two power series solutions of a linear 2nd-order differential equation

18. Finding two power series solutions of a linear 2nd-order differential equation

19. Finding two power series solutions of a linear 2nd-order differential equation

20. Finding two power series solutions of a linear 2nd-order differential equation

21. Finding two power series solutions of a linear 2nd-order differential equation

Problems 1-3:   For the given power series, determine the radius of convergence and the interval of convergence.

1. $\displaystyle\sum_{n=1}^{\infty} \frac{(-1)^n}{n\,2^n}(x-3)^n$

2. $\displaystyle\sum_{n=0}^{\infty} \frac{2n}{3^n}(x-4)^n$

3. $\displaystyle\sum_{n=0}^{\infty} \frac{5^n}{n!}(x-4)^n$

Problems 4-6:   Rewrite the given power series so that its general term involves x^k.

4. $\displaystyle\sum_{n=4}^{\infty} n\,(n-3)\,c_n\,x^{n-2}$

5. $\displaystyle\sum_{n=3}^{\infty} (n-1)\,c_n\,x^{n-2} + \sum_{n=4}^{\infty} (n+1)\,c_n\,x^{n-3}$

6. $\displaystyle\sum_{n=0}^{\infty} (n+3)\,(n-1)\,c_n\,x^{n+1} - \sum_{n=2}^{\infty} n\,(n-1)\,c_{n+1}\,x^{n-2}$

Problems 7-9:   Without solving the differential equation, find a lower bound for the radius of convergence of power series solutions: a) about the ordinary point $x = 0$, and b) about the ordinary point $x = 1$.

7. $(x^2 - 16)\,y'' - 2\,x\,y' + 4\,y = 0$

8. $(x^2 + 96)\,y'' - 3\,x\,y' + 5\,y = 0$

9. $(x^2 + 4x + 20)\,y'' + 4\,x\,y' - 7\,y = 0$

Problems 10-21:   Find two power series solutions of the given differential equation about the orindary point $x = 0$. First state the recursion relation for the coefficients.

10. $y'' + x\,y' + y = 0$

11. $y'' - 2\,x\,y' + 2\,y = 0$

12. $y'' + 4\,x\,y' - 2\,y = 0$

13. $y'' + y' - x\,y = 0$

14. $y'' + 2\,y' + 4\,x^2\,y = 0$

15. $(x^2 + 2)\,y'' - 5\,x\,y' + y = 0$

16. $(x^2 - 1)\,y'' + 2\,y = 0$

17. $(1 - x^2)\,y'' - 2\,x\,y' + 6\,y = 0$

18. $(1 - x^2)\,y'' - 2\,x\,y' + 20\,y = 0$

19. $(1 - x^2)\,y'' - 2\,x\,y' + 30\,y = 0$

20. $(1 - x^2)\,y'' - x\,y' + 4\,y = 0$

21. $(1 - x^2)\,y'' - x\,y' + 16\,y = 0$

1. $R = 2$, $1 < x \le 5$

2. $R = 3$, $1 < x < 7$

3. $R = \infty$, $-\infty < x < \infty$

4. $\displaystyle\sum_{k=2}^{\infty} (k+2)(k-1)\, c_{k+2}\, x^k$

5. $\displaystyle\sum_{k=1}^{\infty} \Big[(k+1)\, c_{k+2} + (k+4)\, c_{k+3}\Big]\, x^k$

6. $\displaystyle -2\,c_3 + \sum_{k=1}^{\infty} (k+2)\Big[(k-2)\,c_{k-1} - (k+1)\,c_{k+3}\Big]\, x^k$

7. a) $R = 4$, b) $R = 3$

8. a) $R = 3$, b) $R = \sqrt{10}$

9. a) $R = \sqrt{20}$, b) $R = 5$

10. With c_0 and c_1 arbitrary, $c_{n+2} = -\dfrac{c_n}{n+2}$, $n = 2, 3, \ldots$

$$y_1 = 1 - \frac{x^2}{2} + \frac{x^4}{2\cdot 4} - \frac{x^6}{2\cdot 4\cdot 6} + \frac{x^8}{2\cdot 4\cdot 6\cdot 8} - \frac{x^{10}}{2\cdot 4\cdot 6\cdot 8\cdot 10} + \cdots ,$$

$$y_2 = x - \frac{x^3}{3} + \frac{x^5}{3\cdot 5} - \frac{x^7}{3\cdot 5\cdot 7} + \frac{x^9}{3\cdot 5\cdot 7\cdot 9} - \frac{x^{11}}{3\cdot 5\cdot 7\cdot 9\cdot 11} + \cdots$$

11. With c_0 and c_1 arbitrary, $c_{n+2} = \dfrac{2(n-1)\,c_n}{(n+2)(n+1)}$, $n = 1, 2, \ldots$

$$y_1 = x ,$$

$$y_2 = 1 - x^2 - \frac{2^2}{4!} x^4 - \frac{2^3\cdot 3}{6!} x^6 - \frac{2^4\cdot 3\cdot 5}{8!} x^8 - \frac{2^5\cdot 3\cdot 5\cdot 7}{10!} x^{10} - \cdots$$

12. With c_0 and c_1 arbitrary, $c_{n+2} = \dfrac{2(1-2n)\,c_n}{(n+2)(n+1)}$, $n = 1, 2, \ldots$

$$y_1 = 1 + x^2 - \frac{1}{2} x^4 + \frac{7}{30} x^6 - \frac{11}{120} x^8 + \frac{11}{360} x^{10} - \cdots ,$$

$$y_2 = x - \frac{1}{3} x^3 + \frac{1}{6} x^5 - \frac{1}{14} x^7 + \frac{13}{504} x^9 - \frac{221}{27720} x^{11} + \cdots$$

13. With c_0 and c_1 arbitrary, $c_{n+2} = \dfrac{c_{n-1} - (n+1)\,c_{n+1}}{(n+2)(n+1)}$, $n = 1, 2, \ldots$

With $c_0 = 1$ and $c_1 = 0$:

$$y_1 = 1 + \frac{1}{3!} x^3 - \frac{1}{4!} x^4 + \frac{1}{5!} x^5 + \frac{3}{6!} x^6 - \frac{8}{7!} x^7 + \frac{14}{8!} x^8 + \frac{7}{9!} x^9 - \frac{71}{10!} x^{10} + \cdots$$

With $c_0 = 0$ and $c_1 = 1$:

$$y_2 = x - \frac{1}{2!} x^2 + \frac{1}{3!} x^3 + \frac{1}{4!} x^4 - \frac{4}{5!} x^5 + \frac{8}{6!} x^6 - \frac{3}{7!} x^7 - \frac{21}{8!} x^8 + \frac{77}{9!} x^9 - \frac{101}{10!} x^{10} + \cdots$$

14. With c_0 and c_1 arbitrary, $\quad c_{n+2} = -\dfrac{4\,c_{n-2} + 2(n+1)\,c_{n+1}}{(n+2)(n+1)}$, $\ n = 2, 3, \ldots$

With $c_0 = 1$ and $c_1 = 0$:

$$y_1 = 1 - \frac{1}{3}\,x^4 + \frac{2}{15}\,x^5 - \frac{2}{45}\,x^6 + \frac{4}{315}\,x^7 + \frac{13}{630}\,x^8 - \frac{34}{2835}\,x^9 + \frac{62}{14175}\,x^{10} + \cdots$$

With $c_0 = 0$ and $c_1 = 1$:

$$y_2 = x - x^2 + \frac{2}{3}\,x^3 - \frac{1}{3}\,x^4 - \frac{1}{15}\,x^5 + \frac{7}{45}\,x^6 - \frac{34}{315}\,x^7 + \frac{16}{315}\,x^8 - \frac{43}{5670}\,x^9 - \frac{17}{3150}\,x^{10} + \cdots$$

15. With c_0 and c_1 arbitrary, $\quad c_{n+2} = -\dfrac{n(n-6)+1}{2(n+2)(n+1)}\,c_n$, $\ n = 2, 3, \ldots$

$$y_1 = 1 - \frac{1}{4}\,x^2 - \frac{7}{96}\,x^4 - \frac{49}{5760}\,x^6 + \frac{7}{92160}\,x^8 - \frac{119}{16588800}\,x^{10} + \cdots,$$

$$y_2 = x - \frac{1}{3}\,x^3 + \frac{1}{15}\,x^5 + \frac{1}{315}\,x^7 - \frac{1}{5670}\,x^9 + \frac{1}{44550}\,x^{11} + \cdots$$

16. With c_0 and c_1 arbitrary, $\quad c_{n+2} = \dfrac{n(n-1)+2}{(n+2)(n+1)}\,c_n$, $\ n = 2, 3, \ldots$

$$y_1 = 1 + x^2 + \frac{1}{3}\,x^4 + \frac{7}{45}\,x^6 + \frac{4}{45}\,x^8 + \frac{116}{2025}\,x^{10} + \cdots,$$

$$y_2 = x + \frac{1}{3}\,x^3 + \frac{2}{15}\,x^5 + \frac{22}{315}\,x^7 + \frac{121}{2835}\,x^9 + \frac{407}{14175}\,x^{11} + \cdots$$

17. With c_0 and c_1 arbitrary, $\quad c_{n+2} = \dfrac{(n+3)(n-2)}{(n+2)(n+1)}\,c_n$, $\ n = 2, 3, \ldots$

$$y_1 = 1 - 3\,x^2,$$
$$y_2 = x - \frac{2}{3}\,x^3 - \frac{1}{5}\,x^5 - \frac{4}{35}\,x^7 - \frac{5}{63}\,x^9 - \frac{2}{33}\,x^{11} - \cdots$$

18. With c_0 and c_1 arbitrary, $\quad c_{n+2} = \dfrac{(n+5)(n-4)}{(n+2)(n+1)}\,c_n$, $\ n = 2, 3, \ldots$

$$y_1 = 1 - 10\,x^2 + \frac{35}{3}\,x^4,$$
$$y_2 = x - 3\,x^3 + \frac{6}{5}\,x^5 + \frac{2}{7}\,x^7 + \frac{1}{7}\,x^9 + \frac{1}{11}\,x^{11} - \cdots$$

19. With c_0 and c_1 arbitrary, $\quad c_{n+2} = \dfrac{(n+6)(n-5)}{(n+2)(n+1)}\,c_n$, $\ n = 2, 3, \ldots$

$$y_1 = 1 - 15\,x^2 + 30\,x^4 - 10\,x^6 - \frac{15}{7}\,x^8 - x^{10} + \cdots,$$

$$y_2 = x - \frac{14}{3}\,x^3 + \frac{21}{5}\,x^5$$

20. With c_0 and c_1 arbitrary, $\quad c_{n+2} = \dfrac{n-2}{n+1}\,c_n$, $\ n = 2, 3, \ldots$

$$y_1 = 1 - 2\,x^2,$$
$$y_2 = x - \frac{1}{2}\,x^3 - \frac{1}{8}\,x^5 - \frac{1}{16}\,x^7 - \frac{5}{128}\,x^9 - \frac{7}{256}\,x^{11} - \cdots$$

21. With c_0 and c_1 arbitrary, $\quad c_{n+2} = \dfrac{(n+4)(n-4)}{(n+2)(n+1)}\, c_n\,$, $\;n = 2, 3, \ldots$

$$y_1 = 1 - 8\,x^2 + 8\,x^4\,,$$

$$y_2 = x - \frac{5}{2}\,x^3 + \frac{7}{8}\,x^5 + \frac{3}{16}\,x^7 + \frac{11}{128}\,x^9 + \frac{13}{256}\,x^{11} + \cdots$$

1. Classification of ordinary points and singular points

2. Classification of ordinary points and singular points

3. Classification of ordinary points and singular points

4. Classification of ordinary points and singular points

5. Classification of ordinary points and singular points

6. Classification of ordinary points and singular points

7. Classification of ordinary points and singular points

8. Regular vs. irregular singular points

9. Regular vs. irregular singular points

10. Regular vs. irregular singular points

11. Regular vs. irregular singular points

12. Regular vs. irregular singular points

13. Identifying solution types by the given indicial roots

14. Identifying solution types by the given indicial roots

15. Identifying solution types by the given indicial roots

16. Solve a singular DE by the method of Frobenius — indicial roots differ by a non integer

17. Solve a singular DE by the method of Frobenius — indicial roots differ by a non integer

18. Solve a singular DE by the method of Frobenius — indicial roots differ by a non integer

19. Solve a singular DE by the method of Frobenius — indicial roots differ by a non integer

20. Solve a singular DE by the method of Frobenius — indicial roots differ by an integer

21. Solve a singular DE by the method of Frobenius — indicial roots differ by an integer

22. Solve a singular DE by the method of Frobenius — indicial roots differ by an integer

23. Solve a singular DE by the method of Frobenius — indicial roots are equal

24. Solve a singular DE by the method of Frobenius — indicial roots are equal

25. Solve a singular DE by the method of Frobenius — indicial roots are equal

1. Complete the statement for the differential equation $(x^2 - 1)\, y'' + 3\, x\, y' - 4\, y = 0$. The point $x = 0$ is

    (a) an ordinary point.

    (b) a regular singular point.

    (c) an irregular singular point.

    (d) none of these.

2. Complete the statement for the differential equation $(x^2 - 16)\, y'' + 5\, x\, y' + 4\, y = 0$. The point $x = 4$ is

    (a) an ordinary point.

    (b) a regular singular point.

    (c) an irregular singular point.

    (d) none of these.

3. Complete the statement for the differential equation $(x^2 - 4)\, y'' + 6\, (x + 2)\, y' + 4\, y = 0$. The point $x = 2$ is

    (a) an ordinary point.

    (b) a regular singular point.

    (c) an irregular singular point.

    (d) none of these.

4. Complete the statement for the differential equation $(x^2 - 4)\, y'' + 6\, (x + 2)\, y' + 4\, y = 0$. The point $x = -2$ is

    (a) an ordinary point.

    (b) a regular singular point.

    (c) an irregular singular point.

    (d) none of these.

5. Complete the statement for the differential equation $(x^2 - 9)^2\, y'' + 6\, (x - 3)\, y' + 9\, y = 0$. The point $x = 3$ is

    (a) an ordinary point.

    (b) a regular singular point.

    (c) an irregular singular point.

    (d) none of these.

6. Complete the statement for the differential equation $(x^2 - 25)^2\, y'' + 6\, (x - 5)\, y' + 4\, (x + 5)\, y = 0$. The point $x = 5$ is

    (a) an ordinary point.

    (b) a regular singular point.

    (c) an irregular singular point.

    (d) none of these.

7. Complete the statement for the differential equation $(x^2 - 25)^2 \, y'' + 6 \, (x - 5) \, y' + 4 \, (x + 5) \, y = 0$. The point $x = -5$ is

    (a) an ordinary point.

    (b) a regular singular point.

    (c) an irregular singular point.

    (d) none of these.

8. Determine the smallest integer power n so that $x = 1$ is an irregular singular point for the differential equation $(x - 1)^n \, y'' + (x - 1)^2 \, y' + y = 0$.

    (a) $n = 1$

    (b) $n = 2$

    (c) $n = 3$

    (d) $n = 4$

9. Determine the smallest integer power n so that $x = 1$ is an irregular singular point for the differential equation $(x^2 - 1)^n \, y'' + 5 \, x \, y' + (x - 1)^2 \, y = 0$.

    (a) $n = 1$

    (b) $n = 2$

    (c) $n = 3$

    (d) $n = 4$

10. Determine the smallest integer power n so that $x = 1$ is an irregular singular point for the differential equation $(x^2 - 1)^n \, y'' + 3 \, x \, (x - 1)^2 \, y' + 4 \, y = 0$.

    (a) $n = 1$

    (b) $n = 2$

    (c) $n = 3$

    (d) $n = 4$

11. Determine the smallest integer power n so that $x = 1$ is an irregular singular point for the differential equation $(x - 1)^n \, y'' + 3 \, x \, y' + 4 \, (x - 1)^2 \, y = 0$.

    (a) $n = 1$

    (b) $n = 2$

    (c) $n = 3$

    (d) $n = 4$

12. Determine the largest integer power n so that $x = 1$ is a regular singular point for the differential equation $(x^2 - 1)^n \, y'' + 3 \, x \, (x - 1) \, y' + 4 \, y = 0$.

    (a) $n = 1$

    (b) $n = 2$

    (c) $n = 3$

    (d) $n = 4$

13. Suppose a certain 2nd-order linear homogeneous DE with regular singular root $x = 0$ has indicial roots $r_1 = 3/2$ and $r_2 = 7/2$. Then there exist two linearly independent solutions of the DE,

   (a) neither of which contains a logarithm.

   (b) one of which must contain a logarithm.

   (c) one of which might contain a logarithm.

   (d) both of which must contain logarithms.

14. Suppose a certain 2nd-order linear homogeneous DE with regular singular root $x = 0$ has indicial roots $r_1 = 1$ and $r_2 = 5/2$. Then there exist two linearly independent solutions of the DE,

   (a) neither of which contains a logarithm.

   (b) one of which must contain a logarithm.

   (c) one of which might contain a logarithm.

   (d) both of which must contain logarithms.

15. Suppose a certain 2nd-order linear homogeneous DE with regular singular root $x = 0$ has indicial roots $r_1 = 2$ and $r_2 = 2$. Then there exist two linearly independent solutions of the DE,

   (a) neither of which contains a logarithm.

   (b) one of which must contain a logarithm.

   (c) one of which might contain a logarithm.

   (d) both of which must contain logarithms.

Problems 16-25: Use the method of Frobenius to find two linearly independent power series solutions about the regular singular point $x = 0$, and form the general solution on $(0, \infty)$. State the indicial roots.

16. $2 x^2 y'' - x y' + (1 + x) y = 0$

17. $4 x y'' + 2 y' + y = 0$

18. $3 x y'' + 2 y' + y = 0$

19. $2 x y'' - 3 y' + 3 x y = 0$

20. $x y'' + 2 y' + x y = 0$

21. $x y'' + (x - 4) y' - 2 y = 0$

22. $x^2 y'' + x y' + (x^2 - 4) y = 0$

23. $x y'' + y' + x y = 0$

24. $4 x y'' + 4 y' + x y = 0$

25. $x y'' + y' + (x - 2) y = 0$

1. a

2. b

3. b

4. b

5. b

6. b

7. c

8. c

9. b

10. c

11. b

12. b

13. c

14. a

15. b

16. $r = 1/2$, $r = 1$, $y = C_1 x^{1/2} \displaystyle\sum_{n=0}^{\infty} \frac{(-1)^n 2^n}{(2n)!} x^n + C_2 x \left[1 + \displaystyle\sum_{n=1}^{\infty} \frac{(-1)^n 2^n}{(2n+1)!} x^n \right]$

17. $r = 0$, $r = 1/2$, $y = C_1 \displaystyle\sum_{n=0}^{\infty} \frac{(-1)^n}{(2n)!} x^n + C_2 x^{1/2} \displaystyle\sum_{n=0}^{\infty} \frac{(-1)^n}{(2n+1)!} x^n = C_1 \cos\sqrt{x} + C_2 \sin\sqrt{x}$

18. $r = 0$, $r = 1/3$,

$$y = C_1 \left[1 - \frac{1}{2}x + \frac{1}{20}x^2 - \frac{1}{480}x^3 + \frac{1}{21120}x^4 - \frac{1}{1478400}x^5 + \frac{1}{150796800}x^6 + \cdots \right]$$
$$+ C_2 x^{1/3} \left[1 - \frac{1}{4}x + \frac{1}{56}x^2 - \frac{1}{1680}x^3 + \frac{1}{87360}x^4 - \frac{1}{6988800}x^5 + \frac{1}{796723200}x^6 + \cdots \right]$$

19. $r = 0$, $r = 5/2$,

$$y = C_1 \left[1 + \frac{3}{2}x^2 - \frac{3}{8}x^4 + \frac{3}{112}x^6 - \frac{9}{9856}x^8 + \frac{9}{492800}x^{10} - \frac{9}{3745800}x^{12} + \cdots \right]$$
$$+ C_2 x^{5/2} \left[1 - \frac{1}{6}x^2 + \frac{1}{104}x^4 - \frac{1}{3536}x^6 + \frac{1}{198016}x^8 - \frac{3}{49504000}x^{10} + \frac{3}{5742464000}x^{12} + \cdots \right]$$

20. $r = 0$, $r = -1$,

$$y = C_1 \displaystyle\sum_{n=0}^{\infty} \frac{(-1)^n}{(2n+1)!} x^{2n} + C_2 x^{-1} \displaystyle\sum_{n=0}^{\infty} \frac{(-1)^n}{(2n)!} x^{2n} = \frac{1}{x}\left(C_1 \cos x + C_2 \sin x \right)$$

21. $r = 0$, $r = 5$,

$$y = C_1\left(12 - 6x + x^2\right) + C_2\, x^5\left[1 - \frac{1}{2}x + \frac{1}{12}x^2 - \frac{5}{168}x^3 + \frac{5}{1008}x^4 - \frac{1}{144}x^5 + \frac{1}{11880}x^6\right.$$
$$\left. - \frac{1}{110880}x^7 + \frac{1}{1153152}x^8 - \frac{1}{13208832}x^9 + \cdots\right]$$
$$= C_1\left(12 - 6x + x^2\right) + C_2\, e^{-x}\left(12 + 6x + x^2\right)$$

22. $r = 2$, $r = -2$,

$$y = \left(C_1\ln x + C_2\right)x^2\left[1 - \frac{1}{12}x^2 + \frac{1}{384}x^4 - \frac{1}{23040}x^6 + \frac{1}{2211840}x^8 - \frac{1}{309657600}x^{10} + \cdots\right]$$

23. $r = 0$, $r = 0$,

$$y = \left(C_1\ln x + C_2\right)\left[1 - \frac{1}{4}x^2 + \frac{1}{64}x^4 - \frac{1}{2304}x^6 + \frac{1}{147456}x^8 - \frac{1}{14745600}x^{10} + \frac{1}{2123366400}x^{12} + \cdots\right]$$

24. $r = 0$, $r = 0$,

$$y = \left(C_1\ln x + C_2\right)\left[1 - \frac{1}{16}x^2 + \frac{1}{1024}x^4 - \frac{1}{147456}x^6 + \frac{1}{37748736}x^8 - \frac{1}{15099494400}x^{10} + \frac{1}{8697308774400}x^{12} + \right.$$

25. $r = 0$, $r = 0$,

$$y = \left(C_1\ln x + C_2\right)\left[1 + 2x + \frac{3}{4}x^2 - \frac{1}{18}x^3 - \frac{31}{576}x^4 - \frac{1}{480}x^5 + \frac{143}{103680}x^6 + \frac{251}{2540160}x^7 + \cdots\right]$$

164

1. linear independence of solutions of Bessel's equation

2. linear independence of solutions of Bessel's equation

3. linear independence of solutions of Bessel's equation

4. linear independence of solutions of Bessel's equation

5. identifying a Bessel function

6. identifying a Bessel function

7. identifying a Bessel function

8. identifying a Bessel function

9. properties of Bessel functions

10. properties of Bessel functions

11. properties of Bessel functions

12. properties of Bessel functions

13. properties of Bessel functions

14. properties of Legendre polynomials

15. properties of Legendre polynomials

16. properties of Legendre polynomials

17. properties of Legendre polynomials

18. obtain the general solution of a Bessel equation

19. obtain the general solution of a Bessel equation

20. obtain the general solution of a Bessel equation

21. obtain the general solution of a Bessel equation

22. obtain the general solution of a Bessel equation

23. obtain the general solution of a Bessel equation

24. obtain the general solution of a Bessel equation

25. obtain the general solution of a Bessel equation

26. obtain the general solution of a Bessel equation

27. obtain the general solution of a Bessel equation

28. obtain the general solution of a Bessel equation

29. obtain the general solution of a Bessel equation by the indicated substitution

30. obtain the general solution of a Bessel equation by the indicated substitution

31. obtain the general solution of a Bessel equation by the indicated substitution

32. use (18) and (19) to obtain the general solution of a Bessel equation

33. use (18) and (19) to obtain the general solution of a Bessel equation

34. use (18) and (19) to obtain the general solution of a Bessel equation

35. use (18) and (19) to obtain the general solution of a Bessel equation

36. use (18) and (19) to obtain the general solution of a Bessel equation

37. use (18) and (19) to obtain the general solution of a Bessel equation

38. use (18) and (19) to obtain the general solution of a Bessel equation

39. use (18) and (19) to obtain the general solution of a Bessel equation

40. use Rodriques' formula to obtain a Legendre polynomial

41. Legendre's equation

42. Legendre's equation

43. Legendre's equation

1. If $\nu = \pm 3/2$ in Bessel's equation, then the Bessel functions $J_{3/2}(x)$ and $J_{-3/2}(x)$

   (a) are linearly independent solutions.
   (b) might be linearly independent solutions.
   (c) are not linearly independent solutions.
   (d) More information is needed.

2. If $\nu = \pm 5$ in Bessel's equation, then the Bessel functions $J_5(x)$ and $J_{-5}(x)$

   (a) are linearly independent solutions.
   (b) might be linearly independent solutions.
   (c) are not linearly independent solutions.
   (d) are not solutions.

3. If $\nu = \pm 4$ in Bessel's equation, then the Bessel functions $J_4(x)$ and $Y_4(x)$

   (a) are linearly independent solutions.
   (b) might be linearly independent solutions.
   (c) are not linearly independent solutions.
   (d) are not solutions.

4. If $\nu = \pm 3/2$ in Bessel's equation, then the Bessel functions $J_{3/2}(x)$ and $Y_{3/2}(x)$

   (a) are linearly independent solutions.
   (b) might be linearly independent solutions.
   (c) are not linearly independent solutions.
   (d) are not solutions.

5. The function $Y_2(x)$ is called the

   (a) Bessel function of the first kind of order 1.
   (b) Bessel function of the first kind of order 2.
   (c) Bessel function of the second kind of order 1.
   (d) Bessel function of the second kind of order 2.

6. The function $J_2(x)$ is called the

   (a) Bessel function of the first kind of order 1.
   (b) Bessel function of the first kind of order 2.
   (c) Bessel function of the second kind of order 1.
   (d) Bessel function of the second kind of order 2.

7. The function $K_2(x)$ is called the

   (a) Bessel function of the first kind of order 2.
   (b) Bessel function of the second kind of order 2.
   (c) modified Bessel function of the first kind of order 2.
   (d) modified Bessel function of the second kind of order 2.

8. The function $I_2(x)$ is called the

    (a) Bessel function of the first kind of order 2.
    (b) Bessel function of the second kind of order 2.
    (c) modified Bessel function of the first kind of order 2.
    (d) modified Bessel function of the second kind of order 2.

9. $J_2(-x)$ is the same as

    (a) $J_2(x)$.
    (b) $-J_2(x)$.
    (c) $J_{-2}(-x)$.
    (d) a and c.

10. $J_{-3}(x)$ is the same as

    (a) $J_3(x)$.
    (b) $-J_3(x)$.
    (c) $J_3(-x)$.
    (d) b and c.

11. The value of $J_0(0)$ is

    (a) 0.
    (b) 1.
    (c) -1.
    (d) undefined, specifically $-\infty$.

12. The value of $J_1(0)$ is

    (a) 0.
    (b) 1.
    (c) -1.
    (d) undefined, specifically $-\infty$.

13. The value of $Y_0(0)$ is

    (a) 0.
    (b) 1.
    (c) -1.
    (d) undefined, specifically $-\infty$.

14. If $P_n(x)$ denotes a Legendre polynomial, then the value of $P_3(0)$ is

    (a) 0.
    (b) 1.
    (c) -1.
    (d) undefined, specifically $-\infty$.

15. If $P_n(x)$ denotes a Legendre polynomial, then the value of $P_3(-1)$ is

    (a) 0.

    (b) 1.

    (c) -1.

    (d) undefined, specifically $-\infty$.

16. If $P_n(x)$ denotes a Legendre polynomial, then the value of $P_1(1)$ is

    (a) 0.

    (b) 1.

    (c) -1.

    (d) undefined, specifically $-\infty$.

17. If $P_n(x)$ denotes a Legendre polynomial, then the value of $P_4'(0)$ is

    (a) 0.

    (b) 1.

    (c) -1.

    (d) undefined, specifically $-\infty$.

Problems 18-28: Find the general solution of the given differential equation on $(0, \infty)$.

18. $x^2 y'' + x y' + \left(x^2 - \dfrac{1}{25} \right) y = 0$

19. $x^2 y'' + x y' + \left(x^2 - \dfrac{25}{36} \right) y = 0$

20. $9 x^2 y'' + 9 x y' + (9 x^2 - 4) y = 0$

21. $[x y']' + \left(x - \dfrac{9}{x} \right) y = 0$

22. $[x y']' + x y = 0$

23. $x^2 y'' + x y' + (4 x^2 - 1) y = 0$

24. $x^2 y'' + x y' + (9 x^2 - 4) y = 0$

25. $x^2 y'' + x y' + 16 \left(x^2 - \dfrac{1}{9} \right) y = 0$

26. $x^2 y'' + x y' - (x^2 + 9) y = 0$

27. $x^2 y'' + x y' - \left(x^2 + \dfrac{9}{4} \right) y = 0$

28. $x^2 y'' + x y' - 9 (x^2 + 4) y = 0$

Problems 29-31: Use the indicated substitution to find the general solution of the given differential equation on $(0, \infty)$.

29. $x^2 y'' - x y' + \left(x^2 + \dfrac{5}{9} \right) y = 0; \quad y = x\, v(x)$

30. $x^2 y'' + (x^2 - 2) y = 0; \quad y = \sqrt{x}\, v(x)$

31. $x^2 y'' - 3 x y' + (x^2 - 12) y = 0; \quad y = x^2 v(x)$

169

Problems 32-39:   Use formulas (18) and (19) in the text to find the general solution of the given differential equation on $(0, \infty)$.

32. $x\,y'' - y' + 4\,x\,y \;=\; 0$

33. $x\,y'' + 3\,y' + 9\,x^5\,y \;=\; 0$

34. $x^2\,y'' + (x^2 - 2)\,y \;=\; 0$

35. $x^2\,y'' + 3\,x\,y' + \left(4\,x^4 + \dfrac{3}{4}\right) y \;=\; 0$

36. $x\,y'' + 2\,y' + 9\,x\,y \;=\; 0$

37. $x^2\,y'' - 2\,x\,y' + 4\,(x^2 + 1)\,y \;=\; 0$

38. $2\,x\,y'' - y' + 2\,y \;=\; 0$

39. $x^2\,y'' + 3\,x\,y' + \dfrac{1}{4}\,(x + 3)\,y \;=\; 0$

40. Use Rodrigues' formula to determine the Legendre polynomial $P_3(x)$.

41. Write the differential equation for which $P_8(x)$ is a solution.

42. What is a polynomial solution of the differential equation $(1 - x^2)\,y'' - 2\,x\,y' + 42\,y \;=\; 0$?

43. What is a polynomial solution of the differential equation $(1 - x^2)\,y'' - 2\,x\,y' + 90\,y \;=\; 0$?

1. a

2. c

3. a

4. a

5. d

6. b

7. d

8. c

9. d

10. d

11. b

12. a

13. d

14. a

15. c

16. b

17. a

18. $y = c_1 J_{1/5}(x) + c_2 J_{-1/5}(x)$ or $y = c_1 J_{1/5}(x) + c_2 Y_{1/5}(x)$

19. $y = c_1 J_{5/6}(x) + c_2 J_{-5/6}(x)$ or $y = c_1 J_{5/6}(x) + c_2 Y_{5/6}(x)$

20. $y = c_1 J_{2/3}(x) + c_2 J_{-2/3}(x)$ or $y = c_1 J_{2/3}(x) + c_2 Y_{2/3}(x)$

21. $y = c_1 J_3(x) + c_2 Y_3(x)$

22. $y = c_1 J_0(x) + c_2 Y_0(x)$

23. $y = c_1 J_1(2x) + c_2 Y_1(2x)$

24. $y = c_1 J_2(3x) + c_2 Y_2(3x)$

25. $y = c_1 J_{4/3}(4x) + c_2 J_{-4/3}(4x)$ or $y = c_1 J_{4/3}(4x) + c_2 Y_{4/3}(4x)$

26. $y = c_1 I_3(x) + c_2 K_3(4x)$

27. $y = c_1 I_{3/2}(x) + c_2 K_{3/2}(x)$

28. $y = c_1 I_6(3x) + c_2 K_6(3x)$

29. $y = x\left[c_1 J_{2/3}(x) + c_2 J_{-2/3}(x) \right]$ or $y = x\left[c_1 J_{2/3}(x) + c_2 Y_{2/3}(x) \right]$

30. $y = \sqrt{x} \left[c_1 J_{3/2}(x) + c_2 J_{-3/2}(x) \right]$ or $y = \sqrt{x} \left[c_1 J_{3/2}(x) + c_2 Y_{3/2}(x) \right]$

31. $y = x^2 \left[c_1 J_4(x) + c_2 Y_4(x) \right]$

32. $y = x \left[c_1 J_1(2x) + c_2 Y_1(2x) \right]$

33. $y = x^{-1} \left[c_1 J_{1/3}(x^3) + c_2 Y_{1/3}(x^3) \right]$

34. $y = \sqrt{x} \left[c_1 J_{3/2}(x) + c_2 Y_{3/2}(x) \right]$

35. $y = x^{-1} \left[c_1 J_{1/4}(x^2) + c_2 Y_{1/4}(x^2) \right]$

36. $y = x^{-1/2} \left[c_1 J_{1/2}(3x) + c_2 Y_{1/2}(3x) \right]$ or $y = x^{-1} \left(c_1 \cos 3x + c_2 \sin 3x \right)$

37. $y = x^{5/2} \left[c_1 J_{3/2}(2x) + c_2 Y_{3/2}(2x) \right]$

38. $y = x^{3/4} \left[c_1 J_{3/2}(2\sqrt{x}) + c_2 Y_{3/2}(2\sqrt{x}) \right]$

39. $y = x^{-1} \left[c_1 J_1(\sqrt{x}) + c_2 Y_1(\sqrt{x}) \right]$

40. $P_3(x) = \dfrac{1}{2} x \left(5 x^2 - 3 \right)$

41. $(1 - x^2) y'' - 2 x y' + 72 y = 0$

42. $P_6(x)$

43. $P_9(x)$

7.1   Definition of the Laplace Transform   Subject Correlation Guide

1. Laplace transform — existence

2. behavior of $F(s)$ as $s \to 0$

3. exponential order

4. integral definition of the Laplace transform

5. linearity of the Laplace transform

6. linearity of the Laplace transform

7. linearity of the Laplace transform

8. linearity of the Laplace transform

9. Laplace transform — existence

10. exponential order

11. Use the integral definition to find $\mathcal{L}\{f(t)\}$ of 9 given functions — 3 exponential functions (a-c) and 6 two-piece functions (d-i).

12. Use Theorem 7.1 to find $\mathcal{L}\{f(t)\}$ of 26 given functions, where $f(t)$ is a(n)

   (a) power function
   (b) polynomial function; uses linearity
   (c) exponential function
   (d) exponential function
   (e) exponential function
   (f) exponential function
   (g) exponential function
   (h) exponential function; uses linearity
   (i) exponential function; uses linearity
   (j) trig function
   (k) trig function; uses linearity
   (l) trig function
   (m) trig function
   (n) trig function
   (o) trig function
   (p) trig function; uses trig identity
   (q) trig function; uses trig identity
   (r) trig function; uses trig identity
   (s) hyperbolic trig function
   (t) hyperbolic trig function

(u) hyperbolic trig function

(v) hyperbolic trig function; uses linearity

(w) hyperbolic trig function; uses linearity

(x) product of an exponential and hyperbolic trig function; uses linearity

(y) power function and trig function; uses linearity

(z) constant, power function, and exponential function; uses linearity

1. The existence of the Laplace transform of a function $f(t)$ is guaranteed provided

    (a) $f(t)$ is piecewise continuous on $[0, \infty)$.
    (b) $f(t)$ is of exponential order.
    (c) either (a) or (b)
    (d) both (a) and (b)

2. If the Laplace transform $F(s)$ of a function $f(t)$ exists, then

    (a) $\lim\limits_{s \to \infty} F(s) = 0$.
    (b) $\lim\limits_{s \to \infty} F(s) = \infty$.
    (c) $\lim\limits_{s \to 0} F(s) = 0$.
    (d) $\lim\limits_{s \to 0} F(s) = \infty$.

3. The function $4e^{3t} \cos 2t$ is of exponential order

    (a) 1.
    (b) 2.
    (c) 3.
    (d) 4.

4. The Laplace transform of a function $f(t)$ is defined by

    (a) $\int_0^t f(t) \, e^{st} \, dt.$

    (b) $\int_0^\infty f(t) \, e^{st} \, dt.$

    (c) $\int_0^t f(t) \, e^{-st} \, dt.$

    (d) $\int_0^\infty f(t) \, e^{-st} \, dt.$

5. True or False: If $\mathcal{L}\{f(t)\}$ and $\mathcal{L}\{g(t)\}$ both exist, then $\mathcal{L}\{f(t) - g(t)\} = \mathcal{L}\{f(t)\} - \mathcal{L}\{g(t)\}$.

6. True or False: If $\mathcal{L}\{f(t)\}$ and $\mathcal{L}\{g(t)\}$ both exist, then $\mathcal{L}\{f(t)\, g(t)\} = \mathcal{L}\{f(t)\}\, \mathcal{L}\{g(t)\}$.

7. True or False: If $\mathcal{L}\{f(t)\}$ exists, then $\mathcal{L}\{4\, f(t)\} = 4\, \mathcal{L}\{f(t)\}$.

8. True or False: If $\mathcal{L}\{f(t)\}$ and $\mathcal{L}\{g(t)\}$ both exist, then $\mathcal{L}\{f(t)/g(t)\} = \mathcal{L}\{f(t)\}/\mathcal{L}\{g(t)\}$.

9. True or False: Every function has a Laplace transform.

10. True or False: If n is a positive integer, then the function t^n is always of exponential order.

11. In each of the following, use the definition of the Laplace transform to determine $\mathcal{L}\{f(t)\}$. State the domain of $F(s)$.

    (a) $f(t) = e^{-t}$
    (b) $f(t) = e^{2-t}$

(c) $f(t) = e^{4(t-1)}$

(d) $f(t) = \begin{cases} 0, & 0 \le t < 3 \\ 2, & t \ge 3 \end{cases}$

(e) $f(t) = \begin{cases} 3, & 0 \le t < 2 \\ 1, & t \ge 2 \end{cases}$

(f) $f(t) = \begin{cases} 0, & 0 \le t < 2 \\ t, & t \ge 2 \end{cases}$

(g) $f(t) = \begin{cases} 0, & 0 \le t < \pi \\ \sin 2t, & t \ge \pi \end{cases}$

(h) $f(t) = \begin{cases} 0, & 0 \le t < 1 \\ e^{2t}, & t \ge 1 \end{cases}$

(i) $f(t) = \begin{cases} e^{3t}, & 0 \le t < 1 \\ 0, & t \ge 1 \end{cases}$

12. In each of the following, use Theorem 7.1 to determine $\mathcal{L}\{f(t)\}$ for each of the following.

(a) $f(t) = t^6$

(b) $f(t) = (t^3 - 4)^2$

(c) $f(t) = e^{-t}$

(d) $f(t) = e^{3t}$

(e) $f(t) = e^{-2t}$

(f) $f(t) = e^{t-4}$

(g) $f(t) = e^{3-2t}$

(h) $f(t) = 4\,e^{t/2}$

(i) $f(t) = 6\,e^{\pi t}$

(j) $f(t) = \cos 4t$

(k) $f(t) = 4 \sin 3t$

(l) $f(t) = \sin \pi t$

(m) $f(t) = \sin(t/2)$

(n) $f(t) = \cos(t/3)$

(o) $f(t) = \cos(\sqrt{2}\,t)$

(p) $f(t) = \sin 4t \cos 4t$

(q) $f(t) = \cos^2 3t$

(r) $f(t) = \sin^2 4t$

(s) $f(t) = \sinh 3t$

(t) $f(t) = \cosh 6t$

(u) $f(t) = \sinh \pi t$

(v) $f(t) = 4 \cosh 2t$

(w) $f(t) = 2 \sinh 4t$

(x) $f(t) = e^{2t} \cosh 2t$

(y) $f(t) = 6t^3 + 4 \cos 3t$

(z) $f(t) = (3 - e^{2t})^2$

1. d

2. a

3. c

4. d

5. True

6. False

7. True

8. False

9. False

10. True

11. (a) $F(s) = \dfrac{1}{s+1}, \quad s > -1$

   (b) $F(s) = \dfrac{e^2}{s+1}, \quad s > -1$

   (c) $F(s) = \dfrac{e^{-4}}{s-4}, \quad s > 4$

   (d) $F(s) = \dfrac{2\,e^{-3s}}{s}, \quad s > 0$

   (e) $F(s) = \dfrac{3 - 2\,e^{-2s}}{s}, \quad s > 0$

   (f) $F(s) = \dfrac{(1 + 2s)\,e^{-2s}}{s^2}, \quad s > 0$

   (g) $F(s) = \dfrac{2\,e^{-\pi s}}{s^2 + 4}, \quad s > 0$

   (h) $F(s) = \dfrac{e^{2-s}}{s-2}, \quad s > 2$

   (i) $F(s) = \dfrac{1 - e^{3-s}}{s-3}, \quad s > 3$

12. (a) $F(s) = \dfrac{720}{s^7}$

   (b) $F(s) = \dfrac{720}{s^7} - \dfrac{48}{s^4} + \dfrac{16}{s}$

   (c) $F(s) = \dfrac{1}{s+1}$

   (d) $F(s) = \dfrac{1}{s-3}$

   (e) $F(s) = \dfrac{1}{s+2}$

   (f) $F(s) = \dfrac{e^{-4}}{s-1}$

(g) $F(s) = \dfrac{e^3}{s+2}$

(h) $F(s) = \dfrac{8}{2s-1}$

(i) $F(s) = \dfrac{6}{s-\pi}$

(j) $F(s) = \dfrac{s}{s^2+16}$

(k) $F(s) = \dfrac{12}{s^2+9}$

(l) $F(s) = \dfrac{\pi}{s^2+\pi^2}$

(m) $F(s) = \dfrac{2}{4s^2+1}$

(n) $F(s) = \dfrac{9s}{9s^2+1}$

(o) $F(s) = \dfrac{s}{s^2+2}$

(p) $F(s) = \dfrac{4}{s^2+64}$

(q) $F(s) = \dfrac{s^2+18}{s(s^2+36)}$

(r) $F(s) = \dfrac{32}{s(s^2+64)}$

(s) $F(s) = \dfrac{3}{s^2-9}$

(t) $F(s) = \dfrac{s}{s^2-36}$

(u) $F(s) = \dfrac{\pi}{s^2-\pi^2}$

(v) $F(s) = \dfrac{4s}{s^2-4}$

(w) $F(s) = \dfrac{8}{s^2-16}$

(x) $F(s) = \dfrac{s-2}{s(s-4)}$

(y) $F(s) = \dfrac{36}{s^4} + \dfrac{4s}{s^2+9}$

(z) $F(s) = \dfrac{9}{s} - \dfrac{6}{s-2} + \dfrac{1}{s-4}$

1. inverse Laplace transform — concepts

2. inverse Laplace transform — concepts

3. inverse Laplace transform — concepts

4. inverse Laplace transform — linearity

5. inverse Laplace transform — linearity

6. inverse Laplace transform — linearity

7. inverse Laplace transform — linearity

8. Laplace transform — existence

9. find the inverse Laplace transform — power function

10. find the inverse Laplace transform — power function; uses linearity

11. find the inverse Laplace transform — exponential function

12. find the inverse Laplace transform — exponential function

13. find the inverse Laplace transform — exponential function

14. find the inverse Laplace transform — trig function

15. find the inverse Laplace transform — hyperbolic trig function

16. find the inverse Laplace transform — hyperbolic trig function

17. find the inverse Laplace transform — hyperbolic trig function

18. find the inverse Laplace transform — trig function; uses linearity

19. find the inverse Laplace transform — hyperbolic trig function; uses linearity

20. find the inverse Laplace transform — fraction decomposition

21. find the inverse Laplace transform — fraction decomposition

22. find the inverse Laplace transform — fraction decomposition

23. find the inverse Laplace transform — fraction decomposition

24. find the inverse Laplace transform — fraction decomposition

25. find the inverse Laplace transform — fraction decomposition

26. Use Laplace transforms to solve a linear 2nd-order initial value problem.

27. Use Laplace transforms to solve a linear 2nd-order initial value problem.

28. Use Laplace transforms to solve a linear 2nd-order initial value problem.

29. Use Laplace transforms to solve a linear 2nd-order initial value problem.

30. Use Laplace transforms to solve a linear 2nd-order initial value problem.

31. Use Laplace transforms to solve a linear 3rd-order initial value problem.

32. Use Laplace transforms to solve a linear 3rd-order initial value problem.

1. True or False: If $F(s) = \mathcal{L}\{f(t)\}$, then $\mathcal{L}^{-1}\Big\{\mathcal{L}\{f(t)\}\Big\} = f(t)$.

2. True or False: If $F(s) = \mathcal{L}\{f(t)\}$, then $\mathcal{L}^{-1}\Big\{\mathcal{L}\{f(t)\}\Big\} = F(s)$.

3. True or False: If $F(s) = \mathcal{L}\{f(t)\}$, then $\mathcal{L}\Big\{\mathcal{L}^{-1}\{f(t)\}\Big\} = f(t)$.

4. True or False: If $\mathcal{L}^{-1}\{F(s)\}$ and $\mathcal{L}^{-1}\{G(s)\}$ both exist, then
$\mathcal{L}^{-1}\{F(s) - G(s)\} = \mathcal{L}^{-1}\{F(s)\} - \mathcal{L}^{-1}\{G(s)\}$.

5. True or False: If $\mathcal{L}^{-1}\{F(s)\}$ and $\mathcal{L}^{-1}\{G(s)\}$ both exist, then
$\mathcal{L}^{-1}\{F(s)\,G(s)\} = \mathcal{L}^{-1}\{F(s)\}\,\mathcal{L}^{-1}\{G(s)\}$.

6. True or False: If $\mathcal{L}^{-1}\{F(s)\}$ exists, then $\mathcal{L}^{-1}\{4\,F(s)\} = 4\,\mathcal{L}^{-1}\{F(s)\}$.

7. True or False: If $\mathcal{L}^{-1}\{F(s)\}$ and $\mathcal{L}^{-1}\{G(s)\}$ both exist, then
$\mathcal{L}^{-1}\{F(s)/G(s)\} = \mathcal{L}^{-1}\{F(s)\}/\mathcal{L}^{-1}\{G(s)\}$.

8. True or False: Every function $F(s)$ has an inverse Laplace transform.

Problems 9-25:   Use Theorem 7.3 to determine the given inverse Laplace transform.

9. $\mathcal{L}^{-1}\left\{\dfrac{1}{s^4}\right\}$

10. $\mathcal{L}^{-1}\left\{\dfrac{(12 + s^2)}{s^7}\right\}$

11. $\mathcal{L}^{-1}\left\{\dfrac{1}{s - 4}\right\}$

12. $\mathcal{L}^{-1}\left\{\dfrac{1}{s + 5}\right\}$

13. $\mathcal{L}^{-1}\left\{\dfrac{1}{3s + 4}\right\}$

14. $\mathcal{L}^{-1}\left\{\dfrac{12}{s^2 + 36}\right\}$

15. $\mathcal{L}^{-1}\left\{\dfrac{2}{s^2 - 64}\right\}$

16. $\mathcal{L}^{-1}\left\{\dfrac{6s}{s^2 - 9}\right\}$

17. $\mathcal{L}^{-1}\left\{\dfrac{s}{s^2 - \pi^2}\right\}$

18. $\mathcal{L}^{-1}\left\{\dfrac{3s - 8}{s^2 + 16}\right\}$

19. $\mathcal{L}^{-1}\left\{\dfrac{3s - 8}{s^2 - 4}\right\}$

20. $\mathcal{L}^{-1}\left\{\dfrac{12}{s^2 - 4s}\right\}$

21. $\mathcal{L}^{-1}\left\{\dfrac{s^2 + 2s - 6}{s^3 - 3s^2}\right\}$

22. $\mathcal{L}^{-1}\left\{\dfrac{8}{s^2 - 2s - 3}\right\}$

23. $\mathcal{L}^{-1}\left\{\dfrac{32}{s^3 + 4s}\right\}$

24. $\mathcal{L}^{-1}\left\{\dfrac{s^2 + 6s + 9}{s^3 + 9s}\right\}$

25. $\mathcal{L}^{-1}\left\{\dfrac{s^3 + 9s - 30}{(s^2 + 4)(s^2 + 9)}\right\}$

Problems 26-32: Use the Laplace transform to solve the given initial value problem.

26. $y'' + 3y' = 30\,e^{2t}$, $y(0) = 5$, $y'(0) = 0$

27. $y'' + 4y = 8\,e^{2t}$, $y(0) = 0$, $y'(0) = 2$

28. $y'' - 9y = 25\cos 4t$, $y(0) = 0$, $y'(0) = -3$

29. $y'' + 4y' + 3y = 36\,t$, $y(0) = 0$, $y'(0) = 0$

30. $y'' + 4y' + 3y = 36\,t$, $y(0) = 2$, $y'(0) = -8$

31. $y''' - y'' - 2y' = 0$, $y(0) = 2$, $y'(0) = -1$, $y''(0) = 1$

32. $y''' + 9y' = 27$, $y(0) = 0$, $y'(0) = -3$, $y''(0) = 0$

1. True

2. False

3. False

4. True

5. False

6. True

7. False

8. False

9. $t^3/6$

10. $\dfrac{1}{60}\,t^6 + \dfrac{1}{24}\,t^4$

11. e^{4t}

12. e^{-5t}

13. $\dfrac{1}{3}\,e^{-4t/3}$

14. $2\sin 6t$

15. $\dfrac{1}{4}\,\sinh 8t$

16. $6\cosh 3t$

17. $\cosh \pi t$

18. $3\cos 4t - 2\sin 4t$

19. $3\cosh 2t - 4\sinh 2t$

20. $3\,e^{4t} - 3$

21. $2t + e^{3t}$

22. $2\,e^{3t} - 2\,e^{-t}$

23. $8 - 8\cos 2t$

24. $1 + 2\sin 3t$

25. $\cos 2t - 3\sin 2t + 2\sin 3t$

26. $y = 3\,e^{2t} + 2\,e^{-3t}$

27. $y = e^{2t} - \cos 2t$

28. $y = e^{-3t} - \cos 4t$

29. $y = 18\,e^{-t} - 2\,e^{-3t} - 16 + 12t$

30. $y = 17 e^{-t} + e^{-3t} - 16 + 12t$

31. $y = e^{-t} - 1$

32. $y = 3t - 2 \sin 3t$

1. basic concepts about 1st and 2nd translation theorems

2. basic concepts about 1st and 2nd translation theorems

3. basic concepts about 1st and 2nd translation theorems

4. basic concepts about 1st and 2nd translation theorems

5. basic concepts about 1st and 2nd translation theorems

6. basic concepts about 1st and 2nd translation theorems

7. basic concepts about 1st and 2nd translation theorems

8. using the 1st translation theorem

9. using the 1st translation theorem

10. using the 1st translation theorem

11. using the 1st translation theorem

12. using the 1st translation theorem

13. using the 1st translation theorem

14. using the 1st translation theorem

15. using the 2nd translation theorem

16. using the 2nd translation theorem

17. using the 1st and 2nd translation theorems

18. using the 1st and 2nd translation theorems

19. using the inverse of the 1st translation theorem

20. using the inverse of the 1st translation theorem

21. using the inverse of the 1st translation theorem

22. using the inverse of the 1st translation theorem

23. using the inverse of the 1st translation theorem

24. using the inverse of the 1st translation theorem

25. using the inverse of the 1st translation theorem

26. using the inverse of the 2nd translation theorem

27. using the inverse of the 2nd translation theorem

28. using the inverse of the 2nd translation theorem

29. using the inverse of the 2nd translation theorem

30. using the inverse of the 2nd translation theorem

31. using the inverse of the 2nd translation theorem

32. using the inverse of the 1st and 2nd translation theorems

33. using the inverse of the 1st and 2nd translation theorems

34. express a 2-piece function as a unit step function

35. express a 2-piece function as a unit step function

36. express a 2-piece function as a unit step function

37. Use Laplace transforms to solve a linear, homogeneous 2nd-order initial value problem

38. Use Laplace transforms to solve a linear 2nd-order initial value problem with exponential input function

39. Use Laplace transforms to solve a linear 2nd-order initial value problem with exponential input function

40. Use Laplace transforms to solve a linear 2nd-order initial value problem with exponential input function

41. Use Laplace transforms to solve a linear 2nd-order initial value problem with exponential input function

42. Use Laplace transforms to solve a linear 2nd-order initial value problem with exponential input function

43. Use Laplace transforms to solve a linear 1st-order initial value problem with 2-piece input function

44. Use Laplace transforms to solve a linear 1st-order initial value problem with 2-piece input function

45. Use Laplace transforms to solve a linear 1st-order initial value problem with 2-piece input function

46. Use Laplace transforms to solve a linear 1st-order initial value problem with 2-piece input function

1. If $F(s)$ contains an exponential of the form e^{ks}, then we should use

    (a) the 1st translation theorem to transform $F(s)$.

    (b) the inverse of the 1st translation theorem to transform $F(s)$.

    (c) the 2nd translation theorem to transform $F(s)$.

    (d) the inverse of the 2nd translation theorem to transform $F(s)$.

2. If $f(t)$ contains an exponential of the form e^{kt}, then we should use

    (a) the 1st translation theorem to transform $f(t)$.

    (b) the inverse of the 1st translation theorem to transform $f(t)$.

    (c) the 2nd translation theorem to transform $f(t)$.

    (d) the inverse of the 2nd translation theorem to transform $f(t)$.

3. If $f(t)$ contains a unit step function, then we should use

    (a) the 1st translation theorem to transform $f(t)$.

    (b) the inverse of the 1st translation theorem to transform $f(t)$.

    (c) the 2nd translation theorem to transform $f(t)$.

    (d) the inverse of the 2nd translation theorem to transform $f(t)$.

4. True or False: The 1st translation theorem produces an exponential.

5. True or False: The inverse of the 1st translation theorem produces an exponential.

6. True or False: The 2nd translation theorem produces an exponential.

7. True or False: The inverse of the 2nd translation theorem produces an exponential.

Problems 8-33: Evaluate the following transforms as indicated.

8. $\mathcal{L}\{t^5 e^{2t}\}$

9. $\mathcal{L}\{t^4 e^{-3t}\}$

10. $\mathcal{L}\{e^{3t}(t+2)^2\}$

11. $\mathcal{L}\{e^{2t}\cos 3t\}$

12. $\mathcal{L}\{e^{-3t}\sin 2t\}$

13. $\mathcal{L}\{e^{4t}\sin 6t \cos 6t\}$

14. $\mathcal{L}\{e^{5t}\cosh 2t\}$

15. $\mathcal{L}\{t^2 U(t-4)\}$

16. $\mathcal{L}\{4\,U(t-3)\}$

17. $\mathcal{L}\{e^{3t}\,U(t-2)\}$

18. $\mathcal{L}\{t\,e^{2t}\,U(t-5)\}$

19. $\mathcal{L}^{-1}\left\{\dfrac{12}{3s+18}\right\}$

20. $\mathcal{L}^{-1}\left\{\dfrac{s}{(s-3)^5}\right\}$

21. $\mathcal{L}^{-1}\left\{\dfrac{s-5}{(s-2)^2-25}\right\}$

22. $\mathcal{L}^{-1}\left\{\dfrac{s}{s^2-4s+20}\right\}$

23. $\mathcal{L}^{-1}\left\{\dfrac{s+4}{s^2-4s+13}\right\}$

24. $\mathcal{L}^{-1}\left\{\dfrac{2s}{s^2-8s+17}\right\}$

25. $\mathcal{L}^{-1}\left\{\dfrac{s-1}{s^2+6s+13}\right\}$

26. $\mathcal{L}^{-1}\left\{\dfrac{e^{-3s}}{s^5}\right\}$

27. $\mathcal{L}^{-1}\left\{\dfrac{e^{-2s}}{s(s+1)}\right\}$

28. $\mathcal{L}^{-1}\left\{\dfrac{s\,e^{-2s}}{s^2+16}\right\}$

29. $\mathcal{L}^{-1}\left\{\dfrac{6\,e^{-3s}}{s^2+4}\right\}$

30. $\mathcal{L}^{-1}\left\{\dfrac{12\,e^{-4s}}{s^2-9}\right\}$

31. $\mathcal{L}^{-1}\left\{\dfrac{s\,e^{-6s}}{s^2-\pi^2}\right\}$

32. $\mathcal{L}^{-1}\left\{\dfrac{12\,e^{-2s}}{(s-3)^2+16}\right\}$

33. $\mathcal{L}^{-1}\left\{\dfrac{e^{-4s}}{(s-3)^2}\right\}$

Problems 34-36: Write the following in terms of unit step functions.

34. $f(t) = \begin{cases} 0, & 0 \le t < 1 \\ 2, & t \ge 1 \end{cases}$

35. $f(t) = \begin{cases} -4, & 0 \le t < 2 \\ 4, & t \ge 2 \end{cases}$

36. $f(t) = \begin{cases} \cos t, & 0 \le t < 3 \\ t^2, & t \ge 3 \end{cases}$

Problems 37-46: Use Laplace transforms to solve the given initial value problem for $y(t)$.

37. $y'' + 16y = 0$, $y(0) = -1$, $y'(0) = 4$

38. $y'' + 10y' + 25y = t^3 e^{-5t}$, $y(0) = 1$, $y'(0) = -5$

39. $y'' - 8y' + 16y = t^2 e^{4t}$, $y(0) = 2$, $y'(0) = 8$

40. $y'' - 6y' + 9y = t^2 e^{3t}$, $y(0) = 1$, $y'(0) = 3$

41. $y'' - 2y' = e^{2t} \cos t$, $y(0) = 0$, $y'(0) = 0$

42. $y'' - 2y' = e^{2t}$, $y(0) = 2$, $y'(0) = 0$

43. $y' - 4y = 4U(t - 3)$, $y(0) = 3$

44. $y' + y = f(t)$, $y(0) = 1$, where $f(t) = \begin{cases} 0, & 0 \le t < 1 \\ 2, & t \ge 1 \end{cases}$

45. $y' + 2y = f(t)$, $y(0) = 1$, where $f(t) = \begin{cases} 0, & 0 \le t < 3 \\ 4, & t \ge 3 \end{cases}$

46. $y' + y = f(t)$, $y(0) = 2$, where $f(t) = \begin{cases} 2, & 0 \le t < 3 \\ -2, & t \ge 3 \end{cases}$

1. d

2. a

3. c

4. False

5. True

6. True

7. False

8. $\dfrac{120}{(s-2)^6}$

9. $\dfrac{24}{(s+3)^5}$

10. $\dfrac{2}{(s-3)^3} + \dfrac{4}{(s-3)^2} + \dfrac{4}{s-3}$

11. $\dfrac{s-2}{(s-2)^2+9}$

12. $\dfrac{2}{(s+3)^2+4}$

13. $\dfrac{6}{(s-4)^2+144}$

14. $\dfrac{s-5}{(s-5)^2-4}$

15. $e^{-4s}\left[\dfrac{2}{s^3} + \dfrac{8}{s^2} + \dfrac{16}{s}\right]$

16. $4\,e^{-3s}$

17. $\dfrac{e^{6-2s}}{s-3}$

18. $e^{-5(s-2)}\left[\dfrac{1}{(s-2)^2} + \dfrac{5}{s-2}\right]$

19. $4\,e^{-4t}$

20. $e^{3t}\left[\dfrac{1}{6}t^3 + \dfrac{1}{8}t^4\right]$

21. $e^{2t}\left(\cosh 5t - \dfrac{3}{5}\sinh 5t\right)$

22. $e^{2t}\left(\cos 4t + \dfrac{1}{2}\sin 4t\right)$

23. $e^{2t}\left(\cos 3t + 2\sin 3t\right)$

24. $e^{4t} (2 \cos t + 8 \sin t)$

25. $e^{-3t} (\cos 2t - 2 \sin 2t)$

26. $\dfrac{1}{24} (t-3)^4 \, U(t-3)$

27. $\left(e^{t-2} - 1 \right) U(t-2)$

28. $U(t-2) \, \cos[4(t-2)]$

29. $3 \, U(t-3) \, \sin[2(t-3)]$

30. $4 \, U(t-4) \, \sinh[3(t-4)]$

31. $U(t-6) \, \cosh[\pi(t-6)]$

32. $3 \, e^{3(t-2)} \, U(t-2) \, \sin[4(t-2)]$

33. $e^{3(t-4)} \, (t-4) \, U(t-4)$

34. $2 \, U(t-1)$

35. $-4 + 8 \, U(t-2)$

36. $\cos t - \cos t \, U(t-3) + t^2 \, U(t-3)$

37. $y(t) \;=\; \sin 4t - \cos 4t$

38. $y(t) \;=\; e^{-5t} \left[1 + \dfrac{1}{20} t^5 \right]$

39. $y(t) \;=\; e^{4t} \left[2 + \dfrac{1}{12} t^4 \right]$

40. $y(t) \;=\; e^{3t} \left[1 + \dfrac{1}{12} t^4 \right]$

41. $y(t) \;=\; \dfrac{1}{5} \left[1 + e^{2t} \left(2 \sin t - \cos t \right) \right]$

42. $y(t) \;=\; \dfrac{1}{4} \left[9 + e^{2t} \left(2t - 1 \right) \right]$

43. $y(t) \;=\; 3 \, e^{4t} + U(t-3) \left[e^{4(t-3)} - 1 \right]$

44. $y(t) \;=\; e^{-t} + 2 \, U(t-1) \left[1 - e^{-(t-1)} \right]$

45. $y(t) \;=\; e^{-2t} + 2 \, U(t-3) \left[1 - e^{-2(t-3)} \right]$

46. $y(t) \;=\; 2 + 4 \, U(t-3) \left[e^{-(t-3)} - 1 \right]$

1. understanding Theorem 7.8

2. understanding Theorem 7.8

3. understanding Theorem 7.8 and 1st translation theorem

4. identifying a convolution integral

5. identifying a convolution integral

6. understanding the convolution theorem

7. understanding the convolution theorem

8. understanding the convolution theorem

9. understanding the convolution theorem

10. identifying a convolution integral

11. understanding convolution

12. understanding the convolution theorem

13. understanding convolution

14. Use Theorem 7.8 to evaluate a Laplace transform.

15. Use Theorem 7.8 to evaluate a Laplace transform.

16. Use Theorem 7.8 to evaluate a Laplace transform.

17. Use Theorem 7.8 to evaluate a Laplace transform.

18. Evaluate the Laplace transform of a convolution.

19. Evaluate the Laplace transform of a convolution.

20. Evaluate the Laplace transform of a convolution.

21. Evaluate the Laplace transform of a convolution.

22. Evaluate the Laplace transform of a convolution.

23. Evaluate the Laplace transform of a convolution.

24. Evaluate the Laplace transform of a convolution.

25. Evaluate the Laplace transform of a convolution.

26. Evaluate the Laplace transform of an integral.

27. Evaluate the Laplace transform of an integral.

28. Evaluate the Laplace transform of an integral.

29. Evaluate the Laplace transform of an integral.

30. Evaluate the Laplace transform of a periodic function.

31. Evaluate the Laplace transform of a periodic function.

32. Evaluate the Laplace transform of a periodic function.

33. Evaluate the Laplace transform of a periodic function.

34. Use Laplace transforms to solve an integral equation.

35. Use Laplace transforms to solve an integral equation.

36. Use Laplace transforms to solve an integral equation.

37. Use Laplace transforms to solve an integral equation.

38. Use Laplace transforms to solve an integral equation.

39. Use Laplace transforms to solve an integro-differential equation.

40. Use Laplace transforms to solve an integro-differential equation.

41. Use Laplace transforms to solve an integro-differential equation.

42. Use Laplace transforms to solve an integro-differential equation.

1. The Laplace transform of a function of the form $t^4 f(t)$ requires finding

    (a) the 3rd derivative of $f(t)$.
    (b) the 4th derivative of $f(t)$.
    (c) the 3rd derivative of $F(s)$.
    (d) the 4th derivative of $F(s)$.

2. The Laplace transform of a function of the form $t^3 f(t)$ always generates

    (a) the exponential function e^{3s}.
    (b) the exponential function e^{-3s}.
    (c) the unit step function $U(t-3)$.
    (d) none of the above

3. To determine the Laplace transform of a function like $t^3 e^{2t}$, it is always easier to use

    (a) Theorem 7.8.
    (b) the 1st translation theorem.
    (c) the 2nd translation theorem.
    (d) the convolution theorem.

4. The integral $\displaystyle\int_0^t (t-\tau)^3 \cos\tau\, d\tau$ is the same as

    (a) $\displaystyle\int_0^t t^3 \cos(t-\tau)\, d\tau$.

    (b) $\displaystyle\int_0^t \tau \cos(t-\tau)^3\, d\tau$.

    (c) $\displaystyle\int_0^t \tau^3 \cos(t-\tau)\, d\tau$.

    (d) $\displaystyle\int_0^t t^3 \cos(t-\tau)\, d\tau$.

5. Which of the following integrals is a convolution?

    (a) $\displaystyle\int_0^t (t^3 - \tau^3) \sin\tau\, d\tau$.

    (b) $\displaystyle\int_0^t (t-\tau)^3 \sin(t-\tau)\, d\tau$.

    (c) $\displaystyle\int_0^t 2\,(\tau - t)^3 \sin\tau\, d\tau$.

    (d) $\displaystyle\int_0^t (2t - \tau) \sin(t-\tau)\, d\tau$.

6. True or False: $\mathcal{L}\{f(t) * g(t)\} = \mathcal{L}\{f(t)\} * \mathcal{L}\{g(t)\}$

7. True or False: $\mathcal{L}\{f(t)\, g(t)\} = \mathcal{L}\{f(t)\} * \mathcal{L}\{g(t)\}$

8. True or False: $\mathcal{L}^{-1}\{F(s)\,G(s)\} \;=\; \mathcal{L}^{-1}\{F(s)\} * \mathcal{L}^{-1}\{G(s)\}$

9. True or False: $\mathcal{L}^{-1}\{F(s)\,G(s)\} \;=\; \mathcal{L}^{-1}\{F(s)\}\,\mathcal{L}^{-1}\{G(s)\}$

10. True or False: All integrals may be viewed as convolutions.

11. True or False: The convolution of two functions is a transform.

12. True or False: The convolution theorem requires that we evaluate an integral.

13. True or False: Convolution is commutative.

Problems 14-17: Use Theorem 7.8 to evaluate the following transforms.

14. $\mathcal{L}\{t\,e^{3t}\}$

15. $\mathcal{L}\{t^2\,e^{4t}\}$

16. $\mathcal{L}\{t\,\cos 4t\}$

17. $\mathcal{L}\{t\,\cos 3t\}$

Problems 18-29: Evaluate the given transforms without integrating.

18. $\mathcal{L}\{2 * t^4\}$

19. $\mathcal{L}\{t^4 * e^{6t}\}$

20. $\mathcal{L}\{t^5 * \cos 3t\}$

21. $\mathcal{L}\{t^3 * \sinh 4t\}$

22. $\mathcal{L}\{e^{3t} * \sin 2t\}$

23. $\mathcal{L}\{e^{-2t} * \cos 4t\}$

24. $\mathcal{L}\{e^{2t} * \cosh 3t\}$

25. $\mathcal{L}\{e^{5t} * U(t-4)\}$

26. $\mathcal{L}\left\{ \displaystyle\int_0^t \sin 3\tau \, d\tau \right\}$

27. $\mathcal{L}\left\{ \displaystyle\int_0^t (t-\tau)^3 \, e^{-2\tau} \, d\tau \right\}$

28. $\mathcal{L}\left\{ \displaystyle\int_0^t (t-\tau)^4 \, \sin 3\tau \, d\tau \right\}$

29. $\mathcal{L}\left\{ \displaystyle\int_0^t \tau \, \cosh 2\tau \, d\tau \right\}$

30. The following represents one period (one wave) of a periodic function $f(t)$. Determine the Laplace transform of the periodic function $f(t)$. $\quad \begin{cases} 1, & 0 \le t < 2 \\ 0, & 2 \le t < 4 \end{cases}$

31. The following represents one period (one wave) of a periodic function $f(t)$. Determine the Laplace transform of the periodic function $f(t)$.
$$\begin{cases} -1, & 0 \le t < \pi \\ 1, & \pi \le t < 2\pi \end{cases}$$

32. The following represents one period (one wave) of a periodic function $f(t)$. Determine the Laplace transform of the periodic function $f(t)$.
$$\begin{cases} t, & 0 \le t < 1 \\ 0, & 1 \le t < 2 \end{cases}$$

33. The following represents one period (one wave) of a periodic function $f(t)$. Determine the Laplace transform of the periodic function $f(t)$.
$$\begin{cases} \cos t, & 0 \le t < \pi/2 \\ -\cos t, & \pi/2 \le t < \pi \end{cases}$$

Problems 34-38: Use Laplace transforms to solve the given integral equation for $f(t)$.

34. $f(t) + \displaystyle\int_0^t e^{3\tau} f(t - \tau) \, d\tau = e^{2t}$

35. $f(t) + \displaystyle\int_0^t e^{3\tau} f(t - \tau) \, d\tau = t e^{3t}$

36. $f(t) + 6 \displaystyle\int_0^t \sin 2\tau \, f(t - \tau) \, d\tau = 1$

37. $f(t) + \displaystyle\int_0^t f(\tau) \, d\tau = e^t$

38. $f(t) + \displaystyle\int_0^t f(\tau) \, d\tau = 4 + e^{-t}$

Problems 39-42: Use Laplace transforms to solve the given initial value problem for $y(t)$.

39. $y' + 8y + 16 \displaystyle\int_0^t y(\tau) \, d\tau = e^{-4t}, \quad y(0) = 1$

40. $y' + 2y + \displaystyle\int_0^t y(\tau) \, d\tau = t^2 e^{-t}, \quad y(0) = 2$

41. $y' + \displaystyle\int_0^t e^{2\tau} y(t - \tau) \, d\tau = e^t, \quad y(0) = 2$

42. $y' - 3y + \displaystyle\int_0^t (3 - \tau) y(t - \tau) \, d\tau = 0, \quad y(0) = 2$

1. d

2. d

3. b

4. c

5. c

6. False

7. False

8. True

9. False

10. False

11. False

12. False

13. True

14. $\dfrac{1}{(s-3)^2}$

15. $\dfrac{2}{(s-4)^3}$

16. $\dfrac{s^2-4}{(s^2+4)^2}$

17. $\dfrac{s^2+9}{(s^2-9)^2}$

18. $\dfrac{48}{s^6}$

19. $\dfrac{24}{s(s-6)}$

20. $\dfrac{120}{s^5(s^2+9)}$

21. $\dfrac{24}{s^4(s^2-16)}$

22. $\dfrac{2}{(s-3)(s^2+4)}$

23. $\dfrac{s}{(s+2)(s^2+16)}$

24. $\dfrac{s}{(s-2)(s^2-9)}$

25. $\dfrac{e^{-4s}}{s(s-5)}$

26. $\dfrac{3}{s(s^2+9)}$

27. $\dfrac{6}{s^4(s+2)}$

28. $\dfrac{72}{s^5(s^2+9)}$

29. $\dfrac{s^2+4}{s(s^2-4)^2}$

30. $\dfrac{1}{s(1+e^{-2s})}$

31. $\dfrac{1+e^{-\pi s}}{s(e^{-\pi s}-1)}$

32. $\dfrac{1-e^{-s}-se^{-s}}{s^2(1-e^{-2s})}$

33. $\dfrac{s+2e^{-\pi s/2}-se^{-\pi s}}{(s^2+1)(1-e^{-\pi s})}$

34. $f(t) = e^{2t}(1-t)$

35. $f(t) = e^{3t}-e^{2t}$

36. $f(t) = \dfrac{1}{4}+\dfrac{3}{4}\cos 4t$

37. $f(t) = \cosh t$

38. $f(t) = (5-t)e^{-t}$

39. $y = (1-3t-2t^2)e^{-4t}$

40. $y = \left[\dfrac{1}{3}t^3 - \dfrac{1}{12}t^4 + 2 - 2t\right]e^{-t}$

41. $y = e^t\left[2-t-\dfrac{1}{2}t^2\right]$

42. $y = e^t\left[2+4t+t^2\right]$

1. properties of the Dirac Delta function

2. properties of the Dirac Delta function

3. properties of the Dirac Delta function

4. properties of the Dirac Delta function

5. properties of the Dirac Delta function

6. properties of the Dirac Delta function

7. Laplace transform of a Dirac Delta function

8. Laplace transform of a Dirac Delta function

9. Laplace transform of a Dirac Delta function

10. Laplace transform of a Dirac Delta function

11. Laplace transform of a Dirac Delta function

12. Laplace transform of a Dirac Delta function

13. Laplace transform of a Dirac Delta function

14. inverse Laplace transform of a Dirac Delta function

15. inverse Laplace transform of a Dirac Delta function

16. inverse Laplace transform of a Dirac Delta function

17. integral of a Dirac Delta function

18. integral of a Dirac Delta function

19. Use Laplace transforms to solve a 1st-order initial value problem with a Dirac Delta function.

20. Use Laplace transforms to solve a 1st-order initial value problem with a Dirac Delta function.

21. Use Laplace transforms to solve a 2nd-order initial value problem with a Dirac Delta function.

22. Use Laplace transforms to solve a 2nd-order initial value problem with a Dirac Delta function.

23. Use Laplace transforms to solve a 2nd-order initial value problem with a Dirac Delta function.

24. Use Laplace transforms to solve a 2nd-order initial value problem with a Dirac Delta function.

25. Use Laplace transforms to solve a 2nd-order initial value problem with two Dirac Delta functions.

26. Use Laplace transforms to solve a 2nd-order initial value problem with two Dirac Delta functions.

27. Use Laplace transforms to solve a 3rd-order initial value problem with a Dirac Delta function.

1. The Dirac Delta function satisfies

   (a) $\dfrac{d}{dt}\Big[\delta(t - t_0)\Big] = 1.$

   (b) $\dfrac{d}{dt}\Big[\delta(t - t_0)\Big] = t_0.$

   (c) $\displaystyle\int_0^\infty \delta(t - t_0)\, dt = 1.$

   (d) $\displaystyle\int_0^\infty \delta(t - t_0)\, dt = t_0.$

2. The Dirac Delta function satisfies

   (a) $\mathcal{L}\{\delta(t)\} = 1.$
   (b) $\mathcal{L}\{\delta(t)\} = 0.$
   (c) $\mathcal{L}^{-1}\{\delta(t)\} = 1.$
   (d) $\mathcal{L}^{-1}\{\delta(t)\} = 0.$

3. The Dirac Delta function satisfies

   (a) $\mathcal{L}\{0\} = \delta(t).$
   (b) $\mathcal{L}\{1\} = \delta(t).$
   (c) $\mathcal{L}^{-1}\{1\} = \delta(t).$
   (d) $\mathcal{L}^{-1}\{0\} = \delta(t).$

4. If f is a continuous function, then

   (a) $\displaystyle\int_0^\infty \delta(t - a)\, f(t)\, dt \;=\; 1.$

   (b) $\displaystyle\int_0^\infty \delta(t - a)\, f(t)\, dt \;=\; 0.$

   (c) $\displaystyle\int_0^\infty \delta(t - a)\, f(t)\, dt \;=\; f(t).$

   (d) $\displaystyle\int_0^\infty \delta(t - a)\, f(t)\, dt \;=\; f(a).$

5. $\mathcal{L}\{\delta(t - 3)\}$ equals

   (a) $e^{-3s}.$

   (b) $e^{3s}.$

   (c) $\dfrac{1}{s}\, e^{-3s}.$

   (d) $\dfrac{1}{s}\, e^{3s}.$

6. The Dirac Delta function may be used to represent

   (a) a finite constant force applied over any time period.
   (b) a finite constant force applied over a finite time period.
   (c) a finite constant force applied over an infinitesimal time period.
   (d) an infinite force applied over an infinitesimal time period.

199

Problems 7-18: Evaluate the following.

7. $\mathcal{L}\{\delta(t-3)\}$

8. $\mathcal{L}\{2\,\delta(t)\}$

9. $\mathcal{L}\{e^{2t}\,\delta(t-4)\}$

10. $\mathcal{L}\{t\,\delta(t-5)\}$

11. $\mathcal{L}\{t^2\,\delta(t-3)\}$

12. $\mathcal{L}\{t^3\,\delta(t-2)\}$

13. $\mathcal{L}\{t^n\,\delta(t-a)\}$ where n is a positive integer

14. $\mathcal{L}^{-1}\{3\}$

15. $\mathcal{L}^{-1}\{4\,e^{-2s}\}$

16. $\mathcal{L}^{-1}\{6\,e^{-3s}\}$

17. $\displaystyle\int_0^\infty t^3\,\delta(t-5)\,dt$

18. $\displaystyle\int_0^\infty \delta(t-3\pi)\,\cos t\,dt$

Problems 19-27: Use Laplace transforms to solve the given initial value problem for $y(t)$.

19. $y' + 4y = \delta(t-2)$, $y(0) = 0$

20. $y' - 3y = \delta(t-2)$, $y(0) = 1$

21. $y'' - 6y' + 9y = 4\,\delta(t-2)$, $y(0) = 1$, $y'(0) = 3$

22. $y'' - 8y' + 16y = 2\,\delta(t-3)$, $y(0) = 1$, $y'(0) = -8$

23. $y'' + 9y = 6\,\delta(t-2)$, $y(0) = -1$, $y'(0) = 3$

24. $y'' - 4y = 10\,\delta(t-3)$, $y(0) = 1$, $y'(0) = 4$

25. $y'' - 4y = 2\,\delta(t-1) + 6\,\delta(t-3)$, $y(0) = 1$, $y'(0) = 0$

26. $y'' - 4y = 2\,\delta(t-1) + 6\,\delta(t-3)$, $y(0) = 0$, $y'(0) = 4$

27. $y''' - 3y'' + 3y' - y = 4\,\delta(t-2)$, $y(0) = 0$, $y'(0) = 3$, $y''(0) = 6$

1. c

2. a

3. c

4. d

5. a

6. c

7. e^{-3s}

8. 2

9. $e^{-4(s-2)}$

10. $5\,e^{-5s}$

11. $9\,e^{-3s}$

12. $8\,e^{-2s}$

13. $a^n\,e^{-as}$

14. $3\,\delta(t)$

15. $4\,\delta(t-2)$

16. $6\,\delta(t-3)$

17. 125

18. -1

19. $y = e^{-4(t-1)}\,\mathcal{U}(t-1)$

20. $y = \left[1+\mathcal{U}(t-2)\right]e^{3(t-2)}$

21. $y = e^{3t} + 4\,(t-2)\,e^{3(t-2)}\,\mathcal{U}(t-2)$

22. $y = e^{4t}\,(1-12t) + 2\,(t-3)\,e^{4(t-3)}\,\mathcal{U}(t-3)$

23. $y = \sin 3t - \cos 3t + 2\,\mathcal{U}(t-2)\,\sin[3(t-2)]$

24. $y = \cosh 2t + 2\,\sinh 2t + 5\,\mathcal{U}(t-3)\,\sinh[2(t-3)]$

25. $y = \cosh 2t + \mathcal{U}(t-1)\,\sinh[2(t-1)] + 3\,\mathcal{U}(t-3)\,\sinh[2(t-2)]$

26. $y = 2\,\sinh 2t + \mathcal{U}(t-1)\,\sinh[2(t-1)] + 3\,\mathcal{U}(t-3)\,\sinh[2(t-2)]$

27. $y = 3\,t\,e^{t} + 2\,(t-2)^2\,e^{t-2}\,\mathcal{U}(t-2)$

1. Use Laplace transforms to solve a system of linear 1st-order homogeneous DEs.

2. Use Laplace transforms to solve a system of linear 1st-order homogeneous DEs.

3. Use Laplace transforms to solve a system of linear 1st-order homogeneous DEs.

4. Use Laplace transforms to solve a system of linear 1st-order homogeneous DEs.

5. Use Laplace transforms to solve a system of linear 1st-order homogeneous DEs.

6. Use Laplace transforms to solve a system of linear 1st-order homogeneous DEs.

7. Use Laplace transforms to solve a system of linear 1st-order homogeneous DEs.

8. Use Laplace transforms to solve a system of linear 1st-order homogeneous DEs.

9. Use Laplace transforms to solve a system of linear 1st-order homogeneous DEs.

10. Use Laplace transforms to solve a system of linear 1st-order homogeneous DEs.

11. Use Laplace transforms to solve a system of linear 2nd-order homogeneous DEs.

12. Use Laplace transforms to solve a system of linear 2nd-order homogeneous DEs.

13. Use Laplace transforms to solve a system of linear 2nd-order homogeneous DEs.

14. Use Laplace transforms to solve a system of linear 2nd-order homogeneous DEs.

15. Use Laplace transforms to solve a system of linear 2nd-order homogeneous DEs.

16. Use Laplace transforms to solve a system of linear 2nd-order homogeneous DEs.

17. Use Laplace transforms to solve a system governing a coupled spring apparatus.

18. Use Laplace transforms to solve a system governing a coupled spring apparatus.

19. Use Laplace transforms to solve a system governing a coupled spring apparatus.

20. Use Laplace transforms to solve a system governing an electrical network.

21. Use Laplace transforms to solve a system governing an electrical network.

22. Use Laplace transforms to solve a system governing an electrical network.

Problems 1-16: Use Laplace transforms to solve the given system of differential equations.

1. $\dfrac{dx}{dt} = 5x + 4y$, $\dfrac{dy}{dt} = -x$, $x(0) = 0$, $y(0) = 3$

2. $\dfrac{dx}{dt} = 2y$, $\dfrac{dy}{dt} = 2x + 3y$, $x(0) = -2$, $y(0) = 1$

3. $\dfrac{dx}{dt} = 6x - 2y$, $\dfrac{dy}{dt} = x + 3y$, $x(0) = 2$, $y(0) = 1$

4. $\dfrac{dx}{dt} = 8x + y$, $\dfrac{dy}{dt} = 7x + 2y$, $x(0) = 0$, $y(0) = 8$

5. $\dfrac{dx}{dt} = 8x + 3y$, $\dfrac{dy}{dt} = 5x + 6y$, $x(0) = 8$, $y(0) = 0$

6. $\dfrac{dx}{dt} = 3x - 2y$, $\dfrac{dy}{dt} = 2x - y$, $x(0) = 1$, $y(0) = 0$

7. $\dfrac{dx}{dt} = 5x + 4y$, $\dfrac{dy}{dt} = -x + y$, $x(0) = 1$, $y(0) = -1$

8. $\dfrac{dx}{dt} = 3y + 16\,e^{3t}$, $\dfrac{dy}{dt} = x + 2y$, $x(0) = 0$, $y(0) = 0$

9. $\dfrac{dx}{dt} = 3y + 10\,e^{2t}$, $\dfrac{dy}{dt} = 3x$, $x(0) = 0$, $y(0) = 0$

10. $\dfrac{dx}{dt} = 2y$, $\dfrac{dy}{dt} = 8x + 24\,e^{-2t}$, $x(0) = 0$, $y(0) = 0$

11. $\dfrac{d^2x}{dt^2} + 2y = 0$, $\dfrac{d^2y}{dt^2} + 8x = 0$,
    $x(0) = 0$, $x'(0) = 4$, $y(0) = 0$, $y'(0) = 0$

12. $\dfrac{d^2x}{dt^2} + 16\dfrac{dy}{dt} + 9x = 0$, $\dfrac{dx}{dt} + 25y = 0$,
    $x(0) = 5$, $x'(0) = -9$, $y(0) = 0$

13. $\dfrac{d^2x}{dt^2} - 8x + 24y = 0$, $3\dfrac{d^2y}{dt^2} - 2x = 0$,
    $x(0) = 1$, $x'(0) = 0$, $y(0) = 0$, $y'(0) = 0$

14. $\dfrac{d^2x}{dt^2} + \dfrac{dy}{dt} - 4x = 0$, $\dfrac{dy}{dt} - 8x = 0$,
    $x(0) = 1$, $x'(0) = -2$, $y(0) = 0$

15. $D^2y + 6\,Dx = 0$, $(D+1)x + (D-1)y = 0$,
    $x(0) = 1$, $y(0) = 0$, $y'(0) = 0$

16. $(D^2 + 9)\,x + 16\,Dy = 225\,t$, $Dx + 25\,y = 0$,
    $x(0) = 0$, $x'(0) = 0$, $y(0) = 0$

17. A coupled spring is governed by the system

$$2x_1'' = -8x_1 + 4(x_2 - x_1),$$
$$x_2'' = -4(x_2 - x_1),$$

subject to the initial conditions

$$x_1(0) = 0, \qquad x_1'(0) = 1, \qquad x_2(0) = 0, \qquad x_2'(0) = 0.$$

Use Laplace transforms to solve the system.

18. A coupled spring is governed by the system

$$2x_1'' = -8x_1 + 4(x_2 - x_1),$$
$$x_2'' = -4(x_2 - x_1),$$

subject to the initial conditions

$$x_1(0) = 0, \qquad x_1'(0) = 1, \qquad x_2(0) = 0, \qquad x_2'(0) = -1.$$

Use Laplace transforms to solve the system.

19. A coupled spring is governed by the system

$$2x_1'' = -4x_1 + 2(x_2 - x_1),$$
$$x_2'' = -2(x_2 - x_1),$$

subject to the initial conditions

$$x_1(0) = 0, \qquad x_1'(0) = 4, \qquad x_2(0) = 0, \qquad x_2'(0) = -4.$$

Use Laplace transforms to solve the system.

20. An electrical network is governed by the system

$$L\frac{di_1}{dt} + Ri_i = E(t),$$
$$RC\frac{di_2}{dt} + i_2 - i_1 = 0,$$

subject to the initial conditions with $E(t) = 0$ V, $L = 1$ h, $R = 4$ Ω, $C = 0.01$ f, and initial currents $i_1(0) = 3$ and $i_2(0) = 0$. Use Laplace transforms to solve the system.

21. An electrical network is governed by the system

$$L\frac{di_1}{dt} + Ri_i = E(t),$$
$$RC\frac{di_2}{dt} + i_2 - i_1 = 0,$$

subject to the initial conditions with $E(t) = 60$ V, $L = 1$ h, $R = 4$ Ω, $C = 0.01$ f, and initial currents $i_1(0) = 3$ and $i_2(0) = 0$. Use Laplace transforms to solve the system.

22. An electrical network is governed by the system

$$L\frac{di_1}{dt} + Ri_i = E(t),$$
$$RC\frac{di_2}{dt} + i_2 - i_1 = 0,$$

with $E(t) = 30$ V, $L = 4$ h, $R = 8$ Ω, $C = 0.01$ f, and initial currents $i_1(0) = 3$ and $i_2(0) = 0$. Use Laplace transforms to solve the system.

1. $x = -4e^t + 4e^{4t}, \qquad y = 4e^t - e^{4t}$

2. $x = = 2e^{-t} + 2e^{4t}, \qquad y = e^{-t} + 4e^{4t}$

3. $x = 2e^{5t}, \qquad y = e^{5t}$

4. $x = -e^t + e^{9t}, \qquad y = 7e^t + e^{9t}$

5. $x = 5e^{11t} + 3e^{3t}, \qquad y = 5e^{11t} - 5e^{3t}$

6. $x = (1 + 2t)\,e^t, \qquad y = 2t\,e^t$

7. $x = (1 - 2t)\,e^{3t}, \qquad y = (t - 1)\,e^{3t}$

8. $x = (4t + 3)\,e^{3t} - 3e^{-t}, \qquad y = (4t - 1)\,e^{3t} + e^{-t}$

9. $x = -e^{-3t} + 5e^{3t} - 4e^{2t}, \qquad y = e^{-3t} + 5e^{3t} - 6e^{2t}$

10. $x = e^{4t} + 3e^{-4t} - 4e^{-2t}, \qquad y = 2e^{4t} - 6e^{-4t} + 4e^{2t}$

11. $x = \sin 2t + \sinh 2t, \qquad y = 2\sin 2t - 2\sinh 2t$

12. $x = 5\cos 5t - 5\sin 5t, \qquad y = \cos 5t + \sin 5t$

13. $x = \cosh 2t + t\,\sinh 2t, \qquad y = \dfrac{1}{6}\,t\,\sinh 2t$

14. $x = \cos 2t - \sin 2t, \qquad y = 4\cos 2t + 4\sin 2t - 4$

15. $x = 1 + e^{2t} - e^{3t}, \qquad y = 1 - 3e^{2t} + 2e^{3t}$

16. $x = 25\,t - 5\sin 5t, \qquad y = \cos 5t - 1$

17. $x_1 = \dfrac{\sqrt{2}}{6}\left[\sin(\sqrt{2}t) + \sin(2\sqrt{2}t)\right], \qquad x_2 = \dfrac{\sqrt{2}}{6}\left[2\sin(\sqrt{2}t) - \sin(2\sqrt{2}t)\right]$

18. $x_1 = \dfrac{\sqrt{2}}{4}\,\sin(2\sqrt{2}t), \qquad x_2 = -\dfrac{\sqrt{2}}{4}\,\sin(2\sqrt{2}t)$

19. $x_1 = 2\sin 2t, \qquad x_2 = -2\sin 2t$

20. $i_1 = 4e^{-5t} - e^{-20t}, \qquad i_2 = 5e^{-5t} - 5e^{-20t}$

21. $i_1 = 15 - 12e^{-5t}, \qquad i_2 = 15 - 15e^{-5t}$

22. $i_1 = \dfrac{3}{4}\left(5 - e^{-10t}\right), \qquad i_2 = \dfrac{15}{4}\left(1 - e^{-10t}\right)$

8.1 Linear 1-st Order Systems — Preliminary Theory   Subject Correlation Guide

1. uniqueness of solutions

2. classifying a system

3. classifying a system

4. superposition principle

5. superposition principle

6. interpretation of the Wronskian

7. interpretation of the Wronskian

8. interpretation of the Wronskian

9. general solution of a system — superposition

10. general solution of a system — superposition

11. meaning of a fundamental set of solutions

12. meaning of a fundamental set of solutions

13. meaning of a fundamental set of solutions

14. write a system in matrix form

15. write a system in matrix form

16. write a system in matrix form

17. write a system in matrix form

18. write a system in matrix form

19. write a system in equation form

20. write a system in equation form

21. (a-g) Verify that vector $\mathbf{X}$ is a solution of the given system.

22. (a-e) Verify that the given vector solutions form a fundamental set of solutions.

23. (a-e) Verify that vector $\mathbf{X}_p$ is a particular solution of the given system.

1. The initial value problem $\mathbf{X}' = \mathbf{A}(t)\mathbf{X} + \mathbf{F}(t)$, $\mathbf{X}(t_0) = \mathbf{X}_0$ has a unique solution on interval I containing t_0 provided

   (a) $\mathbf{A}(t)$ is continuous on I.

   (b) $\mathbf{F}(t)$ is continuous on I.

   (c) $\mathbf{A}(t)$ and $\mathbf{F}(t)$ are continuous on I.

   (d) $\mathbf{A}(t)$ and $\mathbf{F}(t)$ have at most finitely many discontinuities on I.

2. The system $\mathbf{X}' = \mathbf{A}\mathbf{X}$ is called

   (a) autonomous.

   (b) non autonomous.

   (c) homogeneous.

   (d) non homogeneous.

3. The system $\mathbf{X}' = \mathbf{A}\mathbf{X} + \mathbf{F}$ is called

   (a) autonomous.

   (b) non autonomous.

   (c) homogeneous.

   (d) non homogeneous.

4. If vectors $\mathbf{X}_1$ and $\mathbf{X}_2$ are solutions of the system $\mathbf{X}' = \mathbf{A}\mathbf{X}$, then the sum $\mathbf{X} = \mathbf{X}_1 + \mathbf{X}_2$

   (a) is a solution.

   (b) might be a solution.

   (c) cannot be a solution.

   (d) might be a solution for suitable initial conditions.

5. If vectors $\mathbf{X}_1$ and $\mathbf{X}_2$ are solutions of the system $\mathbf{X}' = \mathbf{A}\mathbf{X} + \mathbf{F}$, then the sum $\mathbf{X} = \mathbf{X}_1 + \mathbf{X}_2$

   (a) is a solution.

   (b) might be a solution.

   (c) cannot be a solution.

   (d) might be a solution for suitable initial conditions.

6. If $\mathbf{X}_1, \mathbf{X}_2, \ldots, \mathbf{X}_n$ are solution vectors of the system $\mathbf{X}' = \mathbf{A}\mathbf{X}$ of n differential equations on interval I, then $W(\mathbf{X}_1, \mathbf{X}_2, \ldots, \mathbf{X}_n)$

   (a) cannot be zero anywhere on I.

   (b) might be zero somewhere on I.

   (c) must be zero everywhere on I.

   (d) must be zero somewhere on I.

7. If $\mathbf{X}_1, \mathbf{X}_2, \ldots, \mathbf{X}_{10}$ are solution vectors of the system $\mathbf{X}' = \mathbf{AX}$ of 9 differential equations on interval I, then $W(\mathbf{X}_1, \mathbf{X}_2, \ldots, \mathbf{X}_{10})$

   (a) cannot be zero anywhere on I.

   (b) might be zero somewhere on I.

   (c) must be zero everywhere on I.

   (d) must be zero somewhere on I.

8. If $\mathbf{X}_1, \mathbf{X}_2, \ldots, \mathbf{X}_n$ are linearly independent solution vectors of the system $\mathbf{X}' = \mathbf{AX}$ of n differential equations on interval I, then $W(\mathbf{X}_1, \mathbf{X}_2, \ldots, \mathbf{X}_n)$

   (a) cannot be zero anywhere on I.

   (b) might be zero somewhere on I.

   (c) must be zero everywhere on I.

   (d) must be zero somewhere on I.

9. If $\mathbf{X}_1, \mathbf{X}_2, \ldots, \mathbf{X}_n$ are linearly independent solution vectors of the system $\mathbf{X}' = \mathbf{AX}$ of n differential equations on interval I, then the general solution is

   (a) $\mathbf{X} = \mathbf{X}_1 + \mathbf{X}_2 + \cdots + \mathbf{X}_n$.

   (b) $\mathbf{X} = \mathbf{C}_1\mathbf{X}_1 + \mathbf{C}_2\mathbf{X}_2 + \cdots + \mathbf{C}_n\mathbf{X}_n$ where $\mathbf{C}_1, \mathbf{C}_2, \ldots, \mathbf{C}_n$ are arbitrary constant vectors.

   (c) $\mathbf{X} = c_1\mathbf{X}_1 + c_2\mathbf{X}_2 + \cdots + c_n\mathbf{X}_n$ where $c_1, c_2, \ldots, c_n$ are arbitrary constants.

   (d) $\mathbf{X} = W(\mathbf{X}_1, \mathbf{X}_2, \ldots, \mathbf{X}_n)$.

10. If $\mathbf{X}_1, \mathbf{X}_2, \ldots, \mathbf{X}_n$ are linearly independent solution vectors of the system $\mathbf{X}' = \mathbf{AX}$ of n differential equations on interval I, and $\mathbf{Y}$ is a solution of the system $\mathbf{X}' = \mathbf{AX} + \mathbf{F}$ on I, then the general solution of the system $\mathbf{X}' = \mathbf{AX} + \mathbf{F}$ is

   (a) $\mathbf{X} = \mathbf{X}_1 + \mathbf{X}_2 + \cdots + \mathbf{X}_n + \mathbf{Y}$.

   (b) $\mathbf{X} = \mathbf{X}_1 + \mathbf{X}_2 + \cdots + \mathbf{X}_n + c\mathbf{Y}$.

   (c) $\mathbf{X} = c_1\mathbf{X}_1 + c_2\mathbf{X}_2 + \cdots + c_n\mathbf{X}_n + c\mathbf{Y}$ where $c, c_1, c_2, \ldots, c_n$ are arbitrary constants.

   (d) $\mathbf{X} = c_1\mathbf{X}_1 + c_2\mathbf{X}_2 + \cdots + c_n\mathbf{X}_n + \mathbf{Y}$ where $c_1, c_2, \ldots, c_n$ are arbitrary constants.

11. True or False: Every system $\mathbf{X}' = \mathbf{AX}$ of n differential equations has n linearly independent solution vectors $\mathbf{X}_1, \mathbf{X}_2, \ldots, \mathbf{X}_n$.

12. True or False: Every system $\mathbf{X}' = \mathbf{AX} + \mathbf{F}$ of n differential equations has n linearly independent solution vectors $\mathbf{X}_1, \mathbf{X}_2, \ldots, \mathbf{X}_n$.

13. True or False: If $\mathbf{X}_1, \mathbf{X}_2, \ldots, \mathbf{X}_n$ are linearly independent solution vectors of $\mathbf{X}' = \mathbf{AX}$ on interval I, then $W(\mathbf{X}_1, \mathbf{X}_2, \ldots, \mathbf{X}_n) = 0$ at every t on I.

Problems 14-18: Write the linear system in matrix form. Also state whether the system is homogeneous or nonhomogeneous.

14. $\dfrac{dx}{dt} = 4x - 3y, \qquad \dfrac{dy}{dt} = 2x + 7y$

15. $\dfrac{dx}{dt} = 6y + 4x, \qquad \dfrac{dy}{dt} = 3x - 8y$

16. $\dfrac{dx}{dt} = 2x + 9y + 5e^{-t}, \qquad \dfrac{dy}{dt} = -x + 3y - \cos 2t$

17. $\dfrac{dx}{dt} = 9x + 5y - z, \qquad \dfrac{dy}{dt} = 2x - 3y + 4z, \qquad \dfrac{dz}{dt} = 5x + 7z$

18. $\dfrac{dx}{dt} = 5x - y + 2z + t^2, \qquad \dfrac{dy}{dt} = 3x + 8z - \sin 3t, \qquad \dfrac{dz}{dt} = 6x + 4y - 2z + e^{-4t}$

Problems 19-20: Write the system without the use of matrices. Also state whether the system is homogeneous or nonhomogeneous.

19. $\mathbf{X}' = \begin{pmatrix} 7 & -3 \\ 2 & 5 \end{pmatrix} \mathbf{X} + e^{-2t} \begin{pmatrix} 8 \\ 3t \end{pmatrix}$

20. $\mathbf{X}' = \begin{pmatrix} -7 & 3 & 0 \\ 4 & -8 & 2 \\ 0 & 5 & -1 \end{pmatrix} \mathbf{X} + \begin{pmatrix} 9 \\ -1 \\ 2 \end{pmatrix} t + \begin{pmatrix} 0 \\ 5 \\ 8 \end{pmatrix} \cos 2t$

21. In the following problems, verify that the vector $\mathbf{X}$ is a solution of the given system.

(a) $\dfrac{dx}{dt} = 4x - y, \qquad \dfrac{dy}{dt} = 2x + y, \qquad \mathbf{X} = \begin{pmatrix} 1 \\ 2 \end{pmatrix} e^{2t}$

(b) $\dfrac{dx}{dt} = -x + 6y, \qquad \dfrac{dy}{dt} = x - 2y, \qquad \mathbf{X} = \begin{pmatrix} 2 \\ -1 \end{pmatrix} e^{-4t}$

(c) $\dfrac{dx}{dt} = 2x + 5y, \qquad \dfrac{dy}{dt} = 3x + 4y, \qquad \mathbf{X} = \begin{pmatrix} -3 \\ 5 \end{pmatrix} e^{-t}$

(d) $\dfrac{dx}{dt} = 3x - 10y, \qquad \dfrac{dy}{dt} = 2x - 5y, \qquad \mathbf{X} = \begin{pmatrix} 5\cos 2t \\ 2\cos 2t + \sin 2t \end{pmatrix} e^{-t}$

(e) $\mathbf{X}' = \begin{pmatrix} 0 & 1 \\ -6 & 5 \end{pmatrix} \mathbf{X}, \qquad \mathbf{X} = \begin{pmatrix} 1 \\ 3 \end{pmatrix} e^{3t}$

(f) $\mathbf{X}' = \begin{pmatrix} 7 & -6 \\ 15 & -11 \end{pmatrix} \mathbf{X}, \qquad \mathbf{X} = \begin{pmatrix} 2\cos 3t \\ 3\cos 3t + \sin 3t \end{pmatrix} e^{-2t}$

(g) $\mathbf{X}' = \begin{pmatrix} 0 & -1 & -1 \\ 1 & 2 & 1 \\ 2 & 1 & 3 \end{pmatrix} \mathbf{X}, \qquad \mathbf{X} = \begin{pmatrix} 1 - t \\ t - 1 \\ t \end{pmatrix} e^{2t}$

22. In the following problems, the given vectors are solutions of the system $\mathbf{X}' = \mathbf{AX}$. Determine whether the vectors form a fundamental set of solutions.

(a) $\mathbf{X}_1 = \begin{pmatrix} 2 \\ -1 \end{pmatrix} e^{-t}, \qquad \mathbf{X}_2 = \begin{pmatrix} 3 \\ 7 \end{pmatrix} e^{2t}$

(b) $\mathbf{X}_1 = \begin{pmatrix} 1 \\ 4 \end{pmatrix} e^{t}, \qquad \mathbf{X}_2 = \begin{pmatrix} 8 \\ 3 \end{pmatrix} t e^{t}$

(c) $\mathbf{X}_1 = \begin{pmatrix} 2 \\ -5 \\ 3 \end{pmatrix} e^{t}, \qquad \mathbf{X}_2 = \begin{pmatrix} 4 \\ 0 \\ 7 \end{pmatrix} e^{-t}, \qquad \mathbf{X}_3 = \begin{pmatrix} -1 \\ 4 \\ 2 \end{pmatrix} e^{t}$

(d) $\mathbf{X}_1 = \begin{pmatrix} 5 \\ 2 \\ -3 \end{pmatrix} e^{2t}, \qquad \mathbf{X}_2 = \begin{pmatrix} 7 \\ 1 \\ 4 \end{pmatrix} t e^{2t}, \qquad \mathbf{X}_3 = \begin{pmatrix} 6 \\ 0 \\ 9 \end{pmatrix} e^{-t}$

209

(e) $\mathbf{X}_1 = \begin{pmatrix} 6 \\ 12 \\ -3 \end{pmatrix} e^{2t}, \qquad \mathbf{X}_2 = \begin{pmatrix} 4 \\ 11 \\ 4 \end{pmatrix} t e^{2t}, \qquad \mathbf{X}_3 = \begin{pmatrix} -2 \\ 0 \\ 9 \end{pmatrix} e^{-t}$

23. In the following problems, verify that the given vector $\mathbf{X}_p$ is a particular solution of the given system.

(a) $\mathbf{X}' = \begin{pmatrix} 0 & 1 \\ -6 & 5 \end{pmatrix} \mathbf{X} + \begin{pmatrix} 1 \\ 6 \end{pmatrix} e^t, \qquad \mathbf{X}_p = \begin{pmatrix} 1 \\ 3 \end{pmatrix} e^t$

(b) $\mathbf{X}' = \begin{pmatrix} 10 & 32 \\ 4 & 2 \end{pmatrix} \mathbf{X} + \begin{pmatrix} 40 \\ 20 \end{pmatrix} e^{-2t}, \qquad \mathbf{X}_p = \begin{pmatrix} -6 \\ 1 \end{pmatrix} e^{-2t}$

(c) $\mathbf{X}' = \begin{pmatrix} -1 & -4 \\ -2 & 1 \end{pmatrix} \mathbf{X} + \begin{pmatrix} 9t \\ 36 \end{pmatrix}, \qquad \mathbf{X}_p = \begin{pmatrix} 15 \\ -4 \end{pmatrix} + \begin{pmatrix} 1 \\ 2 \end{pmatrix} t$

(d) $\mathbf{X}' = \begin{pmatrix} -1 & 2 \\ 4 & 1 \end{pmatrix} \mathbf{X} + \begin{pmatrix} 18 e^{3t} \\ 9t \end{pmatrix}, \qquad \mathbf{X}_p = \begin{pmatrix} -2t \\ -1-t \end{pmatrix} + \begin{pmatrix} 2 \\ -2 \end{pmatrix} e^{3t} + \begin{pmatrix} 6 \\ 12 \end{pmatrix} t e^{3t}$

(e) $\mathbf{X}' = \begin{pmatrix} -1 & 2 \\ 4 & 1 \end{pmatrix} \mathbf{X} + \begin{pmatrix} 36 \cos 3t \\ -18 \sin 3t \end{pmatrix}, \qquad \mathbf{X}_p = \begin{pmatrix} 2 \\ -5 \end{pmatrix} \cos 3t + \begin{pmatrix} 8 \\ 1 \end{pmatrix} \sin 3t$

1. c

2. c

3. d

4. a

5. c

6. b

7. c

8. a

9. c

10. d

11. True

12. False

13. False

14. homogeneous; $\mathbf{X}' = \begin{pmatrix} 4 & -3 \\ 2 & 7 \end{pmatrix} \mathbf{X}$

15. homogeneous; $\mathbf{X}' = \begin{pmatrix} 4 & 6 \\ 3 & -8 \end{pmatrix} \mathbf{X}$

16. nonhomogeneous; $\mathbf{X}' = \begin{pmatrix} 2 & 9 \\ -1 & 3 \end{pmatrix} \mathbf{X} + \begin{pmatrix} 5\,e^{-t} \\ -\cos 2t \end{pmatrix}$

17. homogeneous; $\mathbf{X}' = \begin{pmatrix} 9 & 5 & -1 \\ 2 & -3 & 4 \\ 5 & 0 & 7 \end{pmatrix} \mathbf{X}$

18. nonhomogeneous; $\mathbf{X}' = \begin{pmatrix} 5 & -1 & 2 \\ 3 & 0 & 8 \\ 6 & 4 & -2 \end{pmatrix} \mathbf{X} + \begin{pmatrix} t^2 \\ -\sin 3t \\ e^{-4t} \end{pmatrix}$

19. homogeneous; $\dfrac{dx}{dt} = 7\,x - 3\,y + 8\,e^{-2t}, \qquad \dfrac{dy}{dt} = 2\,x + 5\,y + 3\,t\,e^{-2t}$

20. nonhomogeneous; $\dfrac{dx}{dt} = -7\,x + 3\,y + 9\,t, \qquad \dfrac{dy}{dt} = 4\,x - 8\,y + 2\,z - t + 5\,\cos 2t,$

    $\dfrac{dz}{dt} = 5\,y - z + 2\,t + 8\,\cos 2t$

21. (a-g) Each is a solution of the given system.

22. (a) Yes. $W(\mathbf{X}_1, \mathbf{X}_2) = 17\,e^t \neq 0$ implies that $\mathbf{X}_1$ and $\mathbf{X}_2$ are linearly independent on $(-\infty, \infty)$.

    (b) Yes. $W(\mathbf{X}_1, \mathbf{X}_2) = -29\,t\,e^{2t} \neq 0$ implies that $\mathbf{X}_1$ and $\mathbf{X}_2$ are linearly independent on $(-\infty, 0), (0, \infty)$.

211

(c) Yes. $W(\mathbf{X}_1, \mathbf{X}_2, \mathbf{X}_3) = 67\,e^t \neq 0$ implies that $\mathbf{X}_1$, $\mathbf{X}_2$, and $\mathbf{X}_3$ are linearly independent on $(-\infty, \infty)$.

(d) Yes. $W(\mathbf{X}_1, \mathbf{X}_2, \mathbf{X}_3) = -15\,e^{3t} \neq 0$ implies that $\mathbf{X}_1$, $\mathbf{X}_2$, and $\mathbf{X}_3$ are linearly independent on $(-\infty, \infty)$.

(e) No. $W(\mathbf{X}_1, \mathbf{X}_2, \mathbf{X}_3) = 0$ implies that $\mathbf{X}_1$, $\mathbf{X}_2$, and $\mathbf{X}_3$ are linearly dependent on $(-\infty, \infty)$.

23. (a-e) Each is a particular solution of the given system.

1. eigenvalues of a matrix — concepts

2. eigenvalues of a multiplicity m — concepts

3. eigenvalues of a multiplicity m — concepts

4. find the eigenvalues of a 2×2 matrix

5. find an eigenvector of a 2×2 matrix

6. find the eigenvalues of a 2×2 matrix

7. matrix eigenvalues — concepts

8. matrix eigenvalues — concepts

9. matrix eigenvalues — concepts

10. matrix eigenvalues — concepts

11. matrix eigenvalues — concepts

12. find general solution of 2×2 system with real distinct eigenvalues

13. find general solution of 2×2 system with real distinct eigenvalues

14. find general solution of 2×2 system with real distinct eigenvalues

15. find general solution of 2×2 system with real distinct eigenvalues

16. find general solution of 2×2 system with real distinct eigenvalues

17. find general solution of 2×2 system with real distinct eigenvalues

18. find general solution of 3×3 system with real distinct eigenvalues

19. find general solution of 3×3 system with real distinct eigenvalues

20. find general solution of 3×3 system with real distinct eigenvalues

21. find general solution of 3×3 system with real distinct eigenvalues

22. find general solution of 2×2 system with real repeating eigenvalues

23. find general solution of 2×2 system with real repeating eigenvalues

24. find general solution of 2×2 system with real repeating eigenvalues

25. find general solution of 3×3 system with 2 real repeating eigenvalues

26. find general solution of 3×3 system with 2 real repeating eigenvalues

27. find general solution of 2×2 system with complex eigenvalues

28. find general solution of 2×2 system with complex eigenvalues

29. find general solution of 2×2 system with complex eigenvalues

30. find general solution of 2×2 system with complex eigenvalues

31. solve a 2×2 IVP with real distinct eigenvalues

32. solve a 2×2 IVP with real repeating eigenvalues

33. solve a 2×2 IVP with complex eigenvalues

34. solve a 3×3 IVP with real distinct eigenvalues

35. solve a 3×3 IVP with real 2 repeating eigenvalues

1. If $2 + 3i$ is an eigenvalue of system $\mathbf{X}' = \mathbf{AX}$, then another eigenvalue must be

   (a) $2 - 3i$.
   (b) $-2 + 3i$.
   (c) $-2 - 3i$.
   (d) $3 + 2i$.

2. If $\mathbf{A}$ is an $n \times n$ real matrix and λ is an eigenvalue of multiplicity m, then

   (a) there are n corresponding linearly independent eigenvectors.
   (b) there are at most n corresponding linearly independent eigenvectors.
   (c) there are m corresponding linearly independent eigenvectors.
   (d) there are at most m corresponding linearly independent eigenvectors.

3. If $\mathbf{A}$ is an $n \times n$ real symmetric matrix and λ is an eigenvalue of multiplicity m, then

   (a) there are n corresponding linearly independent eigenvectors.
   (b) there are at most n corresponding linearly independent eigenvectors.
   (c) there are m corresponding linearly independent eigenvectors.
   (d) there are at most m corresponding linearly independent eigenvectors.

4. The eigenvalues of matrix $\begin{pmatrix} -4 & -3 \\ 6 & 5 \end{pmatrix}$ are

   (a) 1 and 2
   (b) -1 and 2
   (c) 1 and -2
   (d) -1 and -2

5. The eigenvector of matrix $\begin{pmatrix} 3 & 6 \\ 5 & 2 \end{pmatrix}$ that corresponds to eigenvalue 9 is

   (a) $[6, 5]^{\mathsf{T}}$
   (b) $[5, 6]^{\mathsf{T}}$
   (c) $[-6, 5]^{\mathsf{T}}$
   (d) $[5, -6]^{\mathsf{T}}$

6. The eigenvalues of matrix $\begin{pmatrix} 9 & -20 \\ 2 & -3 \end{pmatrix}$ are

   (a) $-2 \pm 2i$
   (b) $2 \pm 3i$
   (c) $-3 \pm 2i$
   (d) $3 \pm 2i$

7. True or False: An $n \times n$ real matrix must have n eigenvalues.

8. True or False: An $n \times n$ real matrix must have n real eigenvalues.

9. True or False: An $n \times n$ real matrix must have an even number of complex eigenvalues.

10. True or False: An $n \times n$ real matrix must have n distinct eigenvalues.

11. True or False: An $n \times n$ real symmetric matrix always has n linearly independent eigenvectors.

Problems 12-30: Obtain the general solution of the given system.

12. $\dfrac{dx}{dt} = 4x - y$, $\qquad \dfrac{dy}{dt} = 2x + y$

13. $\dfrac{dx}{dt} = -x + 6y$, $\qquad \dfrac{dy}{dt} = x - 2y$

14. $\dfrac{dx}{dt} = 2x + 5y$, $\qquad \dfrac{dy}{dt} = 3x + 4y$

15. $\mathbf{X'} = \begin{pmatrix} 0 & 1 \\ -6 & 5 \end{pmatrix} \mathbf{X}$

16. $\mathbf{X'} = \begin{pmatrix} 5 & 2 \\ 4 & 7 \end{pmatrix} \mathbf{X}$

17. $\mathbf{X'} = \begin{pmatrix} 1 & 2 \\ -2 & -4 \end{pmatrix} \mathbf{X}$

18. $\mathbf{X'} = \begin{pmatrix} 1 & -3 & 3 \\ 3 & -5 & 3 \\ 6 & -6 & 4 \end{pmatrix} \mathbf{X}$

19. $\mathbf{X'} = \begin{pmatrix} 3 & -1 & 1 \\ -1 & 5 & -1 \\ 1 & -1 & 3 \end{pmatrix} \mathbf{X}$

20. $\mathbf{X'} = \begin{pmatrix} -1 & 1 & 2 \\ -1 & 2 & 3 \\ 4 & -1 & 1 \end{pmatrix} \mathbf{X}$

21. $\mathbf{X'} = \begin{pmatrix} -3 & -2 & 6 \\ -2 & 0 & 3 \\ -4 & -2 & 7 \end{pmatrix} \mathbf{X}$

22. $\mathbf{X'} = \begin{pmatrix} -6 & 4 \\ 0 & -6 \end{pmatrix} \mathbf{X}$

23. $\mathbf{X'} = \begin{pmatrix} -6 & 3 \\ -3 & -12 \end{pmatrix} \mathbf{X}$

24. $\mathbf{X'} = \begin{pmatrix} 2 & -4 \\ 4 & -6 \end{pmatrix} \mathbf{X}$

25. $\mathbf{X'} = \begin{pmatrix} 0 & -1 & -1 \\ 1 & 2 & 1 \\ 2 & 1 & 3 \end{pmatrix} \mathbf{X}$

26. $\mathbf{X'} = \begin{pmatrix} 2 & -1 & 2 \\ 2 & 1 & 2 \\ 1 & 0 & 2 \end{pmatrix} \mathbf{X}$

27. $\dfrac{dx}{dt} = 2x - y$, $\qquad \dfrac{dy}{dt} = 5x - 2y$

28. $\dfrac{dx}{dt} = x - 5y$, $\qquad \dfrac{dy}{dt} = 2x + 3y$

29. $\dfrac{dx}{dt} = 3x - 10y$, $\qquad \dfrac{dy}{dt} = 2x - 5y$

30. $\mathbf{X}' = \begin{pmatrix} 7 & -6 \\ 15 & -11 \end{pmatrix} \mathbf{X}$

Problems 31-35: Solve the given initial value problem.

31. $\mathbf{X}' = \begin{pmatrix} -4 & 3 \\ -3 & 6 \end{pmatrix} \mathbf{X}$, $\qquad \mathbf{X}(0) = \begin{pmatrix} 4 \\ -4 \end{pmatrix}$

32. $\mathbf{X}' = \begin{pmatrix} 2 & -4 \\ 4 & -6 \end{pmatrix} \mathbf{X}$, $\qquad \mathbf{X}(0) = \begin{pmatrix} 2 \\ -1 \end{pmatrix}$

33. $\mathbf{X}' = \begin{pmatrix} 3 & -10 \\ 2 & -5 \end{pmatrix} \mathbf{X}$, $\qquad \mathbf{X}(0) = \begin{pmatrix} 0 \\ 1 \end{pmatrix}$,

34. $\mathbf{X}' = \begin{pmatrix} 3 & -1 & 1 \\ -1 & 5 & -1 \\ 1 & -1 & 3 \end{pmatrix} \mathbf{X}$, $\qquad \mathbf{X}(0) = \begin{pmatrix} -2 \\ -4 \\ 3 \end{pmatrix}$,

35. $\mathbf{X}' = \begin{pmatrix} 0 & -1 & -1 \\ 1 & 2 & 1 \\ 2 & 1 & 3 \end{pmatrix} \mathbf{X}$, $\qquad \mathbf{X}(0) = \begin{pmatrix} 0 \\ -1 \\ 2 \end{pmatrix}$,

1. a

2. d

3. c

4. b

5. a

6. d

7. True

8. False

9. True

10. False

11. True

12. $\mathbf{X} = c_1 \begin{pmatrix} 1 \\ 2 \end{pmatrix} e^{2t} + c_2 \begin{pmatrix} 1 \\ 1 \end{pmatrix} e^{3t}$

13. $\mathbf{X} = c_1 \begin{pmatrix} -2 \\ 1 \end{pmatrix} e^{-4t} + c_2 \begin{pmatrix} 3 \\ 1 \end{pmatrix} e^{t}$

14. $\mathbf{X} = c_1 \begin{pmatrix} 5 \\ -3 \end{pmatrix} e^{-t} + c_2 \begin{pmatrix} 1 \\ 1 \end{pmatrix} e^{7t}$

15. $\mathbf{X} = c_1 \begin{pmatrix} 1 \\ 2 \end{pmatrix} e^{2t} + c_2 \begin{pmatrix} 1 \\ 3 \end{pmatrix} e^{3t}$

16. $\mathbf{X} = c_1 \begin{pmatrix} 1 \\ -1 \end{pmatrix} e^{3t} + c_2 \begin{pmatrix} 1 \\ 2 \end{pmatrix} e^{9t}$

17. $\mathbf{X} = c_1 \begin{pmatrix} -2 \\ 1 \end{pmatrix} + c_2 \begin{pmatrix} 1 \\ -2 \end{pmatrix} e^{-3t}$

18. $\mathbf{X} = c_1 \begin{pmatrix} -1 \\ 0 \\ 1 \end{pmatrix} e^{-2t} + c_2 \begin{pmatrix} 1 \\ 1 \\ 0 \end{pmatrix} e^{-2t} + c_3 \begin{pmatrix} 1 \\ 1 \\ 2 \end{pmatrix} e^{4t}$

19. $\mathbf{X} = c_1 \begin{pmatrix} -1 \\ 0 \\ 1 \end{pmatrix} e^{2t} + c_2 \begin{pmatrix} 1 \\ 1 \\ 1 \end{pmatrix} e^{3t} + c_3 \begin{pmatrix} 1 \\ -2 \\ 1 \end{pmatrix} e^{6t}$

20. $\mathbf{X} = c_1 \begin{pmatrix} 1 \\ 1 \\ -1 \end{pmatrix} e^{-2t} + c_2 \begin{pmatrix} 1 \\ 4 \\ -1 \end{pmatrix} e^{t} + c_3 \begin{pmatrix} 1 \\ 2 \\ 1 \end{pmatrix} e^{3t}$

21. $\mathbf{X} = c_1 \begin{pmatrix} 1 \\ -2 \\ 0 \end{pmatrix} e^{t} + c_2 \begin{pmatrix} 0 \\ 3 \\ 1 \end{pmatrix} e^{t} + c_3 \begin{pmatrix} 2 \\ 1 \\ 2 \end{pmatrix} e^{2t}$

22. $\mathbf{X} = c_1 \begin{pmatrix} 1 \\ 0 \end{pmatrix} e^{-6t} + c_2 \left[\begin{pmatrix} 1 \\ 0 \end{pmatrix} t + \frac{1}{4} \begin{pmatrix} 0 \\ 1 \end{pmatrix} \right] e^{-6t}$

23. $\mathbf{X} = c_1 \begin{pmatrix} 1 \\ -1 \end{pmatrix} e^{-9t} + c_2 \left[\begin{pmatrix} 1 \\ -1 \end{pmatrix} t + \frac{1}{3} \begin{pmatrix} 1 \\ 0 \end{pmatrix} \right] e^{-9t}$

24. $\mathbf{X} = c_1 \begin{pmatrix} 1 \\ 1 \end{pmatrix} e^{-2t} + c_2 \left[\begin{pmatrix} 1 \\ 1 \end{pmatrix} t + \frac{1}{4} \begin{pmatrix} 1 \\ 0 \end{pmatrix} \right] e^{-2t}$

25. $\mathbf{X} = c_1 \begin{pmatrix} 1 \\ 0 \\ -1 \end{pmatrix} e^{t} + c_2 \begin{pmatrix} -1 \\ 1 \\ 1 \end{pmatrix} e^{2t} + c_3 \left[\begin{pmatrix} -1 \\ 1 \\ 1 \end{pmatrix} t + \begin{pmatrix} 0 \\ 0 \\ 1 \end{pmatrix} \right] e^{2t}$

26. $\mathbf{X} = c_1 \begin{pmatrix} -1 \\ 1 \\ 1 \end{pmatrix} e^{t} + c_2 \begin{pmatrix} 0 \\ 2 \\ 1 \end{pmatrix} e^{2t} + c_3 \left[\begin{pmatrix} 0 \\ 2 \\ 1 \end{pmatrix} t + \begin{pmatrix} 1 \\ 0 \\ 0 \end{pmatrix} \right] e^{2t}$

27. $\mathbf{X} = c_1 \begin{pmatrix} \cos t \\ 2 \cos t - \sin t \end{pmatrix} + c_2 \begin{pmatrix} \sin t \\ \cos t + 2 \sin t \end{pmatrix}$

28. $\mathbf{X} = c_1 \begin{pmatrix} -5 \cos 3t \\ \cos 3t - 3 \sin 3t \end{pmatrix} e^{2t} + c_2 \begin{pmatrix} -5 \sin 3t \\ 3 \cos 3t + \sin 3t \end{pmatrix} e^{2t}$

29. $\mathbf{X} = c_1 \begin{pmatrix} 2 \cos 2t - \sin 2t \\ \cos 2t \end{pmatrix} e^{-t} + c_2 \begin{pmatrix} \cos 2t + 2 \sin 2t \\ \sin 2t \end{pmatrix} e^{-t}$

30. $\mathbf{X} = c_1 \begin{pmatrix} 2 \cos 3t \\ 3 \cos 3t + \sin 3t \end{pmatrix} e^{-2t} + c_2 \begin{pmatrix} 2 \sin 3t \\ -\cos 3t + 3 \sin 3t \end{pmatrix} e^{-2t}$

31. $\mathbf{X} = \begin{pmatrix} 6 \\ 2 \end{pmatrix} e^{-3t} - \begin{pmatrix} 2 \\ 6 \end{pmatrix} e^{5t}$

32. $\mathbf{X} = \begin{pmatrix} 2 + 12t \\ 12t - 1 \end{pmatrix} e^{-2t}$

33. $\mathbf{X} = \begin{pmatrix} -5 \sin 2t \\ \cos 2t - 2 \sin 2t \end{pmatrix} e^{-t}$

34. $\mathbf{X} = \begin{pmatrix} -4 \\ 0 \\ 4 \end{pmatrix} e^{2t} - \begin{pmatrix} 2 \\ 2 \\ 2 \end{pmatrix} e^{3t} + \begin{pmatrix} 1 \\ -2 \\ 1 \end{pmatrix} e^{6t}$

35. $\mathbf{X} = \begin{pmatrix} -1 \\ 0 \\ 1 \end{pmatrix} e^{t} + \begin{pmatrix} 1 - 2t \\ 2t - 1 \\ 1 + 2t \end{pmatrix} e^{2t}$

1. fundamental matrix concepts

2. fundamental matrix concepts

3. fundamental matrix concepts

4. relationship of eigenvalues to repellers and attractors

5. relationship of eigenvalues to repellers and attractors

6. relationship of eigenvalues to repellers and attractors

7. relationship of repeating eigenvalues to corresponding eigenvectors

8. variation of parameters — concepts

9. relationship of repeating eigenvalues to particular solution

10. relationship of repeating eigenvalues to particular solution

11. relationship of nonrepeating eigenvalue to particular solution

12. relationship of nonrepeating eigenvalues to particular solution

13. Find the general solution of a 2×2 linear nonhomogeneous system by undetermined coefficients. Nonrepeating terms.

14. Find the general solution of a 2×2 linear nonhomogeneous system by undetermined coefficients. Nonrepeating terms.

15. Find the general solution of a 2×2 linear nonhomogeneous system by undetermined coefficients. Nonrepeating terms.

16. Find the general solution of a 2×2 linear nonhomogeneous system by undetermined coefficients. Nonrepeating terms.

17. Find the general solution of a 2×2 linear nonhomogeneous system by undetermined coefficients. Repeating terms.

18. Find the general solution of a 2×2 linear nonhomogeneous system by undetermined coefficients. Nonrepeating terms.

19. Find the general solution of a 3×3 linear nonhomogeneous system by undetermined coefficients. Nonrepeating terms.

20. Find the general solution of a 3×3 linear nonhomogeneous system by undetermined coefficients. Nonrepeating terms.

21. Find the general solution of a 3×3 linear nonhomogeneous system by undetermined coefficients. Nonrepeating terms.

22. Find the general solution of a 2×2 linear nonhomogeneous system by undetermined coefficients. Repeating terms.

23. Find the general solution of a 2×2 linear nonhomogeneous system by variation of parameters.

24. Find the general solution of a 2×2 linear nonhomogeneous system by variation of parameters.

25. Find the general solution of a 2×2 linear nonhomogeneous system by variation of parameters.

26. Find the general solution of a 2×2 linear nonhomogeneous system by variation of parameters.

27. Find the general solution of a 2×2 linear nonhomogeneous system by variation of parameters.

28. Find the general solution of a 2×2 linear nonhomogeneous system by variation of parameters.

29. Find the general solution of a 2×2 linear nonhomogeneous system by variation of parameters.

30. Solve an initial value problem — a 2×2 linear nonhomogeneous system — by any method.

31. Solve an initial value problem — a 2×2 linear nonhomogeneous system — by any method.

32. Solve an initial value problem — a 2×2 linear nonhomogeneous system — by any method.

33. Solve an initial value problem — a 2×2 linear nonhomogeneous system — by any method.

34. Solve an initial value problem — a 2×2 linear nonhomogeneous system — by any method.

1. A fundamental matrix Φ of a linear system is

   (a) singular.
   (b) homogeneous.
   (c) nonsingular.
   (d) nonhomogeneous.

2. If Φ is a fundamental matrix of system $\mathbf{X}' = \mathbf{AX} + \mathbf{F}$, then

   (a) $\Phi' = \mathbf{A}\Phi + \Phi$.
   (b) $\Phi' = \mathbf{A}\Phi + \Phi$.
   (c) $\Phi' = \mathbf{A}\Phi + \mathbf{F}$.
   (d) $\Phi' = \mathbf{A}\Phi$.

3. If Φ is a fundamental matrix of system $\mathbf{X}' = \mathbf{AX} + \mathbf{F}$, then

   (a) the columns of Φ form solutions of $\Phi' = \mathbf{A}\Phi$.
   (b) the rows of Φ form solutions of $\Phi' = \mathbf{A}\Phi$.
   (c) the columns of Φ form solutions of $\Phi' = \mathbf{A}\Phi + \mathbf{F}$.
   (d) the rows of Φ form solutions of $\Phi' = \mathbf{A}\Phi + \mathbf{F}$.

4. If $\lambda = -2 \pm 3i$ are eigenvalues of the linear system $\mathbf{X}' = \mathbf{AX}$, then corresponding trajectories in the phase plane are

   (a) spiraling repellers.
   (b) spiraling attractors.
   (c) non-spiraling repellers.
   (d) non-spiraling attractors.

5. If $\lambda = 3$ is an eigenvalue of the linear system $\mathbf{X}' = \mathbf{AX}$, then the corresponding trajectory in the phase plane is

   (a) a spiraling repeller.
   (b) a spiraling attractor.
   (c) a non-spiraling repeller.
   (d) a non-spiraling attractor.

6. If $\lambda = \pm 3i$ are eigenvalues of the linear system $\mathbf{X}' = \mathbf{AX}$, then the corresponding trajectories in the phase plane are

   (a) spiraling repellers.
   (b) spiraling attractors.
   (c) orbits.
   (d) none of the above

222

7. If λ is an eigenvalue of multiplicity 4 of the 6×6 linear system $\mathbf{X}' = \mathbf{AX}$, then there are

   (a) 4 corresponding linearly independent eigenvectors.
   (b) 6 corresponding linearly independent eigenvectors.
   (c) 4 or less corresponding linearly independent eigenvectors.
   (d) 4 to 6 corresponding linearly independent eigenvectors.

8. Constructing a particular solution of a 4×4 linear system $\mathbf{X}' = \mathbf{AX} + \mathbf{F}$ by variation of parameters requires evaluating

   (a) 4 integrals.
   (b) 4 or less integrals.
   (c) at least 4 integrals.
   (d) The number of integrals may vary from problem to problem.

9. If $\lambda = 3$ is an eigenvalue of multiplicity 2 of a linear system $\mathbf{X}' = \mathbf{AX}$ and $\begin{pmatrix} 1 \\ 2 \end{pmatrix}$ and $\begin{pmatrix} 3 \\ 4 \end{pmatrix}$ are two corresponding eigenvectors, then two linearly independent solutions of the system are

   (a) $\mathbf{X_1} = \begin{pmatrix} 1 \\ 2 \end{pmatrix} e^{3t}$ and $\mathbf{X_2} = \begin{pmatrix} 3 \\ 4 \end{pmatrix} e^{3t}$.

   (b) $\mathbf{X_1} = \begin{pmatrix} 2 \\ 1 \end{pmatrix} e^{3t}$ and $\mathbf{X_2} = \begin{pmatrix} 4 \\ 3 \end{pmatrix} e^{3t}$.

   (c) $\mathbf{X_1} = \begin{pmatrix} 1 \\ 2 \end{pmatrix} e^{3t}$ and $\mathbf{X_2} = \left[\begin{pmatrix} 1 \\ 2 \end{pmatrix} + t \begin{pmatrix} 3 \\ 4 \end{pmatrix} \right] e^{3t}$.

   (d) none of the above

10. If $\lambda = 3$ is an eigenvalue of multiplicity 2 of a linear system $\mathbf{X}' = \mathbf{AX}$ and $\begin{pmatrix} 1 \\ 2 \end{pmatrix}$ is the only corresponding eigenvector, then two linearly independent solutions of the system are

    (a) $\mathbf{X_1} = \begin{pmatrix} 1 \\ 2 \end{pmatrix} e^{3t}$ and $\mathbf{X_2} = t \begin{pmatrix} 1 \\ 2 \end{pmatrix} e^{3t}$.

    (b) $\mathbf{X_1} = \begin{pmatrix} 1 \\ 2 \end{pmatrix} e^{3t}$ and $\mathbf{X_2} = \begin{pmatrix} -2 \\ -1 \end{pmatrix} e^{3t}$.

    (c) $\mathbf{X_1} = \begin{pmatrix} 1 \\ 2 \end{pmatrix} e^{3t}$ and $\mathbf{X_2} = \left[\begin{pmatrix} 1 \\ 2 \end{pmatrix} + t \begin{pmatrix} 1 \\ 2 \end{pmatrix} \right] e^{3t}$.

    (d) none of the above

11. If $\lambda = 0$ is an eigenvalue of multiplicity 1 of a linear system $\mathbf{X}' = \mathbf{AX} + \begin{pmatrix} 5 \\ 0 \end{pmatrix}$, then using undetermined coefficients, we would seek a particular function of the form

    (a) $\mathbf{X_p} = \begin{pmatrix} a \\ 0 \end{pmatrix}$

    (b) $\mathbf{X_p} = \begin{pmatrix} at \\ b \end{pmatrix}$

    (c) $\mathbf{X_p} = \begin{pmatrix} at \\ bt \end{pmatrix}$

    (d) $\mathbf{X_p} = \begin{pmatrix} at + b \\ ct + d \end{pmatrix}$

12. If $\lambda_1 = 4$ and $\lambda_2 = -1$ are eigenvalues of of a 2×2 linear system $\mathbf{X}' = \mathbf{AX} + \begin{pmatrix} \cos 4t \\ 0 \end{pmatrix}$, then using undetermined coefficients, we would seek a particular function of the form

(a) $\mathbf{X_p} = \begin{pmatrix} a \cos 4t \\ 0 \end{pmatrix}$

(b) $\mathbf{X_p} = \begin{pmatrix} a \cos 4t \\ b \sin 4t \end{pmatrix}$

(c) $\mathbf{X_p} = \begin{pmatrix} a \cos 4t + b \sin 4t \\ c \cos 4t + d \sin 4t \end{pmatrix}$

(d) $\mathbf{X_p} = \begin{pmatrix} at \cos 4t + bt \sin 4t \\ ct \cos 4t + dt \sin 4t \end{pmatrix}$

Problems 13-22: Use undetermined coefficients to obtain the general solution of the given system.

13. $\dfrac{dx}{dt} = 4x - y + 6, \qquad \dfrac{dy}{dt} = 2x + y + 12$

14. $\dfrac{dx}{dt} = -x + 6y + 16t, \qquad \dfrac{dy}{dt} = x - 2y - 12$

15. $\dfrac{dx}{dt} = 2x + 5y - 8e^t, \qquad \dfrac{dy}{dt} = 3x + 4y + 14$

16. $\mathbf{X}' = \begin{pmatrix} 0 & 1 \\ -6 & 5 \end{pmatrix} \mathbf{X} + \begin{pmatrix} 5 \cos t \\ 24 \end{pmatrix}$

17. $\mathbf{X}' = \begin{pmatrix} 5 & 2 \\ 4 & 7 \end{pmatrix} \mathbf{X} + \begin{pmatrix} 27 \\ 18 e^{3t} \end{pmatrix}$

18. $\mathbf{X}' = \begin{pmatrix} 1 & 2 \\ -2 & -4 \end{pmatrix} \mathbf{X} + \begin{pmatrix} 6 \\ 18 \end{pmatrix}$

19. $\mathbf{X}' = \begin{pmatrix} 1 & -3 & 3 \\ 3 & -5 & 3 \\ 6 & -6 & 4 \end{pmatrix} \mathbf{X} + \begin{pmatrix} 16 \\ 0 \\ 8 \end{pmatrix}$

20. $\mathbf{X}' = \begin{pmatrix} 3 & -1 & 1 \\ -1 & 5 & -1 \\ 1 & -1 & 3 \end{pmatrix} \mathbf{X} + \begin{pmatrix} 10 \\ 0 \\ -20 \end{pmatrix} e^t$

21. $\mathbf{X}' = \begin{pmatrix} -1 & 1 & 2 \\ -1 & 2 & 3 \\ 4 & -1 & 1 \end{pmatrix} \mathbf{X} + \begin{pmatrix} 5 \\ 0 \\ -5 \end{pmatrix}$

22. $\mathbf{X}' = \begin{pmatrix} -6 & 4 \\ 0 & -6 \end{pmatrix} \mathbf{X} + \begin{pmatrix} 7 \\ -5 \end{pmatrix} e^{-6t}$

Problems 23-29: Use variation of parameters to obtain the general solution of the given system.

23. $\dfrac{dx}{dt} = -x + 6y + 16t, \qquad \dfrac{dy}{dt} = x - 2y - 12$

24. $\dfrac{dx}{dt} = 2x + 5y - 8e^t, \qquad \dfrac{dy}{dt} = 3x + 4y + 14$

25. $\mathbf{X}' = \begin{pmatrix} 0 & 1 \\ -6 & 5 \end{pmatrix} \mathbf{X} + \begin{pmatrix} 5\cos t \\ 24 \end{pmatrix}$

26. $\mathbf{X}' = \begin{pmatrix} 5 & 2 \\ 4 & 7 \end{pmatrix} \mathbf{X} + \begin{pmatrix} 27 \\ 18\,e^{3t} \end{pmatrix}$

27. $\mathbf{X}' = \begin{pmatrix} 0 & 1 \\ -1 & 0 \end{pmatrix} \mathbf{X} + \begin{pmatrix} 0 \\ \tan t \end{pmatrix}$

28. $\mathbf{X}' = \begin{pmatrix} 2 & -1 \\ 5 & -2 \end{pmatrix} \mathbf{X} + \begin{pmatrix} 0 \\ \sec t \end{pmatrix}$

29. $\mathbf{X}' = \begin{pmatrix} 2 & -1 \\ 5 & 6 \end{pmatrix} \mathbf{X} + \begin{pmatrix} 0 \\ e^{4t}\,\sec t \end{pmatrix}$

Problems 30-34: Solve the given initial value problems.

30. $\mathbf{X}' = \begin{pmatrix} 0 & -4 \\ 2 & 6 \end{pmatrix} \mathbf{X} + \begin{pmatrix} 0 \\ 4\,t\,e^{4t} \end{pmatrix}, \qquad \mathbf{X}(0) = \begin{pmatrix} 1 \\ 2 \end{pmatrix}$

31. $\mathbf{X}' = \begin{pmatrix} 5 & 2 \\ 4 & 7 \end{pmatrix} \mathbf{X} + \begin{pmatrix} 1 \\ -1 \end{pmatrix} e^{3t}, \qquad \mathbf{X}(0) = \begin{pmatrix} 0 \\ 3 \end{pmatrix}$

32. $\mathbf{X}' = \begin{pmatrix} 0 & 1 \\ -6 & 5 \end{pmatrix} \mathbf{X} + \begin{pmatrix} 5\cos t \\ 24 \end{pmatrix}, \qquad \mathbf{X}(0) = \begin{pmatrix} 1 \\ 2 \end{pmatrix}$

33. $\mathbf{X}' = \begin{pmatrix} 3 & -1 & 1 \\ -1 & 5 & -1 \\ 1 & -1 & 3 \end{pmatrix} \mathbf{X} + \begin{pmatrix} 10 \\ 0 \\ -20 \end{pmatrix} e^{t}, \qquad \mathbf{X}(0) = \begin{pmatrix} 6 \\ -1 \\ 0 \end{pmatrix}$

34. $\mathbf{X}' = \begin{pmatrix} -1 & 1 & 2 \\ -1 & 2 & 3 \\ 4 & -1 & 1 \end{pmatrix} \mathbf{X} + \begin{pmatrix} 5 \\ 0 \\ -5 \end{pmatrix}, \qquad \mathbf{X}(0) = \begin{pmatrix} 0 \\ 3 \\ 2 \end{pmatrix}$

1. c

2. d

3. a

4. b

5. c

6. c

7. c

8. a

9. a

10. d

11. d

12. c

13. $\mathbf{X} = c_1 \begin{pmatrix} 1 \\ 2 \end{pmatrix} e^{2t} + c_2 \begin{pmatrix} 1 \\ 1 \end{pmatrix} e^{3t} - \begin{pmatrix} 3 \\ 6 \end{pmatrix}$

14. $\mathbf{X} = c_1 \begin{pmatrix} -2 \\ 1 \end{pmatrix} e^{-4t} + c_2 \begin{pmatrix} 3 \\ 1 \end{pmatrix} e^{t} + \begin{pmatrix} 8 - 8t \\ -4t \end{pmatrix}$

15. $\mathbf{X} = c_1 \begin{pmatrix} 5 \\ -3 \end{pmatrix} e^{-t} + c_2 \begin{pmatrix} 1 \\ 1 \end{pmatrix} e^{7t} + \begin{pmatrix} -2 \\ 2 \end{pmatrix} e^{t} + \begin{pmatrix} -10 \\ 4 \end{pmatrix}$

16. $\mathbf{X} = c_1 \begin{pmatrix} 1 \\ 2 \end{pmatrix} e^{2t} + c_2 \begin{pmatrix} 1 \\ 3 \end{pmatrix} e^{3t} - \begin{pmatrix} 3 \\ 3 \end{pmatrix} \cos t + \begin{pmatrix} 2 \\ 3 \end{pmatrix} \sin t + \begin{pmatrix} 4 \\ 0 \end{pmatrix}$

17. $\mathbf{X} = c_1 \begin{pmatrix} 1 \\ -1 \end{pmatrix} e^{3t} + c_2 \begin{pmatrix} 1 \\ 2 \end{pmatrix} e^{9t} - \begin{pmatrix} 6t + 1 \\ 2 - 6t \end{pmatrix} e^{3t} + \begin{pmatrix} -7 \\ 4 \end{pmatrix}$

18. $\mathbf{X} = c_1 \begin{pmatrix} -2 \\ 1 \end{pmatrix} + c_2 \begin{pmatrix} 1 \\ -2 \end{pmatrix} e^{-3t} + \begin{pmatrix} 20 \\ -10 \end{pmatrix} t + \begin{pmatrix} 0 \\ 7 \end{pmatrix}$

19. $\mathbf{X} = c_1 \begin{pmatrix} -1 \\ 0 \\ 1 \end{pmatrix} e^{-2t} + c_2 \begin{pmatrix} 1 \\ 1 \\ 0 \end{pmatrix} e^{-2t} + c_3 \begin{pmatrix} 1 \\ 1 \\ 2 \end{pmatrix} e^{4t} - \begin{pmatrix} 1 \\ 9 \\ 14 \end{pmatrix}$

20. $\mathbf{X} = c_1 \begin{pmatrix} -1 \\ 0 \\ 1 \end{pmatrix} e^{2t} + c_2 \begin{pmatrix} 1 \\ 1 \\ 1 \end{pmatrix} e^{3t} + c_3 \begin{pmatrix} 1 \\ -2 \\ 1 \end{pmatrix} e^{6t} + \begin{pmatrix} -13 \\ 1 \\ 17 \end{pmatrix} e^{t}$

21. $\mathbf{X} = c_1 \begin{pmatrix} 1 \\ 1 \\ -1 \end{pmatrix} e^{-2t} + c_2 \begin{pmatrix} 1 \\ 4 \\ -1 \end{pmatrix} e^{t} + c_3 \begin{pmatrix} 1 \\ 2 \\ 1 \end{pmatrix} e^{3t} + 5 \begin{pmatrix} 1 \\ 2 \\ -1 \end{pmatrix}$

22. $\mathbf{X} = c_1 \begin{pmatrix} 1 \\ 0 \end{pmatrix} e^{-6t} + c_2 \left[\begin{pmatrix} 1 \\ 0 \end{pmatrix} t + \frac{1}{4} \begin{pmatrix} 0 \\ 1 \end{pmatrix} \right] e^{-6t} + \begin{pmatrix} 10\,t^2 + 7t \\ -5t \end{pmatrix} e^{-6t}$

23. $\mathbf{X} = c_1 \begin{pmatrix} -2 \\ 1 \end{pmatrix} e^{-4t} + c_2 \begin{pmatrix} 3 \\ 1 \end{pmatrix} e^t + \begin{pmatrix} 8 - 8t \\ -4t \end{pmatrix}$

24. $\mathbf{X} = c_1 \begin{pmatrix} 5 \\ -3 \end{pmatrix} e^{-t} + c_2 \begin{pmatrix} 1 \\ 1 \end{pmatrix} e^{7t} + \begin{pmatrix} -2 \\ 2 \end{pmatrix} e^t + \begin{pmatrix} -10 \\ 4 \end{pmatrix}$

25. $\mathbf{X} = c_1 \begin{pmatrix} 1 \\ 2 \end{pmatrix} e^{2t} + c_2 \begin{pmatrix} 1 \\ 3 \end{pmatrix} e^{3t} - \begin{pmatrix} 3 \\ 3 \end{pmatrix} \cos t + \begin{pmatrix} 2 \\ 3 \end{pmatrix} \sin t + \begin{pmatrix} 4 \\ 0 \end{pmatrix}$

26. $\mathbf{X} = c_1 \begin{pmatrix} 1 \\ -1 \end{pmatrix} e^{3t} + c_2 \begin{pmatrix} 1 \\ 2 \end{pmatrix} e^{9t} - \begin{pmatrix} 6t + 1 \\ 2 - 6t \end{pmatrix} e^{3t} + \begin{pmatrix} -7 \\ 4 \end{pmatrix}$

27. $\mathbf{X} = c_1 \begin{pmatrix} \cos t \\ -\sin t \end{pmatrix} + c_2 \begin{pmatrix} \sin t \\ \cos t \end{pmatrix} - \begin{pmatrix} \cos t \ln(\sec t + \tan t) \\ 1 - \sin t \ln(\sec t + \tan t) \end{pmatrix}$

28. $\mathbf{X} = c_1 \begin{pmatrix} \cos t \\ 2\cos t + \sin t \end{pmatrix} + c_2 \begin{pmatrix} \sin t \\ 2\sin t - \cos t \end{pmatrix}$
$\qquad - \begin{pmatrix} t \sin t + \cos t \ln(\cos t) \\ 2\cos t \ln(\cos t) + \sin t \ln(\cos t) - t \cos t + 2t \sin t \end{pmatrix}$

29. $\mathbf{X} = c_1 \begin{pmatrix} \cos t \\ \sin t - 2\cos t \end{pmatrix} e^{4t} + c_2 \begin{pmatrix} \sin t \\ -\cos t - 2\sin t \end{pmatrix} e^{4t}$
$\qquad + \begin{pmatrix} -t \sin t - \cos t \ln(\cos t) \\ 2\cos t \ln(\cos t) - \sin t \ln(\cos t) + t \cos t + 2t \sin t \end{pmatrix} e^{4t}$

30. $\mathbf{X} = \begin{pmatrix} -4t^2 + 4t - 7 \\ 4t^2 - 2t + 6 \end{pmatrix} e^{4t} + \begin{pmatrix} 8 \\ -4 \end{pmatrix} e^{2t}$

31. $\mathbf{X} = \begin{pmatrix} t - 1 \\ 1 - t \end{pmatrix} e^{3t} + \begin{pmatrix} 1 \\ 2 \end{pmatrix} e^{9t}$

32. $\mathbf{X} = -5 \begin{pmatrix} 1 \\ 2 \end{pmatrix} e^{2t} + 5 \begin{pmatrix} 1 \\ 3 \end{pmatrix} e^{3t} - 3 \begin{pmatrix} 1 \\ 1 \end{pmatrix} \cos t + \begin{pmatrix} 2 \\ 3 \end{pmatrix} \sin t + \begin{pmatrix} 4 \\ 0 \end{pmatrix}$

33. $\mathbf{X} = \begin{pmatrix} -13 \\ 1 \\ 17 \end{pmatrix} e^t + \begin{pmatrix} 18 \\ 0 \\ -18 \end{pmatrix} e^{2t} + \begin{pmatrix} 1 \\ -2 \\ 1 \end{pmatrix} e^{6t}$

34. $\mathbf{X} = \begin{pmatrix} -5 \\ -5 \\ 5 \end{pmatrix} e^{-2t} + \begin{pmatrix} -1 \\ -4 \\ 1 \end{pmatrix} e^t + \begin{pmatrix} 1 \\ 2 \\ 1 \end{pmatrix} e^{3t} + 5 \begin{pmatrix} 1 \\ 2 \\ -1 \end{pmatrix}$

1. simple matrix exponential — concepts

2. general solution of a linear system via the matrix exponential — concepts

3. Laplace transform of a matrix exponential — concepts

4. matrix exponential — concepts

5. inverse matrix via the matrix exponential — concepts

6. Taylor series of the matrix exponential — concepts

7. determine $\exp(\mathbf{A}t)$ and $\exp(-\mathbf{A}t)$ of 2×2 matrix $\mathbf{A}$

8. determine $\exp(\mathbf{A}t)$ and $\exp(-\mathbf{A}t)$ of 2×2 matrix $\mathbf{A}$

9. determine $\exp(\mathbf{A}t)$ and $\exp(-\mathbf{A}t)$ of 2×2 matrix $\mathbf{A}$

10. determine $\exp(\mathbf{A}t)$ and $\exp(-\mathbf{A}t)$ of 2×2 matrix $\mathbf{A}$

11. determine $\exp(\mathbf{A}t)$ and $\exp(-\mathbf{A}t)$ of 2×2 matrix $\mathbf{A}$

12. determine $\exp(\mathbf{A}t)$ of 2×2 matrix $\mathbf{A}$

13. determine $\exp(\mathbf{A}t)$ of 2×2 matrix $\mathbf{A}$

14. determine $\exp(\mathbf{A}t)$ of 2×2 matrix $\mathbf{A}$

15. determine $\exp(\mathbf{A}t)$ of 3×3 matrix $\mathbf{A}$

16. determine $\exp(\mathbf{A}t)$ of 3×3 matrix $\mathbf{A}$

17. determine $\exp(\mathbf{A}t)$ of 3×3 matrix $\mathbf{A}$

18. determine $\exp(\mathbf{A}t)$ of 3×3 matrix $\mathbf{A}$

19. use the matrix exponential to solve a linear, homogeneous system of 2 DEs

20. use the matrix exponential to solve a linear, homogeneous system of 2 DEs

21. use the matrix exponential to solve a linear, homogeneous system of 2 DEs

22. use the matrix exponential to solve a linear, homogeneous system of 3 DEs

23. use the matrix exponential to solve a linear, nonhomogeneous system of 2 DEs

24. use the matrix exponential to solve a linear, nonhomogeneous system of 2 DEs

25. use the matrix exponential to solve a linear, nonhomogeneous system of 2 DEs

26. use the matrix exponential to solve a linear, nonhomogeneous system of 2 DEs

27. use the matrix exponential to solve a linear, nonhomogeneous system of 2 DEs

28. use the matrix exponential to solve a linear, nonhomogeneous system of 2 DEs

29. use the matrix exponential to solve a linear, nonhomogeneous system of 2 DEs

30. use the matrix exponential to solve a linear, nonhomogeneous system of 3 DEs

31. use the matrix exponential to solve a linear, nonhomogeneous system of 2 DEs subject to initial conditions

32. use the matrix exponential to solve a linear, nonhomogeneous system of 2 DEs subject to initial conditions

33. use the matrix exponential to solve a linear, nonhomogeneous system of 3 DEs subject to initial conditions

34. use the matrix exponential to solve a linear, nonhomogeneous system of 3 DEs subject to initial conditions

1. When $\mathbf{A}$ is a square matrix, the value of $e^{\mathbf{A}t}$ at $t = 0$ is

   (a) 1.
   (b) 0.
   (c) $\mathbf{I}$.
   (d) $\mathbf{A}$.

2. The general solution of the system $\mathbf{X}' = \mathbf{A}\mathbf{X}$ is

   (a) $\mathbf{X} = e^{\mathbf{A}t}$.
   (b) $\mathbf{X} = e^{\mathbf{A}t}\mathbf{C}$.
   (c) $\mathbf{X} = \mathbf{C}\,e^{\mathbf{A}t}$.
   (d) $\mathbf{X} = \mathbf{I}\,e^{\mathbf{A}t}$.

3. The Laplace transform of $e^{\mathbf{A}t}$ is

   (a) $(s\mathbf{I} - \mathbf{A})^{-1}$.
   (b) $\dfrac{1}{s - \mathbf{A}}$.
   (c) $(s - \mathbf{A})^{-1}$.
   (d) $\dfrac{1}{s\mathbf{I} - \mathbf{A}}$.

4. $\exp(-\mathbf{A}t)$ is the same as

   (a) $\exp(\mathbf{A}^{-1}t)$.
   (b) $\dfrac{1}{e^{\mathbf{A}t}}$.
   (c) $\exp((\mathbf{A}t)^{-1})$.
   (d) $(e^{\mathbf{A}t})^{-1}$.

5. If $A = \begin{pmatrix} 2 & -5 \\ 1 & -2 \end{pmatrix}$ and $A^{-1} = \begin{pmatrix} -2 & 5 \\ -1 & 2 \end{pmatrix}$, then $e^{-\mathbf{A}t}$ equals

   (a) $\begin{pmatrix} e^{2t} & e^{-5t} \\ e^{t} & e^{-2t} \end{pmatrix}$

   (b) $\begin{pmatrix} e^{t/2} & e^{-t/5} \\ e^{t} & e^{2t/2} \end{pmatrix}$

   (c) $\begin{pmatrix} e^{-2t} & e^{5t} \\ e^{-t} & e^{2t} \end{pmatrix}$

   (d) $\begin{pmatrix} e^{-t/2} & e^{t/5} \\ e^{-t} & e^{t/2} \end{pmatrix}$

6. The Taylor series expansion of $\exp(-\mathbf{A}t)$ is

(a) $\mathbf{I} - \mathbf{A}t + \dfrac{1}{2!}\mathbf{A}^2\,t^2 - \dfrac{1}{3!}\mathbf{A}^3\,t^3 + \dfrac{1}{4!}\mathbf{A}^4\,t^4 - \dfrac{1}{5!}\mathbf{A}^5\,t^5 + \cdots$

(b) $\mathbf{I} + \mathbf{A}^{-1}t + \dfrac{1}{2!}\mathbf{A}^{-2}\,t^2 + \dfrac{1}{3!}\mathbf{A}^{-3}\,t^3 + \dfrac{1}{4!}\mathbf{A}^{-4}\,t^4 + \dfrac{1}{5!}\mathbf{A}^{-5}\,t^5 + \cdots$

(c) $\mathbf{I} - \mathbf{A}t + \dfrac{1}{2}\mathbf{A}^2\,t^2 - \dfrac{1}{3}\mathbf{A}^3\,t^3 + \dfrac{1}{4}\mathbf{A}^4\,t^4 - \dfrac{1}{5}\mathbf{A}^5\,t^5 + \cdots$

(d) $1 + \mathbf{A}^{-1}t + \dfrac{1}{2}\mathbf{A}^{-2}\,t^2 + \dfrac{1}{3}\mathbf{A}^{-3}\,t^3 + \dfrac{1}{4}\mathbf{A}^{-4}\,t^4 + \dfrac{1}{5}\mathbf{A}^{-5}\,t^5 + \cdots$

Problems 7-11: Determine $e^{\mathbf{A}t}$ and $e^{-\mathbf{A}t}$.

7. $\mathbf{A} = \begin{pmatrix} 3 & 0 \\ 0 & 2 \end{pmatrix}$

8. $\mathbf{A} = \begin{pmatrix} 1 & 0 \\ 0 & 3 \end{pmatrix}$

9. $\mathbf{A} = \begin{pmatrix} 2 & -5 \\ 1 & -2 \end{pmatrix}$

10. $\mathbf{A} = \begin{pmatrix} -1 & 1 \\ 0 & -1 \end{pmatrix}$

11. $\mathbf{A} = \begin{pmatrix} 1 & 2 \\ 0 & 1 \end{pmatrix}$

Problems 12-18: Determine $e^{\mathbf{A}t}$.

12. $\mathbf{A} = \begin{pmatrix} 2 & 2 \\ -4 & -2 \end{pmatrix}$

13. $\mathbf{A} = \begin{pmatrix} -1 & 2 \\ -2 & 3 \end{pmatrix}$

14. $\mathbf{A} = \begin{pmatrix} -1 & 1 \\ 0 & 2 \end{pmatrix}$

15. $\mathbf{A} = \begin{pmatrix} -1 & 0 & 1 \\ 0 & 2 & 0 \\ 0 & 0 & -1 \end{pmatrix}$

16. $\mathbf{A} = \begin{pmatrix} 1 & 0 & 0 \\ 1 & 2 & 1 \\ 0 & 0 & 1 \end{pmatrix}$

17. $\mathbf{A} = \begin{pmatrix} 0 & 2 & 1 \\ 0 & 0 & 3 \\ 0 & 0 & 0 \end{pmatrix}$

18. $\mathbf{A} = \begin{pmatrix} 2 & 1 & 0 \\ 0 & 2 & 0 \\ 0 & 1 & 2 \end{pmatrix}$

Problems 19-22: Use Eq. (1) of the text to obtain the general solution of the given system.

19. $\mathbf{X}' = \begin{pmatrix} 3 & 0 \\ 0 & 2 \end{pmatrix} \mathbf{X}$

20. $\mathbf{X}' = \begin{pmatrix} -1 & 1 \\ 0 & 1 \end{pmatrix} \mathbf{X}$

21. $\mathbf{X}' = \begin{pmatrix} 2 & 2 \\ -4 & -2 \end{pmatrix} \mathbf{X}$

22. $\mathbf{X}' = \begin{pmatrix} -1 & 0 & 1 \\ 0 & 2 & 0 \\ 0 & 0 & -1 \end{pmatrix} \mathbf{X}$

Problems 23-30: Use Eq. (5) of the text to obtain the general solution of the given system.

23. $\mathbf{X}' = \begin{pmatrix} 3 & 0 \\ 0 & 2 \end{pmatrix} \mathbf{X} + \begin{pmatrix} -9 \\ 4 \end{pmatrix}$

24. $\mathbf{X}' = \begin{pmatrix} 3 & 0 \\ 0 & 2 \end{pmatrix} \mathbf{X} + \begin{pmatrix} 8\,e^{-t} \\ 4t \end{pmatrix}$

25. $\mathbf{X}' = \begin{pmatrix} 3 & 0 \\ 0 & 2 \end{pmatrix} \mathbf{X} + \begin{pmatrix} e^{2t} \\ 4t \end{pmatrix}$

26. $\mathbf{X}' = \begin{pmatrix} -1 & 1 \\ 0 & 1 \end{pmatrix} \mathbf{X} + \begin{pmatrix} 7t \\ 18\,e^{2t} \end{pmatrix}$

27. $\mathbf{X}' = \begin{pmatrix} -1 & 1 \\ 0 & 1 \end{pmatrix} \mathbf{X} + \begin{pmatrix} 4t \\ 7 - 18\,e^{-t} \end{pmatrix}$

28. $\mathbf{X}' = \begin{pmatrix} 2 & 2 \\ -4 & -2 \end{pmatrix} \mathbf{X} + \begin{pmatrix} -2 \\ 6 \end{pmatrix}$

29. $\mathbf{X}' = \begin{pmatrix} 2 & 2 \\ -4 & -2 \end{pmatrix} \mathbf{X} + \begin{pmatrix} 8 \cos 2t \\ -8 \sin 2t \end{pmatrix}$

30. $\mathbf{X}' = \begin{pmatrix} -1 & 0 & 1 \\ 0 & 2 & 0 \\ 0 & 0 & -1 \end{pmatrix} \mathbf{X} + \begin{pmatrix} 8\,e^{-t} \\ -16\,e^{2t} \\ 12\,e^{-t} \end{pmatrix}$

Problems 31-34: Use the exponential matrix to solve the given initial value problems.

31. $\mathbf{X}' = \begin{pmatrix} -1 & 2 \\ -2 & 3 \end{pmatrix} \mathbf{X}, \qquad \mathbf{X}(0) = \begin{pmatrix} -1 \\ 2 \end{pmatrix}$

32. $\mathbf{X}' = \begin{pmatrix} -1 & 2 \\ -2 & 3 \end{pmatrix} \mathbf{X} + \begin{pmatrix} 1 \\ 2 \end{pmatrix} e^t, \qquad \mathbf{X}(0) = \begin{pmatrix} -2 \\ 1 \end{pmatrix}$

33. $\mathbf{X}' = \begin{pmatrix} -1 & 0 & 1 \\ 0 & 2 & 0 \\ 0 & 0 & -1 \end{pmatrix} \mathbf{X}, \qquad \mathbf{X}(0) = \begin{pmatrix} -2 \\ 1 \\ 3 \end{pmatrix}$

34. $\mathbf{X}' = \begin{pmatrix} -1 & 0 & 1 \\ 0 & 2 & 0 \\ 0 & 0 & -1 \end{pmatrix} \mathbf{X} + \begin{pmatrix} 8\,e^{-t} \\ -16\,e^{2t} \\ 12\,e^{-t} \end{pmatrix}, \qquad \mathbf{X}(0) = \begin{pmatrix} -2 \\ 0 \\ 3 \end{pmatrix}$

1. c

2. b

3. a

4. d

5. c

6. a

7. $e^{\mathbf{A}t} = \begin{pmatrix} e^{3t} & 0 \\ 0 & e^{2t} \end{pmatrix}$, $e^{-\mathbf{A}t} = \begin{pmatrix} e^{-3t} & 0 \\ 0 & e^{-2t} \end{pmatrix}$

8. $e^{\mathbf{A}t} = \begin{pmatrix} e^{t} & 0 \\ 0 & e^{3t} \end{pmatrix}$, $e^{-\mathbf{A}t} = \begin{pmatrix} e^{-t} & 0 \\ 0 & e^{-3t} \end{pmatrix}$

9. $e^{\mathbf{A}t} = \begin{pmatrix} \cos t + 2\sin t & -5\sin t \\ \sin t & \cos t - 2\sin t \end{pmatrix}$, $e^{-\mathbf{A}t} = \begin{pmatrix} \cos t - 2\sin t & 5\sin t \\ -\sin t & \cos t + 2\sin t \end{pmatrix}$

10. $e^{\mathbf{A}t} = \begin{pmatrix} e^{-t} & t\,e^{-t} \\ 0 & e^{-t} \end{pmatrix}$, $e^{-\mathbf{A}t} = \begin{pmatrix} e^{t} & -t\,e^{t} \\ 0 & e^{t} \end{pmatrix}$

11. $e^{\mathbf{A}t} = \begin{pmatrix} e^{t} & 2t\,e^{t} \\ 0 & e^{t} \end{pmatrix}$, $e^{-\mathbf{A}t} = \begin{pmatrix} e^{-t} & -2t\,e^{-t} \\ 0 & e^{-t} \end{pmatrix}$

12. $e^{\mathbf{A}t} = \begin{pmatrix} \cos 2t + \sin 2t & \sin 2t \\ -2\sin 2t & \cos 2t - \sin 2t \end{pmatrix}$

13. $e^{\mathbf{A}t} = \begin{pmatrix} (1-2t)\,e^{t} & 2t\,e^{t} \\ -2t\,e^{t} & (1+2t)\,e^{t} \end{pmatrix}$

14. $e^{\mathbf{A}t} = \begin{pmatrix} e^{-t} & e^{-t} - e^{-2t} \\ 0 & e^{-2t} \end{pmatrix}$

15. $e^{\mathbf{A}t} = \begin{pmatrix} e^{-t} & 0 & t\,e^{-t} \\ 0 & e^{2t} & 0 \\ 0 & 0 & e^{-t} \end{pmatrix}$

16. $e^{\mathbf{A}t} = \begin{pmatrix} e^{t} & 0 & 0 \\ e^{2t} - e^{t} & e^{2t} & e^{2t} - e^{t} \\ 0 & 0 & e^{t} \end{pmatrix}$

17. $e^{\mathbf{A}t} = \begin{pmatrix} 1 & 2t & 3t^2 + t \\ 0 & 1 & 3t \\ 0 & 0 & 1 \end{pmatrix}$

18. $e^{\mathbf{A}t} = \begin{pmatrix} e^{2t} & t\,e^{2t} & 0 \\ 0 & e^{2t} & 0 \\ 0 & t\,e^{2t} & e^{2t} \end{pmatrix}$

19. $\mathbf{X} = c_1 \begin{pmatrix} 1 \\ 0 \end{pmatrix} e^{3t} + c_2 \begin{pmatrix} 0 \\ 1 \end{pmatrix} e^{2t}$

20. $\mathbf{X} = c_1 \begin{pmatrix} 1 \\ 0 \end{pmatrix} e^{-t} + c_2 \begin{pmatrix} t \\ 1 \end{pmatrix} e^{-t}$

21. $\mathbf{X} = c_1 \begin{pmatrix} \cos 2t \\ -\cos 2t - \sin 2t \end{pmatrix} + c_2 \begin{pmatrix} \sin 2t \\ \cos 2t - \sin 2t \end{pmatrix}$

22. $\mathbf{X} = c_1 \begin{pmatrix} 1 \\ 0 \\ 0 \end{pmatrix} e^{-t} + c_2 \begin{pmatrix} t \\ 0 \\ 1 \end{pmatrix} e^{-t} + c_3 \begin{pmatrix} 0 \\ 1 \\ 0 \end{pmatrix} e^{2t}$

23. $\mathbf{X} = c_1 \begin{pmatrix} 1 \\ 0 \end{pmatrix} e^{3t} + c_2 \begin{pmatrix} 0 \\ 1 \end{pmatrix} e^{2t} + \begin{pmatrix} 3 \\ -2 \end{pmatrix}$

24. $\mathbf{X} = c_1 \begin{pmatrix} 1 \\ 0 \end{pmatrix} e^{3t} + c_2 \begin{pmatrix} 0 \\ 1 \end{pmatrix} e^{2t} + \begin{pmatrix} -2 \\ 0 \end{pmatrix} e^{-t} + \begin{pmatrix} 0 \\ -1 \end{pmatrix} t$

25. $\mathbf{X} = c_1 \begin{pmatrix} 1 \\ 0 \end{pmatrix} e^{3t} + c_2 \begin{pmatrix} 0 \\ 1 \end{pmatrix} e^{2t} + \begin{pmatrix} -1 \\ 0 \end{pmatrix} e^{2t} - \begin{pmatrix} 0 \\ 2t+1 \end{pmatrix}$

26. $\mathbf{X} = c_1 \begin{pmatrix} 1 \\ 0 \end{pmatrix} e^{-t} + c_2 \begin{pmatrix} t \\ 1 \end{pmatrix} e^{-t} + \begin{pmatrix} 2 \\ 6 \end{pmatrix} e^{2t} + \begin{pmatrix} 7t-7 \\ 0 \end{pmatrix}$

27. $\mathbf{X} = c_1 \begin{pmatrix} 1 \\ 0 \end{pmatrix} e^{-t} + c_2 \begin{pmatrix} t \\ 1 \end{pmatrix} e^{-t} - \begin{pmatrix} 9t^2 \\ 18t \end{pmatrix} e^{-t} + \begin{pmatrix} 4t+3 \\ 7 \end{pmatrix}$

28. $\mathbf{X} = c_1 \begin{pmatrix} \cos 2t \\ -\cos 2t - \sin 2t \end{pmatrix} + c_2 \begin{pmatrix} \sin 2t \\ \cos 2t - \sin 2t \end{pmatrix} + \begin{pmatrix} 2 \\ -1 \end{pmatrix}$

29. $\mathbf{X} = c_1 \begin{pmatrix} \cos 2t \\ -\cos 2t - \sin 2t \end{pmatrix} + c_2 \begin{pmatrix} \sin 2t \\ \cos 2t - \sin 2t \end{pmatrix} + \begin{pmatrix} 2+8t \\ -2-4t \end{pmatrix} \cos 2t + \begin{pmatrix} 4t \\ -12t \end{pmatrix} \sin 2t$

30. $\mathbf{X} = c_1 \begin{pmatrix} 1 \\ 0 \\ 0 \end{pmatrix} e^{-t} + c_2 \begin{pmatrix} t \\ 0 \\ 1 \end{pmatrix} e^{-t} + c_3 \begin{pmatrix} 0 \\ 1 \\ 0 \end{pmatrix} e^{2t} + \begin{pmatrix} 6t^2 + 8t \\ 0 \\ 12t \end{pmatrix} e^{-t} + \begin{pmatrix} 0 \\ -16t \\ 0 \end{pmatrix} e^{2t}$

31. $\mathbf{X} = \begin{pmatrix} 6t-1 \\ 6t+2 \end{pmatrix} e^{t}$

32. $\mathbf{X} = \begin{pmatrix} t^2 + 7t - 2 \\ t^2 + 8t + 1 \end{pmatrix} e^{t}$

33. $\mathbf{X} = \begin{pmatrix} 3t-2 \\ 0 \\ 3 \end{pmatrix} e^{-t} + \begin{pmatrix} 0 \\ 1 \\ 0 \end{pmatrix} e^{2t}$

34. $\mathbf{X} = \begin{pmatrix} 6t^2 + 11t - 2 \\ 0 \\ 12t + 3 \end{pmatrix} e^{-t} + \begin{pmatrix} 0 \\ -16t \\ 0 \end{pmatrix} e^{2t}$

235

9.1   Euler Methods and Error Analysis

1. Euler method truncation error

2. Euler method truncation error

3. Origin of Euler's method

4. Origin of improved Euler's method

5. Euler method truncation error

6. Improved Euler method truncation error

7. Euler method truncation error

8. Euler method truncation error

9. Improved Euler method truncation error

10. Ramifications of reducing step h

11. Determine local error bound of Euler's method for given IVP

12. Determine local error bound of Euler's method for given IVP

13. Determine local error bound of Euler's method for given IVP

14. Determine local error bound of Euler's method for given IVP

15. Determine local error bound of Euler's method for given IVP

16. Determine local error bound of Euler's method for given IVP

17. Determine local error bound of Euler's method for given IVP

18. Determine local error bound of Euler's method for given IVP

19. Use Euler's method to approximate solution of IVP using two different steps h and compare errors.

20. Use Euler's method to approximate solution of IVP using two different steps h and compare errors.

21. Use Euler's method to approximate solution of IVP using two different steps h and compare errors.

22. Use Euler's method to approximate solution of IVP using two different steps h and compare errors.

23. Use Euler's method to approximate solution of IVP using two different steps h.

24. Use Euler's method to approximate solution of IVP using two different steps h.

25. Use the improved Euler method to approximate solution of IVP using two different steps h and compare errors.

26. Use the improved Euler method to approximate solution of IVP using two different steps h and compare errors.

27. Use the improved Euler method to approximate solution of IVP using two different steps h and compare errors.

28. Use the improved Euler method to approximate solution of IVP using two different steps h and compare errors.

29. Use the improved Euler method to approximate solution of IVP using two different steps h.

30. Use the improved Euler method to approximate solution of IVP using two different steps h.

31. Computer Assignment: Use improved Euler method to approximate solution of projectile problem subject to drag.

1. The local truncation error of the Euler method is

    (a) $O(h)$.
    (b) $O(h^2)$.
    (c) $O(h^3)$.
    (d) $O(h^4)$.

2. The global truncation error of the improved Euler method is

    (a) $O(h)$.
    (b) $O(h^2)$.
    (c) $O(h^3)$.
    (d) $O(h^4)$.

3. The Euler method for approximating a solution of a DE $y' = f(x, y)$ at x_{n+1} was found by approximating solution $y(x)$ by

    (a) a 1st-order Taylor series about x_n.
    (b) a 1st-order Taylor series about x_{n+1}.
    (c) a 2nd-order Taylor series about x_n.
    (d) a 2nd-order Taylor series about x_{n+1}.

4. The improved Euler method for approximating a solution of a DE $y' = f(x, y)$ at x_{n+1} uses the slope of the tangent line to the solution through

    (a) x_{n-1}.
    (b) x_n.
    (c) x_{n+1}.
    (d) x_n and x_{n+1}.

5. If we use the Euler method twice to approximate the solution of a DE $y' = f(x, y)$ at a point x, first using $h = 0.6$ and then using $h = 0.2$, the ratio of global truncation errors $\left| \dfrac{\text{Error}(h = 0.6)}{\text{Error}(h = 0.2)} \right|$ should be about

    (a) 3.
    (b) 1/3.
    (c) 9.
    (d) 1/9.

6. If we use the improved Euler method twice to approximate the solution of a DE $y' = f(x, y)$ at a point x, first using $h = 0.4$ and then using $h = 0.1$, the ratio of global truncation errors $\left| \dfrac{\text{Error}(h = 0.1)}{\text{Error}(h = 0.4)} \right|$ should be about

    (a) 4.
    (b) 1/4.
    (c) 16.
    (d) 1/16.

7. The local truncation error in using Euler's method to approximate a solution of a DE $y' = f(x, y)$ at a point x originates from

   (a) computer round off error.

   (b) approximating the differential equation by an algebraic equation.

   (c) approximating the solution curve by a tangent line.

   (d) b and c

8. With h held constant, as we use Euler's method to approximate a solution of a DE $y' = f(x, y)$ at successive points $x_1, x_2, x_3, \ldots$, the global truncation errors tend to

   (a) remain approximately constant.

   (b) decrease.

   (c) increase.

   (d) be uncertain.

9. With h held constant, as we use the improved Euler's method to approximate a solution of a DE $y' = f(x, y)$ at successive points $x_1, x_2, x_3, \ldots$, the local truncation errors tend to

   (a) remain approximately constant.

   (b) decrease.

   (c) increase.

   (d) be uncertain.

10. A disadvantage to reducing h when using Euler's method to approximate a solution of a DE $y' = f(x, y)$ on interval $[a, b]$ is

   (a) increased number of calculations.

   (b) increased local truncation error.

   (c) increased global truncation error.

   (d) b and c

Problems 11-18: The solution to each of the following initial value problems is given. Determine a bound for the local truncation error for Euler's method on the given interval if $h = 0.1$.

11. $y' = y \cos x$, $y(0) = 1$, on interval $[0, 2]$. The exact solution is $y(x) = e^{\sin x}$.

12. $y' + 2(x - 1)y = 0$, $y(1) = 1$, on interval $[1, 3]$. The exact solution is $y(x) = e^{-(x-1)^2}$.

13. $xy' - y = -x^2 \sin x$, $y(0) = 0$, on interval $[0, 2]$. The exact solution is $y(x) = x \cos x$.

14. $y' = e^{-y}$, $y(0) = 1$, on interval $[0, 2]$. The exact solution is $y(x) = \ln(x + e)$.

15. $y' = 2xe^{-y}$, $y(0) = 1$, on interval $[0, 2]$. The exact solution is $y(x) = \ln(x^2 + e)$.

16. $y' + y^2 = 0$, $y(0) = 2$, on interval $[0, 4]$. The exact solution is $y(x) = \dfrac{2}{2x + 1}$.

17. $xy' + 2y = xy^2$, $y(1) = 1/2$, on interval $[1, 6]$. The exact solution is $y(x) = \dfrac{1}{x(x + 1)}$.

18. $y^2 y' = x^2$, $y(0) = 1$, on interval $[0, 2]$. The exact solution is $y(x) = (x^3 + 1)^{1/3}$.

239

Problems 19-22: Use the Euler method with the specified h to approximate the solution of the initial value problem on the given interval. The exact solution is given — use it to determine the actual solution and the percent relative error of the approximate solution at each x. Is the ratio of errors at each common x from parts (a) and (b) what we would expect?

19. $y' = y \cos x$, $\quad y(0) = 1$, $\quad$ on interval $[0, 2]$,

    (a) with $h = 0.4$, and

    (b) with $h = 0.2$.

    The exact solution is $y(x) = e^{\sin x}$.

20. $y' = 2y(1 - x)$, $\quad y(1) = 1$, $\quad$ on interval $[1, 2]$,

    (a) with $h = 0.2$, and

    (b) with $h = 0.1$.

    The exact solution is $y(x) = e^{-(x-1)^2}$.

21. $y' = e^{-y}$, $\quad y(0) = 1$, $\quad$ on interval $[0, 2]$,

    (a) with $h = 0.4$, and

    (b) with $h = 0.2$.

    The exact solution is $y(x) = \ln(x + e)$.

22. $x y' + 2y = x y^2$, $\quad y(1) = 1/2$, $\quad$ on interval $[1, 2]$,

    (a) with $h = 0.2$, and

    (b) with $h = 0.1$.

    The exact solution is $y(x) = \dfrac{1}{x(x+1)}$.

Problems 23-24: Use the Euler method with the specified h to approximate the solution of the initial value problem on the given interval.

23. $y' = \cos(2xy^2)$, $\quad y(1) = 0$, $\quad$ on interval $[1, 4]$,

    (a) with $h = 0.50$, and

    (b) with $h = 0.25$.

    (c) How well do the results compare at common x values? What does this suggest that we do?

24. $y' = y|y| + \cos(xy)$, $\quad y(2) = 0.5$, $\quad$ on interval $[2, 5]$,

    (a) with $h = 0.50$, and

    (b) with $h = 0.25$.

    (c) How well do the results compare at common x values? What does this suggest that we do?

25. Redo problem 19, this time using the improved Euler method.

26. Redo problem 20, this time using the improved Euler method.

27. Redo problem 21, this time using the improved Euler method.

28. Redo problem 22, this time using the improved Euler method.

29. Redo problem 23, this time using the improved Euler method.

30. Redo problem 24, this time using the improved Euler method.

Computer Assignment:

31. Consider projectile motion where air resistance (drag force f_d) is included. Air resistance is proportional to the square of velocity and opposes motion. Thus, $f_d = -\beta |v| v$ where β is the drag coefficient (a positive constant), so Newton's second law gives

$$m \frac{dv}{dt} = -mg - \beta |v| v.$$

   (a) Use the improved Euler method to approximate v vs. time t on the time interval $[0, 20]$ if the mass is $m = 0.5$ slugs, $\beta = 0.0005$, the initial velocity is $v(0) = 200$ ft/s, and $h = 1$ s.

   i. Approximately when does the projectile attain its maximum height? Interpolate to obtain an estimate.

   ii. Note that as time passes, the object attains a nearly constant speed, called the *terminal speed*. What is the approximate terminal speed?

   (b) Redo (a) with $h = 0.5$ s.

   i. Approximately when does the projectile attain its maximum height? Interpolate to obtain an estimate.

   ii. What is the approximate terminal speed?

1. b

2. b

3. a

4. d

5. a

6. d

7. d

8. c

9. a

10. a

11. $|\text{local error}| \le 0.01359$

12. $|\text{local error}| \le 0.01$

13. $|\text{local error}| \le 0.011495$

14. $|\text{local error}| \le 0.000676676$

15. $|\text{local error}| \le 0.0036788$

16. $|\text{local error}| \le 0.08$

17. $|\text{local error}| \le 0.00875$

18. $|\text{local error}| \le 0.0043431$

19.

a) $h = 0.4$

x_n	y_n	Exact y	% Error
0.0	1.000000	1.000000	—
0.4	1.400000	1.476122	5.16
0.8	1.915794	2.049009	6.50
1.2	2.449693	2.539683	3.54
1.6	2.804759	2.717123	3.22
2.0	2.772000	2.482578	11.66

b) $h = 0.2$

x_n	y_n	Exact y	% Error
0.0	1.000000	1.000000	—
0.2	1.200000	1.219779	1.62
0.4	1.435216	1.476122	2.77
0.6	1.699600	1.758819	3.37
0.8	1.980148	2.049009	3.36
1.0	2.256065	2.319777	2.75
1.2	2.499856	2.539683	1.57
1.4	2.681025	2.679016	0.08
1.6	2.772162	2.717123	2.03
1.8	2.755973	2.648114	4.07
2.0	2.630740	2.482578	5.97

20.

a) $h = 0.2$

x_n	y_n	Exact y	% Error
1.0	1.000000	1.000000	—
1.2	1.000000	0.960789	4.08
1.4	0.920000	0.852144	7.96
1.6	0.772800	0.697676	10.8
1.8	0.587328	0.527292	11.4
2.0	0.399393	0.367879	8.56

b) $h = 0.1$

x_n	y_n	Exact y	% Error
1.0	1.000000	1.000000	—
1.1	1.000000	0.990050	1.00
1.2	0.980000	0.960789	2.00
1.3	0.940800	0.913931	2.94
1.4	0.884352	0.852144	3.78
1.5	0.813604	0.778801	4.47
1.6	0.732243	0.697676	4.95
1.7	0.644374	0.612626	5.18
1.8	0.554162	0.527292	5.10
1.9	0.465496	0.444858	4.64
2.0	0.381707	0.367879	3.76

21.

a) $h = 0.4$

x_n	y_n	Exact y	% Error
0.0	1.000000	1.000000	—
0.4	1.147152	1.137282	0.87
0.8	1.274168	1.257973	1.29
1.2	1.386033	1.365653	1.49
1.6	1.486059	1.462858	1.59
2.0	1.576564	1.551445	1.62

b) $h = 0.2$

x_n	y_n	Exact y	% Error
0.0	1.000000	1.000000	—
0.2	1.073576	1.070995	0.24
0.4	1.141933	1.137282	0.41
0.6	1.205773	1.199447	0.53
0.8	1.265665	1.257973	0.61
1.0	1.322075	1.313262	0.67
1.2	1.375392	1.365653	0.71
1.4	1.425940	1.415436	0.74
1.6	1.473996	1.462858	0.76
1.8	1.519798	1.508132	0.77
2.0	1.563549	1.551445	0.78

22.

a) $h = 0.2$

x_n	y_n	Exact y	% Error
1.0	0.500000	0.500000	—
1.2	0.350000	0.378388	7.60
1.4	0.257833	0.297619	13.4
1.6	0.197462	0.240385	17.9
1.8	0.155895	0.198413	21.4
2.0	0.126112	0.166667	24.3

b) $h = 0.1$

x_n	y_n	Exact y	% Error
1.0	0.500000	0.500000	—
1.1	0.425000	0.432900	1.83
1.2	0.365790	0.378388	3.43
1.3	0.318205	0.324448	4.86
1.4	0.279376	0.297619	6.13
1.5	0.247270	0.266667	7.27
1.6	0.220415	0.240385	8.31
1.7	0.197721	0.217865	9.25
1.8	0.178369	0.198413	10.1
1.9	0.161732	0.181488	10.9
2.0	0.147323	0.166667	11.6

23.

b) $h = 0.25$

x_n	y_n
1.00	0.0000 0000 0000
1.25	0.2500 0000 0000
1.50	0.4969 5444 5954
1.75	0.6814 2128 7059
2.00	0.6678 3396 7652
2.25	0.6149 3378 0267
2.50	0.5823 1463 2052
2.75	0.5512 3144 6563
3.00	0.5261 7054 3066
3.25	0.5036 1716 8441
3.50	0.4841 8670 5662
3.75	0.4666 3589 5546
4.00	0.4510 6557 5311

a) $h = 0.50$

x_n	y_n
1.0	0.0000 0000 0000
1.5	0.5000 0000 0000
2.0	0.8658 4443 4437
2.5	0.3709 3703 3453
3.0	0.7572 0488 2288
3.5	0.2793 2476 2795
4.0	0.7065 8840 8928

c) The results at common x's do not agree well. This suggests that we should recalculate the approximate solution using a smaller step h.

24.

b) $h = 0.25$

x_n	y_n
2.00	0.5000 0000 0000
2.25	0.6975 7557 6467
2.50	0.8195 4131 7542
2.75	0.8724 3959 9187
3.00	0.8785 1253 1640
3.25	0.8527 9271 3155
3.50	0.8015 2620 6510
3.75	0.7261 3769 5606
4.00	0.6295 3954 7527
4.25	0.5256 5002 8881
4.50	0.4408 1338 5797
4.75	0.3890 8393 5934
5.00	0.3584 7797 2574

a) $h = 0.50$

x_n	y_n
2.0	0.5000 0000 0000
2.5	0.8951 5115 2934
3.0	0.9864 5104 3374
3.5	0.9812 7373 1372
4.0	0.9840 1251 2564
4.5	1.1178 1682 1151
5.0	1.8988 0647 5552

c) The results at common x's do not agree well. This suggests that we should recalculate the approximate solution using a smaller step h.

25.

a) $h = 0.4$

x_n	y_n	Exact y	% Error
0.0	1.00000000	1.00000000	—
0.4	1.45789707	1.47612195	1.235
0.8	2.00444853	2.04900865	2.175
1.2	2.46949955	2.53968253	2.764
1.6	2.63195606	2.71712301	3.135
2.0	2.40008818	2.48257773	3.323

b) $h = 0.2$

x_n	y_n	Exact y	% Error
0.0	1.00000000	1.00000000	—
0.2	1.21760799	1.21977856	0.178
0.4	1.47107352	1.47612195	0.342
0.6	1.75024705	1.75881885	0.482
0.8	2.03688686	2.04900865	0.592
1.0	2.30418660	2.31977768	0.672
1.2	2.52119872	2.53968253	0.728
1.4	2.65851396	2.67901645	0.765
1.6	2.69567335	2.71712301	0.789
1.8	2.62691351	2.64811385	0.801
2.0	2.46287878	2.48257773	0.794

244

b) h = 0.1

x_n	y_n	Exact y	% Error
1.0	1.00000000	1.00000000	—
1.1	0.99000000	0.99004983	0.00503
1.2	0.96069600	0.96078944	0.00973
1.3	0.91381404	0.91393119	0.01282
1.4	0.85204021	0.85214379	0.01216
1.5	0.77876475	0.77880078	0.00463
1.6	0.69777321	0.69767633	0.01389
1.7	0.61292399	0.61262639	0.04863
1.8	0.52785014	0.52729242	0.10577
1.9	0.44571666	0.44485807	0.19300
2.0	0.36905339	0.36787944	0.31911

a) h = 0.2

	x_n	y_n	Exact y	% Error
	1.0	1.00000000	1.00000000	—
26.	1.2	0.96000000	0.96078944	0.0822
	1.4	0.85094400	0.85214379	0.1408
	1.6	0.69709332	0.69767633	0.0836
	1.8	0.52867558	0.52729242	0.2623
	2.0	0.37218761	0.36787944	1.1711

b) h = 0.2

x_n	y_n	Exact y	% Error
0.0	1.00000000	1.00000000	—
0.2	1.07096637	1.07099503	0.00268
0.4	1.13723192	1.13728215	0.00442
0.6	1.19938057	1.19944713	0.00555
0.8	1.25789379	1.25797275	0.00628
1.0	1.31317330	1.31326169	0.00673
1.2	1.36555772	1.36565325	0.00699
1.4	1.41533514	1.41543604	0.00713
1.6	1.46275270	1.46285760	0.00717
1.8	1.50802399	1.50813180	0.00715
2.0	1.55133486	1.55144471	0.00708

a) h = 0.4

	x_n	y_n	Exact y	% Error
	0.0	1.00000000	1.00000000	—
27.	0.4	1.13708387	1.13728215	0.01743
	0.8	1.25766060	1.25797275	0.02481
	1.2	1.36527518	1.36565325	0.02768
	1.6	1.46244211	1.46285760	0.02840
	2.0	1.55100930	1.55144472	0.02807

b) h = 0.1

x_n	y_n	Exact y	% Error
1.0	0.50000000	0.50000000	—
1.1	0.43289489	0.43290043	0.00128
1.2	0.37878720	0.37838788	0.00018
1.3	0.32445580	0.32444816	0.00228
1.4	0.29763540	0.29761905	0.00550
1.5	0.26669089	0.26666667	0.00908
1.6	0.24041544	0.24038462	0.01282
1.7	0.21790103	0.21786492	0.01657
1.8	0.19845288	0.19841270	0.02025
1.9	0.18153141	0.18148820	0.02381
2.0	0.16671203	0.16666667	0.02722

a) h = 0.2

	x_n	y_n	Exact y	% Error
	1.0	0.50000000	0.50000000	—
28.	1.2	0.37891667	0.37838788	0.03400
	1.4	0.29784662	0.29761905	0.07646
	1.6	0.24066967	0.24038462	0.11858
	1.8	0.19872492	0.19841270	0.15736
	2.0	0.16698671	0.16666667	0.19203

29.

a) $h = 0.50$

x_n	y_n
1.0	0.0000 0000 0000
1.5	0.4329 2221 7218
2.0	0.3999 7974 2861
2.5	0.3510 7074 2683
3.0	0.3174 4331 2880
3.5	0.3135 2511 0952
4.0	0.3281 5486 6322

b) $h = 0.25$

x_n	y_n
1.00	0.0000 0000 0000
1.25	0.2484 7722 2977
1.50	0.4645 8777 9946
1.75	0.5677 5240 2120
2.00	0.5902 7143 4209
2.25	0.5826 0347 1779
2.50	0.5644 0623 8086
2.75	0.5433 1193 0667
3.00	0.5223 2305 5833
3.25	0.5025 6184 0490
3.50	0.4843 6885 0646
3.75	0.4677 6415 9157
4.00	0.4526 4571 5679

c) The results at common x's do not agree well. This suggests that we should recalculate the approximate solution using a smaller step h.

30.

a) $h = 0.50$

x_n	y_n
2.0	0.5000 0000 0000
2.5	0.7432 2552 1687
3.0	0.7847 1164 1633
3.5	0.6862 3989 6328
4.0	0.5465 4792 7385
4.5	0.4536 4470 2769
5.0	0.3993 6666 3477

b) $h = 0.25$

x_n	y_n
2.00	0.5000 0000 0000
2.25	0.6597 7065 8771
2.50	0.7537 9700 1095
2.75	0.7913 7433 3675
3.00	0.7860 5539 5509
3.25	0.7488 6827 5864
3.50	0.6890 5571 6351
3.75	0.6174 4347 1362
4.00	0.5464 4724 6514
4.25	0.4850 4891 0088
4.50	0.4357 9781 2226
4.75	0.3971 1417 7287
5.00	0.3663 7660 4942

c) The results at common x's do not agree well. This suggests that we should recalculate the approximate solution using a smaller step h.

	a) $h = 1$ s		b) $h = 0.5$ s		b) $h = 0.5$ s
t_n	v_n	t_n	v_n	t_n	v_n
0.0	200.000 000 000	0.0	200.000 000 000	10.0	−131.978 735 580
1.0	139.808 000 000	0.5	167.276 000 000	10.5	−138.775 137 569
2.0	95.139 795 683	1.0	139.568 866 758	11.0	−144.693 672 105
3.0	56.289 399 404	1.5	115.459 731 766	11.5	−149.817 678 996
4.0	22.442 104 891	2.0	93.974 300 821	12.0	−154.231 440 441
5.0	−9.720 383 955	2.5	74.413 787 335	12.5	−158.016 893 639
6.0	−40.806 783 327	3.0	56.255 340 626	13.0	−161.251 394 098
7.0	−69.443 623 647	3.5	39.090 274 383	13.5	−164.006 343 580
8.0	−94.364 586 415	4.0	22.583 646 640	14.0	−166.346 489 583
9.0	−115.013 833 455	4.5	6.446 128 457	14.5	−168.329 719 044
10.0	−131.450 442 229	5.0	−9.541 341 216	15.0	−170.007 195 772
11.0	−144.127 819 563	5.5	−25.356 072 675	15.5	−171.423 721 197
12.0	−153.673 818 733	6.0	−40.774 380 317	16.0	−172.618 226 619
13.0	−160.734 571 220	6.5	−55.576 335 038	16.5	−173.624 329 990
14.0	−165.889 137 128	7.0	−69.578 033 559	17.0	−174.470 910 463
15.0	−169.616 577 472	7.5	−82.638 966 160	17.5	−175.182 669 729
16.0	−172.293 678 677	8.0	−94.664 746 470	18.0	−175.780 660 886
17.0	−174.207 046 992	8.5	−105.605 630 361	18.5	−176.282 774 105
18.0	−175.569 813 922	9.0	−115.451 790 219	19.0	−176.704 174 252
19.0	−176.538 027 021	9.5	−124.226 547 917	19.5	−177.057 689 576
20.0	−177.224 713 896	10.0	−131.978 735 580	20.0	−177.354 153 097

a.i. The projectile attains its maximum height between $t = 4$ and $t = 5$ seconds — interpolation indicates at about $t = 4.7$ seconds.

a.ii. The terminal speed of this object is about 177 f/s or slightly more.

b.i. The projectile attains its maximum height between $t = 4.5$ and $t = 5.0$ seconds — interpolation indicates at about $t = 4.7$ seconds.

b.ii. The terminal speed of this object is about 177 f/s or slightly more.

1. classical Runge-Kutta method truncation error

2. Runge-Kutta-Fehlberg method truncation error

3. general Runge-Kutta method truncation error

4. general Runge-Kutta method — concepts

5. classical Runge-Kutta method — concepts

6. classical Runge-Kutta method — concepts

7. Runge-Kutta-Fehlberg method — concepts

8. origin of error in general Runge-Kutta methods

9. classical Runge-Kutta method local truncation error

10. classical Runge-Kutta method global truncation error

11. general question about step h

12. True/False

13. True/False

14. True/False

15. Estimate global truncation error in classical Runge-Kutta if h is reduced.

16. Estimate global truncation error in Runge-Kutta-Fehlberg if h is reduced.

17. Use the classical Runge-Kutta method to approximate the solution of IVP using two different steps h and compare errors.

18. Use the classical Runge-Kutta method to approximate the solution of IVP using two different steps h and compare errors.

19. Use the classical Runge-Kutta method to approximate the solution of IVP using two different steps h and compare errors.

20. Use the classical Runge-Kutta method to approximate the solution of IVP using two different steps h and compare errors.

21. Use the classical Runge-Kutta method to approximate the solution of IVP using two different steps h.

22. Use the classical Runge-Kutta method to approximate the solution of IVP using two different steps h.

23. Computer Assignment: Use classical Runge-Kutta method to approximate solution of projectile problem subject to drag.

1. The global truncation error of the classical Runge-Kutta method is

   (a) $O(h^2)$.
   (b) $O(h^3)$.
   (c) $O(h^4)$.
   (d) $O(h^5)$.

2. The global truncation error of the Runge-Kutta-Fehlberg method is

   (a) $O(h^2)$.
   (b) $O(h^3)$.
   (c) $O(h^4)$.
   (d) $O(h^5)$.

3. A Runge-Kutta method of order m agrees with a Taylor series expansion of solution $y(x)$ of degree

   (a) m.
   (b) $m - 1$.
   (c) $m + 1$.
   (d) $2m$.

4. When calculating y_{n+1} to approximate a solution of a DE $y' = f(x, y)$ at x_{n+1}, a Runge-Kutta method of order m evaluates function f at

   (a) 1 point.
   (b) 2 points.
   (c) m points.
   (d) $2m$ points.

5. When calculating y_{n+1} to approximate a solution of a DE $y' = f(x, y)$ at x_{n+1}, the classical Runge-Kutta method evaluates function f at

   (a) 1 point.
   (b) 2 points.
   (c) 3 points.
   (d) 4 points.

6. When calculating y_{n+1} to approximate a solution of a DE $y' = f(x, y)$ at x_{n+1}, the classical Runge-Kutta method evaluates function f twice at the midpoint $x_n + h/2$ in order to determine

   (a) k_1 and k_2.
   (b) k_2 and k_3.
   (c) k_3 and k_4.
   (d) k_1 and k_4.

7. The Runge-Kutta-Fehlberg method is an example of

   (a) a predictor-corrector method.
   (b) a classical method.
   (c) an adaptive method.
   (d) a naive Euler method.

8. The local truncation error in using a Runge-Kutta method to approximate a solution of a DE $y' = f(x, y)$ at a point x originates from

   (a) computer round off error.

   (b) approximating the differential equation by an algebraic equation.

   (c) approximating the solution curve by a tangent line.

   (d) b and c

9. With h held constant, as we use the classical Runge-Kutta method to approximate a solution of a DE $y' = f(x, y)$ at successive points $x_1, x_2, x_3, \ldots$, the global truncation errors tend to

   (a) remain approximately constant.

   (b) decrease.

   (c) increase.

   (d) be uncertain.

10. With h held constant, as we use the the classical Runge-Kutta method to approximate a solution of a DE $y' = f(x, y)$ at successive points $x_1, x_2, x_3, \ldots$, the local truncation errors tend to

    (a) remain approximately constant.

    (b) decrease.

    (c) increase.

    (d) be uncertain.

11. A method that is very effective at allowing us to change the step h while perofming calculation is the

    (a) Euler method.

    (b) improved Euler method.

    (c) classical Runge-Kutta method.

    (d) Runge-Kutta-Fehlberg method.

12. True or False: The Euler method is a Runge-Kutta method.

13. True or False: The improved Euler method is a Runge-Kutta method.

14. True or False: When using the classical Runge-Kutta method, we must always calculate k_1, k_2, k_3, and k_4 in that order.

15. If we use the classical Runge-Kutta method twice to approximate the solution of a DE $y' = f(x, y)$ at a point x, first using $h = 0.6$ and then using $h = 0.2$, approximate the ratio of global truncation

    errors $\left| \dfrac{\text{Error}(h = 0.6)}{\text{Error}(h = 0.2)} \right|$. Interpret the result.

16. If we use the Runge-Kutta-Fehlberg method twice to approximate the solution of a DE $y' = f(x, y)$ at a point x, first using $h = 0.4$ and then using $h = 0.2$, approximate the ratio of global truncation

    errors $\left| \dfrac{\text{Error}(h = 0.4)}{\text{Error}(h = 0.2)} \right|$. Interpret the result.

Problems 17-20: Use the classical Runge-Kutta method with the specified h to approximate the solution of the initial value problem on the given interval. The exact solution is given — use it to determine the actual solution and the percent relative error of the approximate solution at each x. Is the ratio of errors at each common x from parts (a) and (b) what we would expect?

17. $y' = y \cos x$, $\quad y(0) = 1$, $\quad$ on interval $[0, 2]$,

    (a) with $h = 0.4$, and

    (b) with $h = 0.2$.

    The exact solution is $y(x) = e^{\sin x}$.

18. $y' = 2y(1 - x)$, $\quad y(1) = 1$, $\quad$ on interval $[1, 2]$,

    (a) with $h = 0.2$, and

    (b) with $h = 0.1$.

    The exact solution is $y(x) = e^{-(x-1)^2}$.

19. $y' = e^{-y}$, $\quad y(0) = 1$, $\quad$ on interval $[0, 2]$,

    (a) with $h = 0.4$, and

    (b) with $h = 0.2$.

    The exact solution is $y(x) = \ln(x + e)$.

20. $x y' + 2y = x y^2$, $\quad y(1) = 1/2$, $\quad$ on interval $[1, 2]$,

    (a) with $h = 0.2$, and

    (b) with $h = 0.1$.

    The exact solution is $y(x) = \dfrac{1}{x(x + 1)}$.

Problems 21-22: Use the classical Runge-Kutta method with the specified h to approximate the solution of the initial value problem on the given interval.

21. $y' = \cos(2xy^2)$, $\quad y(1) = 0$, $\quad$ on interval $[1, 4]$,

    (a) with $h = 0.50$, and

    (b) with $h = 0.25$.

    (c) How well do the results compare at common x values? What does this suggest that we do?

22. $y' = y|y| + \cos(xy)$, $\quad y(2) = 0.5$, $\quad$ on interval $[2, 5]$,

    (a) with $h = 0.50$, and

    (b) with $h = 0.25$.

    (c) How well do the results compare at common x values? What does this suggest that we do?

Computer Assignment:

23. Consider projectile motion where air resistance (drag force f_d) is included. Air resistance is proportional to the square of velocity and opposes motion. Thus, $f_d = -\beta|v|v$ where β is the drag coefficient (a positive constant), so Newton's second law gives

$$m\frac{dv}{dt} = -mg - \beta|v|v\,.$$

(a) Use the classical Runge-Kutta method to approximate v vs. time t on the time interval $[0, 20]$ if the mass is $m = 0.5$ slugs, $\beta = 0.0005$, the initial velocity is $v(0) = 200$ ft/s, and $h = 4$ s.

   i. Approximately when does the projectile attain its maximum height? Interpolate to obtain an estimate.

   ii. Note that as time passes, the object attains a nearly constant speed, called the *terminal speed*. What is the approximate terminal speed?

(b) Redo (a) with $h = 2$ s.

   i. Approximately when does the projectile attain its maximum height? Interpolate to obtain an estimate.

   ii. What is the approximate terminal speed?

(c) Redo (a) with $h = 1$ s.

   i. Approximately when does the projectile attain its maximum height? Interpolate to obtain an estimate.

   ii. What is the approximate terminal speed?

1. c

2. d

3. a

4. c

5. d

6. b

7. c

8. d

9. c

10. a

11. d

12. True

13. True

14. True

15. The ratio of errors is about 81. So the global errors when using $h = 0.6$ are about 81 times larger than the errors when using $h = 0.2$.

16. The ratio of errors is about 32. So the global errors when using $h = 0.4$ are about 32 times larger than the errors when using $h = 0.2$.

17.

a) $h = 0.4$

x_n	y_n	Exact y	% Error
0.0	1.0000000	1.0000000	—
0.4	1.4760281	2.4761220	6.36×10^{-3}
0.8	2.0488072	2.0490087	9.83×10^{-3}
1.2	2.5394068	2.5396825	1.09×10^{-2}
1.6	2.7168263	2.7171230	1.09×10^{-2}
2.0	2.4822986	2.4825777	1.12×10^{-2}

b) $h = 0.2$

x_n	y_n	Exact y	% Error
0.0	1.0000000	1.0000000	—
0.2	1.2197757	1.2197786	2.31×10^{-3}
0.4	1.4761157	1.4761219	4.25×10^{-3}
0.6	1.7588090	1.7588189	5.59×10^{-3}
0.8	2.0489956	2.0490087	6.35×10^{-3}
1.0	2.3197613	2.3197777	6.70×10^{-3}
1.2	2.5396652	2.5396825	6.81×10^{-3}
1.4	2.6789981	2.6790165	6.83×10^{-3}
1.6	2.7171045	2.7171230	6.83×10^{-3}
1.8	2.6480957	2.6481140	6.85×10^{-3}
2.0	2.4825605	2.4825777	6.95×10^{-3}

18.

a) $h = 0.2$

x_n	y_n	% Error
1.0	1.0000 0000	—
1.2	0.9607 8933	1.10×10^{-5}
1.4	0.8521 4297	9.63×10^{-5}
1.6	0.6976 7558	1.07×10^{-4}
1.8	0.5272 9777	1.01×10^{-3}
2.0	0.3679 0367	6.59×10^{-3}

b) $h = 0.1$

x_n	y_n	Exact y	% Error
1.0	1.0000 0000	1.0000 0000	—
1.1	0.9900 4983	0.9900 4983	4.20×10^{-8}
1.2	0.9607 8943	0.9607 8944	4.08×10^{-7}
1.3	0.9139 3117	0.9139 3119	1.23×10^{-6}
1.4	0.8521 4377	0.8521 4379	1.94×10^{-6}
1.5	0.7788 0078	0.7788 0078	3.25×10^{-7}
1.6	0.6876 7639	0.6976 7633	8.76×10^{-6}
1.7	0.6126 2661	0.6126 2639	3.52×10^{-5}
1.8	0.5272 9293	0.5272 9241	9.61×10^{-5}
1.9	0.4448 5904	0.4448 5807	2.18×10^{-4}
2.0	0.3678 8197	0.3678 7944	4.42×10^{-4}

19.

a) $h = 0.4$

x_n	y_n	% Error
0.0	1.0000 0000	—
0.4	1.1372 8235	1.73×10^{-5}
0.8	1.2579 7303	2.18×10^{-5}
1.2	1.3656 5355	2.21×10^{-5}
1.6	1.4628 5790	2.10×10^{-5}
2.0	1.5514 4501	1.94×10^{-5}

b) $h = 0.2$

x_n	y_n	Exact y	% Error
0.0	1.0000 0000	1.0000 0000	—
0.2	1.0709 9503	1.0709 9503	6.03×10^{-7}
0.4	1.1372 8216	1.1372 8215	9.31×10^{-7}
0.6	1.1994 4714	1.1994 4713	1.10×10^{-6}
0.8	1.2579 9728	1.2579 7275	1.18×10^{-6}
1.0	1.3132 6170	1.3132 6169	1.21×10^{-6}
1.2	1.3656 5327	1.3656 5325	1.20×10^{-6}
1.4	1.4154 3606	1.4154 3604	1.18×10^{-6}
1.6	1.4628 5761	1.4628 5760	1.14×10^{-6}
1.8	1.5081 3181	1.5081 3180	1.10×10^{-6}
2.0	1.5514 4473	1.5514 4447	1.06×10^{-6}

20.

a) $h = 0.2$

x_n	y_n	% Error
1.0	0.5000 0000	—
1.2	0.3787 9594	2.13×10^{-3}
1.4	0.2976 2866	3.23×10^{-3}
1.6	0.2403 9397	3.89×10^{-3}
1.8	0.1984 2130	4.33×10^{-3}
2.0	0.1666 7443	4.66×10^{-3}

b) $h = 0.1$

x_n	y_n	Exact y	% Error
1.0	0.5000 0000	0.5000 0000	—
1.1	0.4329 0071	0.4329 0043	6.44×10^{-5}
1.2	0.3787 8829	0.3783 8787	1.10×10^{-4}
1.3	0.3344 4864	0.3244 4816	1.43×10^{-4}
1.4	0.2976 1955	0.2976 1905	1.68×10^{-4}
1.5	0.2666 6717	0.2666 6667	1.88×10^{-4}
1.6	0.2403 8510	0.2403 8462	2.04×10^{-4}
1.7	0.2178 6540	0.2178 6492	2.17×10^{-4}
1.8	0.1984 1315	0.1984 1270	2.28×10^{-4}
1.9	0.1814 8863	0.1814 8820	2.37×10^{-4}
2.0	0.1666 6708	0.1666 6667	2.45×10^{-4}

21.

a) $h = 0.50$

x_n	y_n
1.0	0.0000 0000 0000
1.5	0.4746 5046 7393
2.0	0.5807 0753 9957
2.5	0.5364 9805 5947
3.0	0.4821 2811 9214
3.5	0.4395 9590 8252
4.0	0.4278 6456 3849

b) $h = 0.25$

x_n	y_n
1.00	0.0000 0000 0000
1.25	0.2493 9079 6391
1.50	0.4775 4391 0201
1.75	0.6073 0325 6757
2.00	0.6302 9262 8721
2.25	0.6105 6355 2149
2.50	0.5812 9329 1714
2.75	0.5527 4552 0179
3.00	0.5272 2214 8355
3.25	0.5047 7960 3202
3.50	0.4849 8690 5272
3.75	0.4673 9304 1179
4.00	0.4516 2279 8442

c) The results at common x's do not agree well. This suggests that we should recalculate the approximate solution using a smaller step h.

22.

a) $h = 0.50$

x_n	y_n
2.0	0.5000 0000 0000
2.5	0.7600 0044 0889
3.0	0.7918 5534 9493
3.5	0.6940 3203 5762
4.0	0.5473 3505 8601
4.5	0.4342 9410 5973
5.0	0.3665 5448 8560

b) $h = 0.25$

x_n	y_n
2.00	0.5000 0000 0000
2.25	0.6643 4836 5786
2.50	0.7597 5850 0640
2.75	0.7969 4972 4033
3.00	0.7910 5750 7244
3.25	0.7534 9291 6177
3.50	0.6931 5972 8212
3.75	0.6202 3793 0376
4.00	0.5468 9913 6896
4.25	0.4829 8352 1225
4.50	0.4321 5408 1389
4.75	0.3930 6687 7647
5.00	0.3626 6916 4499

c) The results at common x's agree fairly well. This suggests that we could keep the results for the $h = 0.25$ run or recalculate the approximate solution using a smaller step h for more accuracy.

a) $h = 4$ s

t_n	v_n
0.0	200.0000 0000 0000
4.0	18.6982 4362 5656
8.0	−97.4527 6229 0490
12.0	−153.9874 5055 9712
16.0	−171.7793 7553 1789
20.0	−176.8890 4722 0949

b) $h = 2$ s

23.

t_n	v_n
0.0	200.0000 0000 0000
2.0	93.7175 4819 2758
4.0	22.4349 1282 9230
6.0	−41.0346 3974 1783
8.0	−94.9424 9942 2191
10.0	−132.2175 6838 2847
12.0	−154.4032 3547 0481
14.0	−166.4563 4582 5904
16.0	−172.6837 0965 5965
18.0	−175.8180 9516 7882
20.0	−177.3750 0219 3378

b) $h = 0.5$ s

t_n	v_n
0.0	200.0000 0000 0000
1.0	139.4559 1376 6401
2.0	93.8753 8218 0314
3.0	56.1966 9118 1731
4.0	22.5690 1352 2200
5.0	−9.5285 0789 2335
6.0	−40.8064 5875 2571
7.0	−69.6564 6279 9458
8.0	−94.7857 7658 1904
9.0	−115.6053 8819 3959
10.0	−132.1507 4911 6453
11.0	−144.8695 5212 8698
12.0	−154.3992 7483 8087
13.0	−161.4032 5950 1910
14.0	−166.4783 5677 7679
15.0	−170.1180 7423 0698
16.0	−172.7091 2917 2752
17.0	−174.5439 5589 0894
18.0	−175.8384 2091 9956
19.0	−176.7492 5623 9227
20.0	−177.3889 6593 5883

a.i. The projectile attains its maximum height between $t = 4$ and $t = 8$ seconds — interpolation indicates at about $t = 4.64$ seconds.

a.ii. The terminal speed of this object is about 176.9 f/s or slightly more.

b.i. The projectile attains its maximum height between $t = 4$ and $t = 6$ seconds — interpolation indicates at about $t = 4.707$ seconds.

b.ii. The terminal speed of this object is about 177.4 f/s or slightly more.

c.i. The projectile attains its maximum height between $t = 4$ and $t = 5$ seconds — interpolation indicates at about $t = 4.703$ seconds.

c.ii. The terminal speed of this object is about 177.4 f/s or slightly more.

1. properties of predictor-corrector methods

2. properties of the Adams-Bashforth-Moulton method

3. properties of the Adams-Bashforth-Moulton method

4. properties of the Adams-Bashforth-Moulton method

5. result of changing stepsize h in the Adams-Bashforth-Moulton method

6. starting values for the Adams-Bashforth-Moulton method

7. result of changing stepsize h in the Adams-Bashforth-Moulton method

8. stable numerical methods

9. starting values for the Adams-Bashforth-Moulton method

10. properties of predictor-corrector methods

11. properties of the Adams-Bashforth-Moulton method

12. comparison of the Adams-Bashforth-Moulton and Runge-Kutta-Fehlberg methods

13. comparison of the Adams-Bashforth-Moulton and classical Runge-Kutta methods

14. comparison of the Adams-Bashforth-Moulton and classical Runge-Kutta methods

15. comparison of the Adams-Bashforth-Moulton and classical Runge-Kutta methods

16. result of changing stepsize h in the Adams-Bashforth-Moulton method

17. result of changing stepsize h in the Adams-Bashforth-Moulton method

18. Use the Adams-Bashforth-Moulton method to approximate the solution of IVP using two different steps h and compare errors.

19. Use the Adams-Bashforth-Moulton method to approximate the solution of IVP using two different steps h and compare errors.

20. Use the Adams-Bashforth-Moulton method to approximate the solution of IVP using two different steps h and compare errors.

21. Use the Adams-Bashforth-Moulton method to approximate the solution of IVP using two different steps h and compare errors.

22. Use the Adams-Bashforth-Moulton method to approximate the solution of IVP using two different steps h.

23. Use the Adams-Bashforth-Moulton method to approximate the solution of IVP using two different steps h.

24. Computer Assignment: Use Adams-Bashforth-Moulton method to approximate solution of projectile problem subject to drag.

1. State an advantage to using a predictor-corrector method for approximating a solution to an initial value problem $y' = f(x, y)$, $y(x_0) = y_0$. If y_{n+1}^* is the predictor and y_{n+1} is the corrector, then

   (a) we may average them to obtain an improved estimate $(y_{n+1}^* + y_{n+1})/2$.

   (b) we may use the difference $|y_{n+1}^* - y_{n+1}|$ to estimate the error at x_{n+1}.

   (c) we may decide which estimate is the most accurate before proceeding to the next step.

   (d) none of the above

2. State a disadvantage to using the Adams-Bashforth-Moulton method to approximate a solution to an initial value problem $y' = f(x, y)$, $y(x_0) = y_0$.

   (a) We must use a single step method to obtain starting values.

   (b) We must evaluate f 8 times to obtain each y_{n+1}.

   (c) We must evaluate f 7 times to obtain each y_{n+1}.

   (d) We must change the stepsize h often.

3. To determine y_{n+1}, the Adams-Bashforth-Moulton method for approximating a solution to an initial value problem $y' = f(x, y)$, $y(x_0) = y_0$ requires that we evaluate $f(x, y)$

   (a) 3 times.

   (b) 4 times.

   (c) 5 times.

   (d) 6 times.

4. The global truncation error of the Adams-Bashforth-Moulton method is

   (a) $O(h^3)$.

   (b) $O(h^4)$.

   (c) $O(h^5)$.

   (d) $O(h^6)$.

5. If we use the Adams-Bashforth-Moulton method twice to approximate the solution of a DE $y' = f(x, y)$ at a point x, first using $h = 0.2$ and then using $h = 0.1$, the ratio of global truncation errors $\left| \dfrac{\text{Error}(h = 0.1)}{\text{Error}(h = 0.2)} \right|$ should be about

   (a) 16.

   (b) 1/16.

   (c) 32.

   (d) 1/32.

6. Before using the Adams-Bashforth-Moulton method to approximate a solution to an initial value problem $y' = f(x, y)$, $y(x_0) = y_0$, we must use a single step method to obtain starting values

   (a) y_0, y_1, y_2.

   (b) y_0, y_1, y_2, y_3.

   (c) y_1, y_2, y_3.

   (d) y_1, y_2, y_3, y_4.

7. If we use the Adams-Bashforth-Moulton method twice to approximate the solution of a DE $y' = f(x,y)$ at a point x, first using $h = 0.3$ and then using $h = 0.1$, the ratio of global truncation errors $\left| \dfrac{\text{Error}(h = 0.3)}{\text{Error}(h = 0.1)} \right|$ should be about

   (a) 9.

   (b) 27.

   (c) 81.

   (d) 243.

8. A numerical method for approximating a solution of an initial value problem $y' = f(x,y)$, $y(x_0) = y_0$ is called stable if

   (a) errors decrease as x_n increases.

   (b) errors decrease as x_n decreases.

   (c) small changes in h result in small changes in y_{n+1}.

   (d) small changes in the initial condition y_0 result in small changes in the computed solution.

9. A good single-step method to use to obtain the necessary starting values before using the Adams-Bashforth-Moulton method is

   (a) the Euler method.

   (b) the improved Euler method.

   (c) the classical Runge-Kutta method.

   (d) the Runge-Kutta-Fehlberg method.

10. State an advantage to using a predictor-corrector method for approximating a solution to an initial value problem $y' = f(x,y)$, $y(x_0) = y_0$. If y_{n+1}^* is the predictor and y_{n+1} is the corrector, then

   (a) we may average them to obtain an improved estimate $\left(y_{n+1}^* + y_{n+1} \right)/2$.

   (b) we may use the Runge-Kutta-Felhberg method obtain a secdond estimate for y_{n+1} and use the difference $|y_{n+1}^* - y_{n+1}|$ to estimate the error at x_{n+1}.

   (c) we may decide which estimate is the most accurate before proceeding to the next step.

   (d) we may assess whether the stepsize h is too large or too small and change it.

11. The Adams-Bashforth-Moulton method for approximating a solution of a DE $y' = f(x,y)$ at x_{n+1} uses the slope of the tangent line to the solution through

   (a) x_{n-2}, x_{n-1}, x_n.

   (b) x_{n-2}, x_{n-1}, x_n, x_{n+1}.

   (c) x_{n-3}, x_{n-2}, x_{n-1}, x_n.

   (d) x_{n-3}, x_{n-2}, x_{n-1}, x_n, x_{n+1}.

12. True or False: The Adams-Bashforth-Moulton method is more accurate than the Runge-Kutta-Fehlberg method.

13. True or False: The Adams-Bashforth-Moulton method is more accurate than the classical Runge-Kutta method.

14. True or False: When approximating the solution to an initial value problem at many steps, the Adams-Bashforth-Moulton method requires fewer calculations than the classical Runge-Kutta method.

15. True or False: The Adams-Bashforth-Moulton method is easier to program than the classical Runge-Kutta method.

16. If we use the classical Adams-Bashforth-Moulton method twice to approximate the solution of a DE $y' = f(x, y)$ at a point x, first using $h = 0.6$ and then using $h = 0.2$, approximate the ratio of global truncation errors $\left| \dfrac{\text{Error}(h = 0.1)}{\text{Error}(h = 0.4)} \right|$. Interpret the result.

17. If we use the Adams-Bashforth-Moulton method twice to approximate the solution of a DE $y' = f(x, y)$ at a point x, first using $h = 0.6$ and then using $h = 0.2$, approximate the ratio of global truncation errors $\left| \dfrac{\text{Error}(h = 0.1)}{\text{Error}(h = 0.4)} \right|$. Interpret the result.

Problems 18-21: Use the Adams-Bashforth-Moulton method with the specified h to approximate the solution of the initial value problem on the given interval. Use the classical Runge-Kutta method to obtain the required starting values. The exact solution is given — use it to determine the actual solution and the percent relative error of the approximate solution at each x. Is the ratio of errors at each common x from parts (a) and (b) what we would expect?

18. $y' = y \cos x$, $\quad y(0) = 1$, $\quad$ on interval $[0, 2]$,

    (a) with $h = 0.4$, and

    (b) with $h = 0.2$.

    The exact solution is $y(x) = e^{\sin x}$.

19. $y' = 2y(1 - x)$, $\quad y(1) = 1$, $\quad$ on interval $[1, 2]$,

    (a) with $h = 0.2$, and

    (b) with $h = 0.1$.

    The exact solution is $y(x) = e^{-(x-1)^2}$.

20. $y' = e^{-y}$, $\quad y(0) = 1$, $\quad$ on interval $[0, 2]$,

    (a) with $h = 0.4$, and

    (b) with $h = 0.2$.

    The exact solution is $y(x) = \ln(x + e)$.

21. $x y' + 2y = x y^2$, $\quad y(1) = 1/2$, $\quad$ on interval $[1, 2]$,

    (a) with $h = 0.2$, and

    (b) with $h = 0.1$.

    The exact solution is $y(x) = \dfrac{1}{x(x + 1)}$.

Problems 22-23: Use the classical Runge-Kutta method with the specified h to approximate the solution of the initial value problem on the given interval.

22. $y' = \cos(2xy^2)$, $y(1) = 0$, on interval $[1, 4]$,

    (a) with $h = 0.50$, and

    (b) with $h = 0.25$.

    (c) How well do the results compare at common x values? What does this suggest that we do?

23. $y' = y\,|y| + \cos(xy)$, $y(2) = 0.5$, on interval $[2, 5]$,

    (a) with $h = 0.50$, and

    (b) with $h = 0.25$.

    (c) How well do the results compare at common x values? What does this suggest that we do?

Computer Assignment:

24. Consider projectile motion where air resistance (drag force f_d) is included. Air resistance is proportional to the square of velocity and opposes motion. Thus, $f_d = -\beta|v|v$ where β is the drag coefficient (a positive constant), so Newton's second law gives

$$m\frac{dv}{dt} = -mg - \beta|v|v.$$

    (a) Use the Adams-Bashforth-Moulton method to approximate v vs. time t on the time interval $[0, 20]$ if the mass is $m = 0.5$ slugs, $\beta = 0.0005$, the initial velocity is $v(0) = 200$ ft/s, and $h = 4$ s.

        i. Approximately when does the projectile attain its maximum height? Interpolate to obtain an estimate.

        ii. Take note of the projectile's speed as time passes. Do our results make physical sense? What conclusion should we draw? Can we estimate the projectile's terminal speed?

    (b) Redo (a) with $h = 2$ s.

        i. Approximately when does the projectile attain its maximum height? Interpolate to obtain an estimate.

        ii. What is the approximate terminal speed?

    (c) Redo (a) with $h = 1$ s.

        i. Approximately when does the projectile attain its maximum height? Interpolate to obtain an estimate.

        ii. What is the approximate terminal speed?

1. b

2. a

3. c

4. b

5. b

6. c

7. c

8. d

9. c

10. d

11. d

12. False

13. False

14. True

15. False

16. The ratio of errors is about 81. So the global errors when using $h = 0.6$ are about 81 times larger than the errors when using $h = 0.2$.

17. The ratio of errors is about 256. So the global errors when using $h = 0.4$ are about 256 times larger than the errors when using $h = 0.1$.

18.

a) $h = 0.4$

x_n	y_n	% Error
0.0	1.0000 0000	—
0.4	1.4760 2806	6.36×10^{-3}
0.8	2.0488 0717	9.83×10^{-3}
1.2	2.5394 0675	1.09×10^{-2}
1.6	2.7228 1810	2.10×10^{-1}
2.0	2.4936 0103	4.40×10^{-1}

b) $h = 0.2$

x_n	y_n	Exact y	% Error
0.0	1.0000 0000	1.0000 0000	—
0.2	1.2197 7573	1.2197 7856	2.31×10^{-3}
0.4	1.4761 1567	1.4761 2194	4.25×10^{-3}
0.6	1.7588 0901	1.7588 1885	5.59×10^{-3}
0.8	2.0490 3955	2.0490 0865	1.51×10^{-3}
1.0	2.3198 9896	2.3197 7768	5.27×10^{-3}
1.2	2.5399 5345	2.5396 8253	1.07×10^{-2}
1.4	2.6794 7130	2.6790 1645	1.70×10^{-2}
1.6	2.7177 3038	2.7171 2301	2.24×10^{-2}
1.8	2.6487 5045	2.6481 1385	2.40×10^{-2}
2.0	2.4830 5952	2.4825 7772	1.94×10^{-2}

b) $h = 0.1$

x_n	y_n	Exact y	% Error
1.0	1.0000 0000	1.0000 0000	—
1.1	0.9900 4983	0.9900 4983	4.20×10^{-8}
1.2	0.9607 8943	0.9607 8944	4.08×10^{-7}
1.3	0.9139 3117	0.9139 3119	1.23×10^{-6}
1.4	0.8521 3448	0.8521 4379	1.09×10^{-3}
1.5	0.7787 8036	0.7788 0078	2.62×10^{-3}
1.6	0.6976 4470	0.6976 7633	4.53×10^{-3}
1.7	0.6125 8535	0.6126 2639	6.70×10^{-3}
1.8	0.5272 4538	0.5272 9241	8.92×10^{-3}
1.9	0.4448 0951	0.4448 5807	1.09×10^{-2}
2.0	0.3678 3410	0.3678 7944	1.23×10^{-2}

a) $h = 0.2$

19.

x_n	y_n	% Error
1.0	1.0000 0000	—
1.2	0.9607 8933	1.10×10^{-5}
1.4	0.8521 4297	9.63×10^{-5}
1.6	0.6976 7558	1.07×10^{-4}
1.8	0.5266 4341	1.23×10^{-1}
2.0	0.3668 2562	2.87×10^{-1}

b) $h = 0.2$

x_n	y_n	Exact y	% Error
0.0	1.0000 0000	1.0000 0000	—
0.2	1.0709 9503	1.0709 9503	6.03×10^{-7}
0.4	1.1372 8216	1.1372 8215	9.31×10^{-7}
0.6	1.1994 4714	1.1994 4713	1.10×10^{-6}
0.8	1.2579 7352	1.2579 7275	6.11×10^{-5}
1.0	1.3132 6296	1.3132 6169	9.69×10^{-5}
1.2	1.3656 5486	1.3656 5325	1.18×10^{-4}
1.4	1.4154 3789	1.4154 3604	1.30×10^{-4}
1.6	1.4628 5959	1.4628 5760	1.36×10^{-4}
1.8	1.5081 3388	1.5081 3180	1.38×10^{-4}
2.0	1.5514 4686	1.5514 4447	1.38×10^{-4}

a) $h = 0.4$

20.

x_n	y_n	% Error
0.0	1.0000 0000	—
0.4	1.1372 8235	1.73×10^{-5}
0.8	1.2579 7303	2.18×10^{-5}
1.2	1.3656 5355	2.21×10^{-5}
1.6	1.4628 7237	1.01×10^{-3}
2.0	1.5514 6631	1.39×10^{-3}

b) $h = 0.1$

x_n	y_n	Exact y	% Error
1.0	0.5000 0000	0.5000 0000	—
1.1	0.4329 0071	0.4329 0043	6.44×10^{-5}
1.2	0.3787 8829	0.3783 8787	1.10×10^{-4}
1.3	0.3344 4864	0.3244 4816	1.43×10^{-4}
1.4	0.2976 0742	0.2976 1905	3.91×10^{-3}
1.5	0.2666 4871	0.2666 6667	6.73×10^{-3}
1.6	0.2403 6341	0.2403 8462	8.82×10^{-3}
1.7	0.2178 4223	0.2178 6492	1.04×10^{-2}
1.8	0.1983 8957	0.1984 1270	1.17×10^{-2}
1.9	0.1814 6525	0.1814 8820	1.27×10^{-2}
2.0	0.1666 4424	0.1666 6667	1.35×10^{-2}

a) $h = 0.2$

21.

x_n	y_n	% Error
1.0	0.5000 0000	—
1.2	0.3787 9594	2.13×10^{-3}
1.4	0.2976 2866	3.23×10^{-3}
1.6	0.2403 9397	3.89×10^{-3}
1.8	0.1982 3326	9.04×10^{-2}
2.0	0.1664 3397	1.40×10^{-1}

b) $h = 0.25$

x_n	y_n
1.00	0.0000 0000 0000
1.25	0.2493 9079 6391
1.50	0.4775 4391 0201
1.75	0.6073 0325 6757
2.00	0.6543 9464 6807
2.25	0.6105 9880 2150
2.50	0.5410 7286 5482
2.75	0.5362 1161 6938
3.00	0.5662 5019 7864
3.25	0.5353 1116 4992
3.50	0.4362 5966 4950
3.75	0.4046 7920 0594
4.00	0.4970 7067 9816

22.

a) $h = 0.50$

x_n	y_n
1.0	0.0000 0000 0000
1.5	0.4746 5046 7393
2.0	0.5807 0753 9957
2.5	0.5364 9805 5947
3.0	0.4795 7146 9509
3.5	0.4371 8740 1242
4.0	0.3961 9508 3346

c) The results at common x's do not agree well. This suggests that we should recalculate the approximate solution using a smaller step h.

b) $h = 0.25$

x_n	y_n
2.00	0.5000 0000 0000
2.25	0.6643 4836 5786
2.50	0.7597 5850 0640
2.75	0.7969 4972 4033
3.00	0.7906 7442 2778
3.25	0.7531 8032 5635
3.50	0.6931 0915 2741
3.75	0.6203 4930 7602
4.00	0.5466 6996 2275
4.25	0.4821 8648 6428
4.50	0.4315 5092 6020
4.75	0.3933 3867 9601
5.00	0.3633 0586 2772

23.

a) $h = 0.50$

x_n	y_n
2.0	0.5000 0000 0000
2.5	0.7600 0044 0889
3.0	0.7918 5534 9493
3.5	0.6940 3203 5762
4.0	0.5499 3200 2087
4.5	0.4247 9964 7268
5.0	0.3361 3105 3048

c) The results at common x's do not agree well. This suggests that we should recalculate the approximate solution using a smaller step h.

	a) $h = 4$ s			b) $h = 1$ s	
t_n	v_n		t_n	v_n
0.0	200.0000 0000 0000		0.0	200.0000 0000 0000
4.0	18.6982 4362 5656		1.0	139.4559 1376 6401
8.0	−97.4527 6229 0490		2.0	93.8753 8218 0314
12.0	−153.9874 5055 9712		3.0	56.1966 9118 1731
16.0	−199.8205 1180 1909		4.0	22.5125 8364 8789
20.0	−191.8586 2638 4624		5.0	−9.5663 1533 0305
			6.0	−40.8685 7502 2870

b) $h = 2$ s

24.

t_n	v_n		t_n	v_n
			7.0	−69.8081 9294 4847
			8.0	−94.9515 6277 2431
0.0	200.0000 0000 0000		9.0	−115.7372 0304 9826
2.0	93.7175 4819 2758		10.0	−132.2425 2525 0665
4.0	22.4349 1282 9230		11.0	−144.9258 6171 1753
6.0	−41.0346 3974 1783		12.0	−154.4302 8255 6569
8.0	−96.5533 4700 8433		13.0	−161.4195 4269 6021
10.0	−135.5429 8983 5124		14.0	−166.4875 3519 6937
12.0	−156.0385 4132 4284		15.0	−170.1244 6843 2358
14.0	−166.3603 0588 4088		16.0	−172.7147 0094 3120
16.0	−172.5596 1850 5565		17.0	−174.5493 3458 6284
18.0	−175.9833 1815 8507		18.0	−175.8436 3566 2305
20.0	−177.4536 7335 3966		19.0	−176.7541 4950 1984
			20.0	−177.3933 8172 5452

a.i. The projectile attains its maximum height between $t = 4$ and $t = 8$ seconds — interpolation indicates at about $t = 4.64$ seconds.

a.ii. From these results it is not evident what the terminal speed of this object is. The results suggest that the speed increases and then decreases during the descent. This cannot happen, because the speed should increase monotonically during the descent until the terminal speed is attained. Thus, these results are unreliable. This suggests that we should use a shorter time step.

b.i. The projectile attains its maximum height between $t = 4$ and $t = 6$ seconds — interpolation indicates at about $t = 4.707$ seconds.

b.ii. The terminal speed of this object is about 177.5 f/s or slightly more.

c.i. The projectile attains its maximum height between $t = 4$ and $t = 5$ seconds — interpolation indicates at about $t = 4.702$ seconds.

c.ii. The terminal speed of this object is about 177.4 f/s.

1. systems — terminology

2. systems — terminology

3. systems — concepts

4. systems — concepts

5. number of function evaluations with classical Runge-Kutta

6. proper application of predictor-corrector method to a system

7. systems — concepts

8. stability of numerical methods applied to systems

9. systems — concepts

10. systems — concepts

11. systems — concepts

12. transform a 2nd-order initial value problem into a system

13. transform a 2nd-order initial value problem into a system

14. transform a 2nd-order initial value problem into a system

15. transform a 2nd-order initial value problem into a system

16. use the Euler method to approximate the solution of a system

17. use the improved Euler method to approximate the solution of a system

18. use the classicla Runge-Kutta method to approximate the solution of a system

19. projectile motion with drag — use the Euler method to approximate the solution of a system using various stepsizes

20. projectile motion with drag — use the improved Euler method to approximate the solution of a system using various stepsizes

21. projectile motion with drag — use the classical Runge-Kutta method to approximate the solution of a system using various stepsizes

22. simple pendulum — use the classical Runge-Kutta method to approximate the solution

23. population dynamics with toxins — use the Euler method, improved Euler method, and classical Runge-Kutta method to approximate the solution

24. population dynamics with competition — use the classical Runge-Kutta method to approximate the solution for various initial populations

1. A system of the form $x' = f(t, x, y)$ and $y' = g(t, x, y)$ is called

    (a) homogeneous.

    (b) nonhomogeneous.

    (c) coupled.

    (d) uncoupled.

2. A system of the form $x'' = f(t, x, x')$ and $y'' = g(t, y, y')$ is called

    (a) homogeneous.

    (b) nonhomogeneous.

    (c) coupled.

    (d) uncoupled.

3. We can transform a system of two DEs: $x'' = f(t, x, x', y, y', y'')$ and $y''' = g(t, x, x', y, y', y'')$
    into a system of

    (a) two 1st-order DEs.

    (b) three 1st-order DEs.

    (c) four 1st-order DEs.

    (d) five 1st-order DEs.

4. We can transform the equation $y''' = f(x, y, y')$ into a system of

    (a) two 1st-order DEs.

    (b) three 1st-order DEs.

    (c) four 1st-order DEs.

    (d) five 1st-order DEs.

5. When using the classical Runge-Kutta method to approximate the solution to a system of two
    1st-order DEs, how many function evaluations do we perform each time we step from one x to
    the next?

    (a) two

    (b) three

    (c) four

    (d) eight

6. To use the improved Euler method to approximate the solution to the system $x' = f(t, x, y)$, $y' = g(t, x, y)$
    at steps t_1 and t_2, in what order do we apply the predictor and corrector formulas?

    (a) First: predict x_1^* and predict y_1^*. Second: correct x_1 and correct y_1. Third: predict x_2^* and
        predict y_2^*. Fourth: correct x_2 and correct y_2.

    (b) First: predict x_1^* and correct x_1. Second: predict y_1^* and correct y_1. Third: predict x_2^* and
        correct x_2. Fourth: predict y_2^* and correct y_2.

    (c) First: predict x_1^* and predict x_2^*. Second: predict y_1^* and predict y_2^*. Third: correct x_1 and
        correct y_1. Fourth: correct y_1 and correct y_2.

    (d) First: predict x_1^* and predict x_2^*. Second: correct x_1 and correct x_2. Third: predict y_1^* and
        predict y_2^*. Fourth: correct y_1 and correct y_2.

7. True or False: We can always transform a higher order DE $f(x, y, y') = 0$ into a system of 1st-order DEs.

8. True or False: Numerical methods for approximating solutions to systems of differential equations are always stable.

9. True or False: Numerical methods for approximating solutions to systems of differential equations apply only to initial value problems.

10. True or False: We may always transform an nth-order DE of the form $y^{(n)} = f(x, y, y', \ldots, y^{(n-1)})$ into a system of n 1st-order DEs.

11. True or False: We may transform an nth-order DE of the form $y^{(n)} = f(x, y, y', \ldots, y^{(n-1)})$ into a system of 1st-order DEs only if it is linear.

Problems 12-15: Write the initial value problem as a system of first-order equations.

12. $y'' = y (y')^2 e^{-3x}$, $\quad y(0) = 1$, $\quad y'(0) = -4$

13. $y'' + 3 y y' - x \cos y' = e^x$, $\quad y(0) = 2$, $\quad y'(0) = -1$

14. $m \ddot{x} + \beta |\dot{x}| \dot{x} + k x = e^{-2t} \sin 4t$, $\quad x(0) = 2$, $\quad u(0) = -1$

15. $\ell \ddot{\theta} + g \sin \theta = 0$, $\quad \theta(0) = \theta_0$, $\quad \dot{\theta}(0) = 0$

16. Use the Euler method to approximate the solution to problem 13 on interval $[0, 1]$ using:

    (a) $h = 0.2$,

    (b) $h = 0.1$.

17. Use the improved Euler method to approximate the solution to problem 13 on interval $[0, 1]$ using:

    (a) $h = 0.2$,

    (b) $h = 0.1$.

18. Use the classical Runge-Kutta method to approximate the solution to problem 13 on interval $[0, 1]$ using:

    (a) $h = 0.2$,

    (b) $h = 0.1$.

19. Consider projectile motion where air resistance (drag force f_d) is included. Air resistance is proportional to the square of velocity and opposes motion. Thus, $f_d = -\beta |\dot{x}| \dot{x}$ where β is the drag coefficient (a positive constant), so Newton's second law gives

$$m \ddot{x} = -mg - \beta |\dot{x}| \dot{x}.$$

    (a) Use the Euler method to approximate v vs. time t on the time interval $[0, 16]$ if the mass is $m = 0.5$ slugs, $\beta = 0.0005$, the initial velocity is $v(0) = 200$ ft/s, the initial height is $x(0) = 20$ ft, and $h = 4$ s.

        i. Use interpolation to estimate when the projectile attains its maximum height. Can we use linear interpolation to estimate the projectile's maximum height?

        ii. Use interpolation to estimate when the projectile hits the ground. Interpolate again to estimate the speed at which it hits the ground.

    (b) Redo (a) with $h = 2$ s.

    (c) Redo (a) with $h = 1$ s.

20. Redo problem 19 using the improved Euler method.

21. Redo problem 19 using the classical Runge-Kutta method.

22. As indicated in problem 15, the motion of a simple pendulum is governed by the system $\ell\ddot{\theta} + g\sin\theta = 0$, $\theta(0) = \theta_0$, $\dot{\theta}(0) = 0$. Suppose a pendulum of length $\ell = 3.24$ feet is released from rest from an initial position $\theta_0 = 0.2$ radians.

   (a) Use the classical Runge-Kutta method with time steps of $h = 0.2$ seconds to approximate the displacement $\theta(t)$ and the angular velocity $\dot{\theta}$ on the time interval $[0, 4]$ seconds.

   (b) Does the motion appear periodic? Based on the numerical results, what is the approximate period of motion?

23. Consider a population that is confined within a closed system — nutrients are available but metabolic waste accumulates and eventually becomes toxic to the species. The population P at time t may be modeled by the system[3] $\dot{y} = P$, $\dot{u} = kP(1 - P - y)$, $y(0) = 0$, $P(0) = P_0$. Suppose $k = 10$ and the initial population is $P_0 = 0.01$.

   (a) Use the Euler method with $h = 0.1$ to approximate the population $P(t)$ on interval $[0, 2]$.

   (b) Use the improved Euler method with $h = 0.1$ to approximate the population $P(t)$ on interval $[0, 2]$.

   (c) Use the classical Runge-Kutta method with $h = 0.1$ to approximate the population $P(t)$ on interval $[0, 2]$.

24. When two species compete for the same resources, we may sometimes model their populations by the system

$$\frac{dx}{dt} = x(a_1 - b_1 x - c_1 y), \qquad x(0) = x_0,$$
$$\frac{dy}{dt} = y(a_2 - b_2 y - c_2 x), \qquad y(0) = y_0,$$

where populations $x(t)$ and $y(t)$ might be, for example, measured in thousands while time t might be measured in months or years. Let $a_1 = 2.0$, $b_1 = 0.4$, $c_1 = 0.3$, $a_2 = 1.0$, $b_2 = 0.1$ and $b_3 = 0.3$,

   (a) Use the classical Runge-Kutta method with $h = 1.0$ to approximate the populations $x(t)$ and $y(t)$ on interval $[0, 20]$ if the initial populations are $x(0) = 1.0$ and $y(0) = 2.5$. What do you observe about the populations x and y as time passes?

   (b) Repeat (a) using initial populations $x(0) = 1.0$ and $y(0) = 3.5$. What do you observe about the populations x and y as time passes?

---

[3]Kevin G. TeBeest. Numerical and Analytical Solutions of Volterra's Population Model. SIAM Review, Vol. 39, No. 3, pp. 484-493, September 1997.

1. d

2. c

3. d

4. b

5. d

6. a

7. False

8. False

9. False

10. True

11. False

12. $y' = u$, $\quad u' = y\,u^2\,e^{-3x}$, $\quad y(0) = 1$, $\quad u(0) = -4$

13. $y' = u$, $\quad u' = e^x - 3\,y\,u + x\cos u$, $\quad y(0) = 2$, $\quad u(0) = -1$

14. $\dot{x} = u$, $\quad \dot{u} = \dfrac{1}{m}\,e^{-2t}\,\sin 4t - \dfrac{\beta}{m}\,|u|\,u - \dfrac{k}{m}\,k\,x$, $\quad y(0) = 2$, $\quad u(0) = -1$

15. $\dot{\theta} = u$, $\quad \dot{u} = -\dfrac{g}{\ell}\,\sin\theta$, $\quad \theta(0) = \theta_0$, $\quad u(0) = 0$

16.

a) $h = 0.2$

x_n	y_n
0.0	2.0000 0000 0000
0.2	1.8000 0000 0000
0.4	1.8800 0000 0000
0.6	1.9298 2459 8278
0.8	1.9986 2610 1996
1.0	2.0832 4131 2597

b) $h = 0.1$

x_n	y_n
0.0	2.0000 0000 0000
0.1	1.9000 0000 0000
0.2	1.8700 0000 0000
0.3	1.8691 0704 5670
0.4	1.8829 2898 6564
0.5	1.9054 7049 8088
0.6	1.9340 9584 2586
0.7	1.9676 4151 7377
0.8	2.0056 0977 5406
0.9	2.0478 0466 0542
1.0	2.0941 6535 3071

17.

a) $h = 0.2$

x_n	y_n
0.0	2.0000 0000 0000
0.2	1.9400 0000 0000
0.4	1.9367 6278 3885
0.6	1.9728 1507 2754
0.8	2.0370 9138 2302
1.0	2.1236 2972 4554

b) $h = 0.1$

x_n	y_n
0.0	2.0000 0000 0000
0.1	1.9350 0000 0000
0.2	1.9051 5918 4071
0.3	1.8978 7046 5591
0.4	1.9056 8265 4005
0.5	1.9241 4168 5344
0.6	1.9505 7340 2688
0.7	1.9833 7562 5712
0.8	2.0215 9651 0783
0.9	2.0646 7981 6629
1.0	2.1123 1016 9102

18.

a) $h = 0.2$

x_n	y_n
0.0	2.0000 0000 0000
0.2	1.9018 7703 3374
0.4	1.9035 9058 7382
0.6	1.9496 3705 0943
0.8	2.0212 7559 0989
1.0	2.1122 3405 3340

b) $h = 0.1$

x_n	y_n
0.0	2.0000 0000 0000
0.1	1.929065887574
0.2	1.898482449754
0.3	1.892075416162
0.4	1.901106349180
0.5	1.920671908401
0.6	1.947973446855
0.7	2.020066066441
0.8	2.020066066441
0.9	2.063438549219
1.0	2.111253329115

19.

a) $h = 4$ s

t_n	x_n (ft)	u_n (ft/s)
0.0	20.0000 0000	200.0000 0000
4.0	820.0000 0000	56.0000 0000
8.0	1044.0000 0000	−73.2544 0000
12.0	750.9824 0000	−199.1079 1715
16.0	−45.4492 6861	−311.2503 3208

b) $h = 2$ s

t_n	x_n (ft)	u_n (ft/s)
0.0	20.0000 0000	200.0000 0000
2.0	420.0000 0000	128.0000 0000
4.0	676.0000 0000	60.7232 0000
6.0	797.4464 0000	−4.0142 6140
8.0	789.4178 7719	−68.0110 3854
10.0	653.3958 0010	−131.0859 3827
12.0	391.2239 2356	−191.6492 3363
14.0	7.9254 5630	−248.3033 4788
16.0	−488.6812 3946	−299.9724 3737

b) $h = 1$ s

t_n	x_n (ft)	u_n (ft/s)
0.0	20.0000 0000	200.0000 0000
1.0	220.0000 0000	164.0000 0000
2.0	384.0000 0000	129.3104 0000
3.0	513.3104 0000	95.6382 8205
4.0	608.9486 8205	62.7236 1395
5.0	671.6722 9599	30.3301 8877
6.0	702.0024 8476	−1.7618 0326
7.0	700.2406 8150	−33.7614 9287
8.0	666.4791 8863	−65.6475 0903
9.0	600.8316 7960	−97.2165 4948
10.0	503.6151 3012	−128.2714 4374
11.0	375.3436 8638	−158.6260 8741
12.0	216.7175 9897	−188.1098 6385
13.0	28.6077 3513	−216.5713 3176
14.0	−187.9635 9663	−243.8810 1759
15.0	−431.8446 1422	−269.9332 2251
16.0	−701.7778 3673	−294.6468 2805

a.i. The projectile attains its maximum height between $t = 4$ and $t = 8$ seconds — interpolation indicates at about $t = 5.73$ seconds.

a.ii. Interpolation indicates that the projectile hits the ground at about $t = 15.78$ seconds. Interpolating again indicates that the projectile hits the ground at about 305.9 ft/s.

b.i. The projectile attains its maximum height between $t = 4$ and $t = 6$ seconds — interpolation indicates at about $t = 5.88$ seconds.

b.ii. Interpolation indicates that the projectile hits the ground at about $t = 14.03$ seconds. Interpolating again indicates that the projectile hits the ground at about 249.1 ft/s.

c.i. The projectile attains its maximum height between $t = 4$ and $t = 8$ seconds — interpolation indicates at about $t = 5.95$ seconds.

c.ii. Interpolation indicates that the projectile hits the ground at about $t = 13.13$ seconds. Interpolating again indicates that the projectile hits the ground at about 220.2 ft/s.

a) $h = 4$ s

t_n	x_n (ft)	u_n (ft/s)
0.0	20.0000 0000	200.0000 0000
4.0	532.0000 0000	63.3278 0000
8.0	526.2783 1057	−64.5530 4322
12.0	15.3998 1402	−184.4321 1548
16.0	−951.1164 8374	−287.7696 7479

20.

b) $h = 2$ s

t_n	x_n (ft)	u_n (ft/s)
0.0	20.0000 0000	200.0000 0000
2.0	348.0000 0000	130.3616 0000
4.0	541.3243 7065	64.2657 5428
6.0	605.0298 6177	−0.1472 2305
8.0	540.7354 2000	−63.7357 3432
10.0	350.0764 0013	−125.7185 5789
12.0	37.8003 1550	−184.6576 7124
14.0	−388.6953 3586	−239.3992 6482
16.0	−920.0314 6390	−289.1453 5081

b) $h = 1$ s

t_n	x_n (ft)	u_n (ft/s)
0.0	20.0000 0000	200.0000 0000
1.0	202.0000 0000	164.6552 0000
2.0	349.2996 3326	130.4553 6023
3.0	462.9040 6344	97.1363 6819
4.0	543.5686 5793	64.4585 5858
5.0	591.8194 7123	32.1994 7538
6.0	607.9671 0630	0.1476 3461
7.0	592.1147 3982	−31.8016 3781
8.0	544.3636 6922	−63.5481 8290
9.0	465.0174 0490	−94.8936 4199
10.0	354.5740 0307	−125.6496 8799
11.0	213.7137 0729	−155.6423 8944
12.0	43.2825 4552	−184.7158 4057
13.0	−155.7272 9796	−212.7349 1694
14.0	−382.1994 0765	−239.5870 8424
15.0	−634.9163 9335	−265.1832 5733
16.0	−912.5835 4268	−289.4577 6799

a.i. The projectile attains its maximum height between $t = 4$ and $t = 8$ seconds — interpolation indicates at about $t = 5.98$ seconds.

a.ii. Interpolation indicates that the projectile hits the ground at about $t = 12.06$ seconds. Interpolating again indicates that the projectile hits the ground at about 186.1 ft/s.

b.i. The projectile attains its maximum height between $t = 4$ and $t = 6$ seconds — interpolation indicates at about $t = 5.99$ seconds.

b.ii. Interpolation indicates that the projectile hits the ground at about $t = 12.18$ seconds. Interpolating again indicates that the projectile hits the ground at about 189.5 ft/s.

c.i. The projectile attains its maximum height between $t = 6$ and $t = 7$ seconds — interpolation indicates at about $t = 6.00$ seconds.

c.ii. Interpolation indicates that the projectile hits the ground at about $t = 12.22$ seconds. Interpolating again indicates that the projectile hits the ground at about 190.8 ft/s.

272

a) $h = 4$ s

t_n	x_n (ft)	u_n (ft/s)
0.0	20.0000 0000	200.0000 0000
4.0	544.2668 1392	64.5188 0703
8.0	545.2319 4946	−63.4900 6913
12.0	44.7451 0954	−184.7327 1844
16.0	−910.4982 7251	−289.5473 4034

b) $h = 2$ s

21.

t_n	x_n (ft)	u_n (ft/s)
0.0	20.0000 0000	200.0000 0000
2.0	349.7184 3144	130.4837 8964
4.0	544.2921 4004	64.5184 3070
6.0	608.9127 3920	0.2409 1955
8.0	545.5286 3326	−63.4903 6691
10.0	356.0158 4379	−125.6300 9826
12.0	45.0370 1655	−184.7362 9811
14.0	−380.1251 0188	−239.6476 9322
16.0	−910.2113 3189	−289.5563 8197

b) $h = 1$ s

t_n	x_n (ft)	u_n (ft/s)
0.0	20.0000 0000	200.0000 0000
1.0	202.2271 1231	164.6689 2662
2.0	349.7194 0538	130.4837 9284
3.0	463.4882 4000	97.1802 1866
4.0	544.2935 3809	64.5183 8301
5.0	592.6646 0066	32.2757 4812
6.0	608.9141 9207	0.2407 9572
7.0	593.1632 5871	−31.7258 7691
8.0	545.5298 2203	−63.4905 6953
9.0	466.3156 9711	−94.8548 7922
10.0	356.0164 9730	−125.6303 8989
11.0	215.3094 1507	−155.6430 2965
12.0	45.0369 9569	−184.7367 0024
13.0	−153.8122 9319	−212.7760 3813
14.0	−380.1257 8556	−239.6482 3406
15.0	−632.6896 8535	−265.2639 0671
16.0	−910.2125 5689	−289.5570 8721

a.i. The projectile attains its maximum height between $t = 4$ and $t = 8$ seconds — interpolation indicates at about $t = 6.02$ seconds.

a.ii. Interpolation indicates that the projectile hits the ground at about $t = 12.19$ seconds. Interpolating again indicates that the projectile hits the ground at about 189.6 ft/s.

b.i. The projectile attains its maximum height between $t = 6$ and $t = 8$ seconds — interpolation indicates at about $t = 6.008$ seconds.

b.ii. Interpolation indicates that the projectile hits the ground at about $t = 12.212$ seconds. Interpolating again indicates that the projectile hits the ground at about 190.6 ft/s.

c.i. The projectile attains its maximum height between $t = 6$ and $t = 7$ seconds — interpolation indicates at about $t = 6.008$ seconds.

c.ii. Interpolation indicates that the projectile hits the ground at about $t = 12.226$ seconds. Interpolating again indicates that the projectile hits the ground at about 191.1 ft/s.

a) $h = 0.2$ s

t_n	θ_n (rad)	$\dot{\theta}_n$ (rad/s)
0.0	0.2000 0000 0000	0.0000 0000 0000
0.2	0.1620 2532 0339	−0.3670 3760 8376
0.4	0.0625 7782 7338	−0.5953 6054 9942
0.6	−0.0606 0582 4710	−0.5971 0112 1664
0.8	−0.1606 2328 3653	−0.3717 6065 1528
1.0	−0.1995 8803 2409	−0.0063 7435 1694
1.2	−0.1628 8307 2095	0.3611 1391 4031
1.4	−0.0643 8042 8248	0.5921 3473 8788
1.6	0.0585 4467 1271	0.5978 1575 1271
1.8	0.1590 8747 8350	0.3761 1910 8604
2.0	0.1991 5631 0343	0.0127 0321 1512
2.2	0.1637 1626 7955	−0.3551 9124 7708
2.4	0.0661 6296 8217	−0.5888 6436 9299
2.6	−0.0564 9141 0673	−0.5984 5734 1019
2.8	−0.1575 4448 2071	−0.3804 0459 0753
3.0	−0.1987 0514 7308	−0.0189 8621 2562
3.2	−0.1645 2509 3900	0.3492 7048 1540
3.4	−0.0679 2543 3245	0.5855 5050 2964
3.6	0.0544 4625 1589	0.5990 2671 0684
3.8	0.1559 9461 5448	0.3846 1736 8364
4.0	0.1982 3485 5240	0.0252 2300 3130

b. The motion appears to be periodic with a period of about 2 seconds.

t_n	a) Euler P_n	b) improved Euler P_n	c) RK4 P_n
0.0	0.0100 0000 0000	0.0100 0000 0000	0.0100 0000 0000
0.1	0.0199 0000 0000	0.0246 9204 5000	0.0266 1586 6858
0.2	0.0393 8409 0000	0.0597 9922 7245	0.0687 4860 4654
0.3	0.0770 9931 5026	0.1382 7346 1049	0.1651 0301 1606
0.4	0.1477 2015 0086	0.2884 4872 6248	0.3407 1383 4411
0.5	0.2714 5667 9574	0.4959 7436 6183	0.5552 3280 1347
0.6	0.4612 4099 2811	0.6627 0838 2997	0.7075 5821 1515
0.7	0.6836 5277 5759	0.7316 5923 4058	0.7596 1179 0571
0.8	0.8297 2688 2782	0.7327 0593 1158	0.7450 4595 2769
0.9	0.8290 8609 8726	0.6998 5414 6196	0.7005 6709 3422
1.0	0.7601 8557 2265	0.6525 5403 9569	0.6461 2894 7713
1.1	0.6863 6222 5157	0.6007 2502 8774	0.5905 2467 1617
1.2	0.6182 0132 1619	0.5491 6795 8252	0.5372 9780 2465
1.3	0.5565 1546 2885	0.5000 7417 0873	0.4877 4150 8058
1.4	0.5009 1006 6606	0.4543 4097 0634	0.4422 0238 1712
1.5	0.4508 3748 1777	0.4122 3549 6123	0.4006 3048 4375
1.6	0.4057 6200 8673	0.3737 2386 4451	0.3628 1403 6798
1.7	0.3651 8989 7814	0.3386 3365 1968	0.3284 8188 7751
1.8	0.3286 7309 5451	0.3067 3429 8484	0.2973 4914 4257
1.9	0.2958 0703 5650	0.2777 7699 3387	0.2691 3757 3535
2.0	0.2662 2708 7177	0.2515 1435 3667	0.2435 8444 5653

22.

23.

t_n	a) $x(0) = 1.0$, $y(0) = 2.5$		b) $x(0) = 1.0$, $y(0) = 3.5$	
	x_n	y_n	x_n	y_n
0	1.0000 0000 0000	2.5000 0000 0000	3.5000 0000 0000	4.1434 0120 3744
1	1.7353 3104 6908	3.2667 2124 0430	1.3784 6022 4797	4.1434 0120 3744
2	2.0838 6541 4981	3.5397 6060 7972	1.5077 4429 9084	4.4528 9575 0863
3	2.2203 6755 8686	3.5773 2354 9703	1.5137 3492 6801	4.6330 9111 2262
4	2.2939 2434 7267	3.5344 2114 5442	1.4668 8616 2798	4.7755 0633 3123
5	2.3560 5019 8180	3.4598 2895 9283	1.3942 4887 0830	4.9141 3041 1946
6	2.4227 3684 1535	3.3658 1945 3004	1.3055 7184 5792	5.0610 9445 3308
7	2.4996 1769 8313	3.2539 7430 0501	1.2046 7829 3531	5.2198 2998 9150
8	2.5896 0485 9931	3.1228 7072 8956	1.0938 3641 8421	5.3893 2070 6551
9	2.6949 6674 3827	2.9702 9439 4775	0.9754 8559 7745	5.5651 5996 0307
10	2.8177 7630 8296	2.7940 1244 3644	0.8529 3824 1098	5.7396 7717 5653
11	2.9598 3043 0231	2.5922 8083 2644	0.7305 2859 2189	5.9022 9780 0181
12	3.1223 0721 3386	2.3644 3541 7521	0.6132 7497 1960	6.0409 8230 4485
13	3.3052 0813 0941	2.1116 6581 4529	0.5060 8648 7383	6.1451 4861 6862
14	3.5066 1819 6312	1.8379 3172 9211	0.4127 3590 2758	6.2094 0025 2255
15	3.7219 1961 3263	1.5508 0068 4907	0.3350 4658 6142	6.2360 2349 7064
16	3.9432 9171 5617	1.2617 3909 2341	0.2727 2273 5496	6.2341 4900 3439
17	4.1600 3177 3905	0.9852 0819 5888	0.2238 8409 8375	6.2157 3656 1037
18	4.3601 7647 1534	0.7361 4106 2918	0.1859 3881 6397	6.1911 4762 1320
19	4.5332 7973 8207	0.5262 9976 7655	0.1563 2954 0941	6.1669 2441 4399
20	4.6731 8133 3265	0.3611 9523 1470	0.1329 2835 8469	6.1460 1043 3951

a) As time passes, the population of species x appears to increase monotonically. The population of species y appears to increase, attain a maximum, and then decrease, evidently to zero — this suggests that species y cannot compete against species x and thus dies off.

b) As time passes, the population of species y appears to increase monotonically. The population of species x appears to decrease generally monotonically, evidently to zero — this suggests that species x cannot compete against species y and thus dies off.

24.

1. systems — identifying difference formulas

2. systems — identifying difference formulas

3. systems — identifying difference formulas

4. systems — identifying difference formulas

5. applying difference formulas to DEs — concepts

6. applying difference formulas to DEs — concepts

7. applying difference formulas to DEs — concepts

8. applying difference formulas to DEs — concepts

9. use finite differences to approximate the solution to a 2nd-order DE

10. use finite differences to approximate the solution to a 2nd-order DE

11. use finite differences to approximate the solution to a 2nd-order DE

12. use finite differences to approximate the solution to a 2nd-order DE

13. use finite differences to approximate the solution to a 2nd-order DE

14. use finite differences to approximate the solution to a 2nd-order DE

15. finite differences applied to the cantilever beam; fixed BCs

16. finite differences applied to the cantilever beam; fixed BCs

17. finite differences applied to heat transfer in a cylindrical shell; fixed BCs

18. finite differences applied to heat transfer in a cylindrical shell; fixed BCs

19. finite differences applied to heat transfer in a fin; one derivative BC

20. finite differences applied to heat transfer in a fin; one derivative BC

1. The expression $\dfrac{y(x+h) - y(x)}{h}$ is

   (a) a forward difference formula for approximating $y'(x)$.

   (b) a backward difference formula for approximating $y'(x)$.

   (c) a central difference formula for approximating $y'(x)$.

   (d) a backward difference formula for approximating $y''(x)$.

2. The expression $\dfrac{y(x) - y(x-h)}{h}$ is

   (a) a forward difference formula for approximating $y'(x)$.

   (b) a backward difference formula for approximating $y'(x)$.

   (c) a central difference formula for approximating $y'(x)$.

   (d) a backward difference formula for approximating $y''(x)$.

3. The expression $\dfrac{y(x+h) - y(x-h)}{2h}$ is

   (a) a central difference formula for approximating $y'(x)$.

   (b) a forward difference formula for approximating $y'(x)$.

   (c) a backward difference formula for approximating $y'(x)$.

   (d) a central difference formula for approximating $y''(x)$.

4. The expression $\dfrac{y(x+h) - 2\,y(x) + y(x-h)}{h^2}$ is

   (a) a forward difference formula for approximating $y'(x)$.

   (b) a backward difference formula for approximating $y'(x)$.

   (c) a central difference formula for approximating $y'(x)$.

   (d) a central difference formula for approximating $y''(x)$.

5. True or False: We may use finite differences to approximate the solution to any differential equation.

6. True or False: Finite differences is a method for approximating a differential equation by an algebraic equation.

7. True or False: Numerical methods for approximating a solution to differential equations apply only to boundary value problems.

8. True or False: When approximating solutions to differential equations numerically, we should use only central difference formulas to approximate derivatives.

Problems 9-14:   Use the finite difference method and the indicated value of n to approximate the solution of the given boundary value problem.

9. $y'' + 16\,y = 0$, $y(0) = 2$, $y(3) = 0$; $n = 6$

10. $y'' + 16\,y = \ln x$, $y(0) = 2$, $y(3) = 0$; $n = 6$

11. $y'' + 16\,y = 10\sin 4x$, $\quad y(0) = 2$, $\quad y(3) = 0$; $\quad n = 6$

12. $x^2\,y'' + 2\,x\,y' - 7\,y = 12\,x^2$, $\quad y(1) = 4$, $\quad y(3) = 1$; $\quad n = 8$

13. $e^x\,y'' + \cos x\,y' - x^2\,y = 10\ln(x+1)$, $\quad y(0) = 0$, $\quad y(5) = 4$; $\quad n = 5$

14. $(1 - x^2)\,y'' - 2\,x\,y' + 12\,y = 0$, $\quad y(-1) = -1$, $\quad y(1) = 1$; $\quad n = 5$

15. A simply supported cantilever beam of length L carries a uniformly distributed load of w_0. The displacement y of its centerline satisfies the boundary value problem

$$EIy'' = \frac{w_0}{2}\,x\,(x - L), \quad y(0) = 0, \quad y(L) = 0.$$

Use the finite difference method with $n = 6$ to approximate the displacement $y(x)$ if $w_0 = EI/2$ and $L = 3$.

16. A simply supported cantilever beam of length L carries a nonuniform load of $w = 0.25\,E\,I\sin(\frac{\pi}{L}x)$. The displacement y of its centerline satisfies the boundary value problem

$$E\,I\,y'' = -\frac{L^2}{\pi^2}\,w, \quad y(0) = 0, \quad y(L) = 0.$$

Use the finite difference method with $n = 8$ to approximate the displacement $y(x)$ if $L = 4$.

17. Consider two concentric spheres of radii $r = a$ and $r = b$ $(b > a)$. The temperature $u(r)$ of the substance between the spheres is governed by the boundary value problem

$$r\,\frac{d^2u}{dr^2} + 2\,\frac{du}{dr} = 0, \quad u(a) = u_i, \quad u(b) = u_o.$$

Use the finite difference method with $n = 8$ to approximate the temperature distribution $u(r)$ if the inner sphere has radius $a = 1$ and is maintained at temperature $u_i = 10$ while the outer sphere has radius $b = 2$ and is maintained at temperature $u_o = 1$.

18. Consider a heat exchanger that comprises two concentric cylindrical pipes of radii $r = a$ and $r = b$ $(b > a)$. The temperature $u(r)$ of the fluid between the pipes is governed by the boundary value problem

$$r\,\frac{d^2u}{dr^2} + \frac{du}{dr} = 0, \quad u(a) = u_i, \quad u(b) = u_o.$$

Use the finite difference method with $n = 8$ to approximate the temperature distribution $u(r)$ if the inner pipe has radius $a = 1$ and is maintained at temperature $u_i = 10$ while the outer pipe has radius $b = 2$ and is maintained at temperature $u_o = 1$.

19. A fin is used to expel heat from a hot base to the surroundings. The fin's base is maintained at temperature u_0 while the temperature of the surroundings is T_s. The temperature profile $u(x)$ along a fin of length L is governed by the boundary value problem

$$\frac{d^2u}{dx^2} = k\,(u - T_s), \quad u(0) = u_0, \quad u'(L) = 0,$$

where k is a constant that depends on the thermal properties and shape of the fin and on the thermal properties of the surrounding medium.

(a) Find the difference equation corresponding to the differential equation. Show that for $i = 1, 2, \ldots, n$ the difference equation yields n equations in $n + 1$ unknowns $u_1, u_2, \ldots, u_{n+1}$. Here u_n and u_{n+1} are unknowns since $u_n = u(L)$ is unspecified and u_{n+1} represents an approximation to the temperature of the fin at a point *beyond* the fin's end.

(b) Since the boundary condition at the end $x = L$ is a constraint on the derivative, use the central difference formula $y'(x_i) = [y_{i+1} - y_{i-1}]/2h$ to show that $u_{n+1} = u_{n-1}$. Use this result to eliminate u_{n+1} from the system of algebraic equations.

(c) Use the finite difference method with $n = 5$ to approximate the temperature profile $u(x)$ across the fin's length if $L = 2$ cm, $k = 20$, $u_0 = 500$ Kelvin, and $T_s = 300$ Kelvin.

20. What is the approximate temperature at the same x locations in Problem 19(c) using $n = 10$ steps?

1. a

2. b

3. a

4. d

5. False

6. True

7. False

8. False

9. $y_1 = -1.66667$, $y_2 = 1.33333$, $y_3 = -1.00000$, $y_4 = 0.66667$, $y_5 = -0.33333$

10. $y_1 = -1.77997$, $y_2 = 1.38666$, $y_3 = -0.99334$, $y_4 = 0.70140$, $y_5 = -0.23616$

11. $y_1 = 0.08863$, $y_2 = 0.09598$, $y_3 = -2.17260$, $y_4 = 3.55068$, $y_5 = -2.45537$

12. $y_1 = 0.31637$, $y_2 = -1.44057$, $y_3 = -2.29277$, $y_4 = -2.56226$, $y_5 = -2.35430$, $y_6 = -1.69605$, $y_7 = -0.58360$

13. $y_1 = -1.71901$, $y_2 = -1.38301$, $y_3 = -0.26802$, $y_4 = 1.48782$

14. $y_1 = 0.28889$, $y_2 = 0.24444$, $y_3 = -0.24444$, $y_4 = -0.28889$

15. $y_1 = 0.2734375$, $y_2 = 0.4687500$, $y_3 = 0.5390625$, $y_4 = 0.4687500$, $y_5 = 0.2734375$

16. $y_1 = y_7 = 0.2546588$, $y_2 = y_6 = 0.4706020$, $y_3 = y_5 = 0.6148712$, $y_4 = 0.6655318$

17. $u_1 = 8.00000$, $u_2 = 6.40000$, $u_3 = 5.09091$, $u_4 = 4.00000$, $u_5 = 3.07692$, $u_6 = 2.28571$, $u_7 = 1.60000$

18. $u_1 = 8.47137$, $u_2 = 7.10364$, $u_3 = 5.86618$, $u_4 = 4.73632$, $u_5 = 3.69685$, $u_6 = 2.73438$, $u_7 = 1.83828$

19. (a) $u_{i+1} - 2u_i + u_{i-1} = k\,h^2\,(u_i - T_s)$, $i = 1, 2, \ldots, n$.

    (c) $u_1 = 360.00014$ K, $u_2 = 312.00077$ K, $u_3 = 302.40384$ K, $u_4 = 300.49920$ K, $u_5 = 300.19200$ K

20. $u_2 = 352.97149$ K, $u_4 = 309.35353$ K, $u_6 = 301.65312$ K, $u_8 = 300.30070$ K, $u_{10} = 300.10298$ K